Readings in Mathematical Social Science

Readings
in
Mathematical Social Science

Edited by

Paul F. Lazarsfeld
Quetelet Professor of Social Science
Columbia University

and

Neil W. Henry
Bureau of Applied Social Research
Columbia University

The M.I.T. Press
Massachusetts Institute of Technology
Cambridge, Massachusetts, and London, England

PMC COLLEGES
LIBRARY
CHESTER, PENNSYLVANIA
74413

Acknowledgments

The publisher and the Bureau of Applied Social Research, Columbia University, acknowledge with thanks permission from the authors and copyright holders to reprint the following selections:

FREDERIC M. LORD, "The Relation of Test Score to the Trait Underlying the Test." Reprinted from *Educational and Psychological Measurement*, XIII, No. 4 (Winter 1953).

W. A. GIBSON, "Three Multivariate Models: Factor Analysis, Latent Structure Analysis, and Latent Profile Analysis." Reprinted from *Psychometrika*, XXIV, No. 3 (September 1959).

PAUL F. LAZARSFELD, "Latent Structure Analysis and Test Theory." Reprinted from *Psychological Scaling*, eds. H. GULLIKSEN and S. MESSICK. New York: John Wiley & Sons, Inc., 1960.

R. DUNCAN LUCE and ALBERT D. PERRY, "A Method of Matrix Analysis of Group Structure." Reprinted from *Psychometrika*, XIV, No. 1 (March 1949).

HERBERT A. SIMON and HAROLD GUETZKOW, "Mechanisms Involved in Pressure Toward Uniformity in Groups." Reprinted from HERBERT A. SIMON, *Models of Man*. New York: John Wiley & Sons, Inc., 1957.

J. G. KEMENY and J. L. SNELL, "A Markov Chain Model in Sociology." Reprinted from J. G. KEMENY and J. L. SNELL, *Mathematical Models in the Social Sciences*. Boston: Ginn & Co., 1962.

JAMES S. COLEMAN, "Reward Structures and the Allocation of Effort." Reprinted with corrections from *Mathematical Methods in Small Group Processes*, eds. JOAN CRISWELL *et al.* Stanford, Calif.: Stanford University Press, 1962.

GERMAIN KREWERAS, "A Model for Opinion Change During Repeated Balloting." Translated from "Un modèle d'évolution de l'opinion exprimée par des votes successifs," *Publications de l'Institut de Statistique de l'Université de Paris*, XIII, No. 1 (1963).

HARRISON C. WHITE, "Models of Kinship Systems with Prescribed Marriage." Reprinted from HARRISON C. WHITE, *An Anatomy of Kinship: Mathematical Models for Structures of Cumulated Roles*. Englewood Cliffs, N.J.: Prentice-Hall, Inc., 1963.

JACOB MARSCHAK, "Efficient and Viable Organizational Forms." Reprinted from *Modern Organizational Theory*, ed. MASON HAIRE. New York: John Wiley & Sons, Inc., 1959.

JAMES G. MARCH, "Party Legislative Representation as a Function of Election Results." Reprinted with corrections from *Public Opinion Quarterly*, XXI (1957).

MARTIN SHUBIK, "Games Decisions and Industrial Organization." Reprinted from *Management Science*, VI, No. 4 (July 1960).

G. TH. GUILBAUD, "Theories of the General Interest and the Logical Problem of Aggregation." Translated from "Les Théories de l'intérêt général et le problème logique de l'agrégation," *Economie Appliquée*, 1952.

L. A. GOODMAN, "Some Possible Effects of Birth Control on the Human Sex Ratio." Reprinted from *Annals of Human Genetics, London*, XXV, No. 75 (1961).

ISADORE BLUMEN, MARVIN KOGAN, and PHILIP J. McCARTHY, "Probability Models for Mobility." Reprinted from ISADORE BLUMEN, MARVIN KOGAN, and PHILIP J. McCARTHY, *The Industrial Mobility of Labor as a Probability Process*. Ithaca, N.Y.: Cornell University Press, 1955.

ROBERT R. BUSH and FREDERICK MOSTELLER, "A Comparison of Eight Models." Reprinted from *Studies in Mathematical Learning Theory*, eds. ROBERT R. BUSH and WILLIAM K. ESTES. Stanford, Calif.: Stanford University Press, 1961.

BENOIT MANDELBROT, "Information Theory and Psycholinguistics: A Theory of Word Frequencies." Adapted and reprinted in part from BENOIT MANDELBROT, "Information Theory and Psycholinguistics," in *Scientific Psychology*, ed. BENJAMIN B. WOLMAN. New York: Basic Books, Inc., 1965. The appendixes were prepared by the author for the present volume.

GEORG RASCH, "An Individualistic Approach to Item Analysis," was written at the editors' invitation for the present volume.

Table of Contents

Section One **Introduction**

Mathematics and the Social Sciences

The application of mathematics to the social sciences has become a topic of great interest in recent years, although it is not, of course, completely new. Economists have worked with mathematical formulations of their theories for a long time, and econometrics is today a well-developed field in its own right. Psychologists have used mathematical tools in certain aspects of their work, especially in the development of tests and in psychophysics. What is new is the increasing development of mathematical models in disciplines that are now sometimes called the behavioral sciences, especially social psychology, sociology, and political science.

These models have a variety of functions. Sometimes they provide a language that tends to clarify the assumptions behind, and the consequences of, ideas that are rather vague when expressed in conventional verbal terms. In other cases mathematical models represent real theories of their own that can be tested against empirical data; some of these models provide rationales for organizing and sifting the increasing amount of data that is available from experiments and surveys. Some social scientists have an additional reason for their interest in mathematical formulations. After all, they reason, mathematics has played a crucial role in the growth of the physical sciences and is becoming increasingly important in biological work; why not see what contribution it might make to the social sciences? Even if this means a considerable amount of trial-and-error procedure, rather than explorations guided by specific problems and established procedures, the effort — with hard work, insight, and luck — might pay off.

The attitude of the mathematician is a considerably more hesitant one. Even if he chooses to work in applied mathematics, he can work with physicists and engineers in areas that have both high prestige and high remuneration. In addition, the natural scientists are more experienced in formulating their problems in mathematical language and may ask only how their equations can be solved. Social scientists often need help in the formulation of the problem itself, but once this has been carried out the problem may become too simple to motivate a mathematician's further effort. As to jobs, the situation is even more paradoxical. The few academic positions newly created in, say, mathematical sociology may go begging because even fewer experienced mathematicians are prepared for, or interested in, filling them. As a result, the number of available positions increases very slowly, and the lack of a broader labor market prevents younger people from being attracted to this "borderline" field.

In spite of these obstacles the interest in mathematical applications to the social sciences continues to grow rapidly, as is best indicated by the rapid increase in the amount of available literature in the United States and Europe, especially in France. During the last ten years American scholars have published numerous volumes on such topics as mathematical psychology and the mathematical study of small groups, including the new *Journal of Mathematical Psychology.* In France a special institute for mathematical social sciences publishes regular reports on its seminars and recently began to issue a periodical, *Mathématiques et sciences humaines.*

A second indicator is the increasing educational effort in the area. The Social Science Research Council has organized numerous seminars, most often to train social scientists in mathematics, but sometimes also to give mathematicians a background in the social sciences. In France the field forms part of the regular instruction at the Hautes Etudes. The present reader grew out of a similar undertaking on the international level.

For several years the social science division of UNESCO has organized a seminar in which a group of mathematicians or social scientists working with mathematical tools have presented their work to a number of young academicians selected from many European countries. These seminars have had to solve a large number of administrative problems. It has been necessary to select from an array of topics much too large to be covered in a few weeks work; the mathematical training of the junior participants has been uneven, reflecting the level of teaching their various countries provided. Most of these difficulties could have been alleviated by distributing appropriate literature in advance of the seminars, but none was available that precisely suited the needs of the participants. The American literature is so specialized that it would have been necessary to provide a large number of books that would have been too expensive to buy and too time-consuming to study in detail. The French literature is written primarily by mathematicians with little concern for the education of an audience of social scientists. To collect in one volume a number of characteristic papers seemed the best solution, and from this recognition the present volume originated.

It is hoped, of course, that the reader will serve a broader audience than the members of the UNESCO seminars. Even in the United States, where so much literature is available, there has been no unified selection of papers cutting across the several disciplines in the social sciences to which mathematics has been applied. The articles in the reader were selected to provide a broad introductory view of this new intellectual field for students with some undergraduate training in mathematics. To those who would use this collection in teaching an introductory course we offer a few suggestions in the last part of this introduction.

The Organization of This Collection

The construction of this reader created its own problems. The term *social science* is vague, and a decision had to be made as to which subject matters should be included. From the beginning it seemed necessary to exclude econometrics and psychophysics, which are established topics with at least a hundred years of literature. This left for further selection nonphysiological psychology, sociology, political science, and anthropology. The next problem was whether these four fields, as units, should form the basis for the volume's organization. A more promising alternative seemed to us to be to organize the papers around the main formal aspects of the subjects to which mathematics has been applied in the last twenty years or so. Thus the volume is now organized into the following divisions:

> Problems of measurement (Section Two)
> The mathematical study of small, homogeneous groups (Section Three)
> The mathematical study of more complex aggregates (Section Four)
> Models analyzing processes (Section Five)

The problem of selection then became urgent within each section, and the guidelines were somewhat different for each. The mathematical foundation of measurement procedures in the social sciences has produced an extensive literature, partly determined by the kind of substantive data from which scales, scores, and indices are being derived. We have concentrated on those techniques that are based essentially on the aggregation of dichotomous items. Here a general theory has evolved that, on the one hand, makes for considerable unification and, on the other hand, permits us to put varying specific techniques into proper perspective.

In the small-group field we have tried to represent several mathematical techniques: classical differential equations, probabilistic approaches of the Poisson and Markov types, and the enumeration techniques of sociometry. With the more complex aggregates we have tried to represent a variety of substantive subject matters: the political body of voters, business organizations, and the anthropologist's primitive tribes. Though the section on processes has a slightly residual character, the central question is: How does change come about? It might be surprising to find learning theory so sparsely represented as well as viewed from the rather narrow perspective of process analysis, since a large literature on mathematical learning theory does exist. We felt that a single selection is all that is needed, with the addition of the bibliographic references, to guide the interested reader toward further study.

We carefully reviewed each paper in the reader to spot places where the authors may have called for more mathematical sophistication than our average reader may have. At such points we added short footnotes to help maintain a fairly even level of difficulty throughout the volume. One further principle of selection might be mentioned. We gave preference to papers that were mathematically not too demanding, that were relatively self-contained, and that stressed basic concepts and results rather than elaborately detailed mathematical presentations. Very often this forced us to eliminate from our earlier, more encompassing list of selections many papers that are of great importance in their own right. We have appended to each section several references that give a general idea of these near misses; these Suggestions for Further Reading should be the first candidates for anyone who wants to pursue the various topics further. At the end of the reader is a list of the major published books in mathematical social science.

Measurement

Now to a more detailed discussion of the papers included in this volume. We have already mentioned that all contributions in the measurement section derive from a unified principle. Leaving aside the specific terminology used, each author begins with the axiom of local independence, which we develop briefly here.

The items of any test are usually highly correlated with each other. This has to be so because they have been selected as indicators of a basic or latent ordering system, which is exactly what the mathematical model tries to detect and to describe. Assuming that we know the "true position" of a person or a group in this intended conceptual scheme, we then make one assumption: that the probability of a combination of responses should be the simple product of the response probabilities for each item. If we could deal with people who are all basically alike, it would be a matter of chance which combinations of items we choose to indicate their latent position. Of course the higher their true score, the more probable it will be that they give a "positive" reply to each item. The following scheme, which elaborates 48 responses to two items, should clarify the idea. A plus sign represents a positive response, a minus sign a negative one.

	+	−	
+	14	10	24
−	10	14	24
	24	24	

$=$

	+	−	
+	1	3	4
−	3	9	12
	4	12	

$\oplus$

	+	−	
+	4	4	8
−	4	4	8
	8	8	

$\oplus$

	+	−	
+	9	3	12
−	3	1	4
	12	4	

On the right side of the equality sign we have three groups of people arranged in order of increasing "latent score" from left to right. The tendency to give positive responses increases from group to group, but within each of the three groups there is no association between the two items. However, when the three groups are combined to produce the table on the left side of the equality sign, an association has appeared between the two items: there appears to be a tendency to give either two positive or two negative responses. All the articles in Section Two use this basic idea: explaining associations between items (such as that on the left of the above figure) by decomposing the population into subsets within which no associations exist.

Beyond this basic idea the various models differ considerably. The papers by Lord and Rasch assume that the probability relation between the answer to a question and the position on the latent dimension has a specific form. Lord is closest to traditional test theory, and what he calls the item characteristic curve is the ogive of the normal distribution. Rasch is guided by a very specific consideration: he wants to be able to compute separately parameters that characterize respondents and parameters that characterize items. This computation must be done for each item and each person separately. He achieves this by giving his item characteristic curves the special form

$$y = \frac{ax}{1 + ax},$$

where a is the easiness of the item, x is the ability of the person, and y is the probability of a correct response. He achieves his goal in a remarkably efficient way.

Gibson's paper is an adaptation of a special case of latent structure analysis. These models were originally developed to separate people into homogeneous types by their item responses. The paper shows that the same typological procedure can also be applied to quantitative test scores. We have included a paper by Lazarsfeld that shows the relation between latent structure analysis and the traditional notion of test score that is the starting point of Lord's paper.

Small Homogeneous Groups

Turning to the formalization of small-group research, we are in a new situation. Laboratory experiments in this field have been one of the most productive developments in social psychology. As a matter of fact, many new dimensions have been added to the notion of "experiment" since the time when the typical procedure was, for example, to have students watch a propaganda film and then to test whether they showed greater changes in attitude than a matched group of students not exposed to the film.

Ingenious ways have been found to broaden the notion of "stimulus." Subjects have been made anxious by various devices, and their ability to perform certain tasks has been compared with that of others in a more normal situation. Experimental environments have been created by mixing genuine and preinstructed subjects. Groups have been made more or less cohesive by manipulating the type of tasks given or the type of rewards offered. Efforts to relate this experimental work to mathematical models have not yet caught up with the wealth of experimental ingenuity, but several trends toward formalization are distinguishable.

The earliest quantitative approach to small groups was Moreno's sociometric technique: The members of a group were asked to select other members according to whether they wanted to work with them, whether they would like to have them as friends, and like criteria. As long as the number of persons involved is small, the structure of the group can easily be perceived by graphic methods: Are the choices mutual or one-sided? Do they form cliques whose members choose each other and not "outsiders"? How long a chain of choices would be needed to connect one participant to some other? However, with groups larger than, say, fifteen persons, graphic representation becomes unmanageable. The mathematical technique that has proved so helpful on this point is the *sociometric matrix* in place of the graph. In each cell of this matrix the relation between the choosers and the chosen can be entered in numerical form, and the usual algebraic operations on the matrices can be given substantive interpretations. Luce and Perry were able to show that matrix multiplications provide a simple way to count how many choices were reciprocated, how many larger clusters exist, and other factors.

The next step beyond the mere description of small-group structures was Herbert Simon's translation of a set of experimental findings into a coherent mathematical language. He had available a number of propositions derived by Festinger from his experiments, which related a set of variables in pairwise combinations. Simon constructed a larger, interrelated system and was able thereby to derive conclusions that were hidden in the earlier formulation. We want to draw special attention to two points in Simon's paper: he proves (1) that one of Festinger's propositions can be derived from the remaining ones and (2) that some of the actual experimental findings acquire a richer interpretation when they are looked upon as implications of a *system* of equations rather than as mere correlations.

The mathematical functions that Simon introduces have no specified form; for his purposes it is enough to know whether they are increasing or decreasing in relation to time. The next step forward comes from mathematical models that permit numerical derivations. Here we selected a work that had three different intellectual phases. The starting point was the famous experiments by Asch that show how the cognitive performances of people are influenced by their social environment. Another psychologist, Bernard Cohen, then developed a mathematical scheme from which Asch's findings could be derived. He could observe, for each subject, a pattern of conforming or nonconforming responses, and he assumed that these were generated by a Markov chain, whose states corresponded to latent, unobservable, psychological states of the individuals. It was difficult, however, to derive the latent transition probabilities from the manifest behavior patterns. The mathematicians Kemeny and Snell later derived an elegant solution for this problem, which has been included in this collection. The original experiments show considerable variations in the performance of a subject. The mathematical model shows that in principle these variations are implied by the probabilistic character of the latent Markov chain. The final section of the Kemeny-Snell paper shows that further refinement of the model is needed to account for all the observed variation.

The Asch experiments were carried out in the setting of small-group research, but the model itself pertains to a hypothetical individual subject. The next paper in this section makes the group itself the object of a formalization. Over a hundred years ago the Belgian mathematician Adolphe Quételet pointed out that biological as well as social phenomena showed distributions that could be accounted for by the probabilities of independent events. Fifty years ago the leaders in the French Durkheim school considered the use of mathematics inappropriate because they thought that probabilistic models violated a basic sociological tenet: social behavior of a group of people who are in interaction cannot be analyzed in terms of "independent events." Since then we have learned that many probability distributions exist that have, built in, the idea of mutual dependence. Thus, for instance, whether a person chooses A rather than B might depend upon how many before him have made such a choice and therefore cannot be modeled by the toss of a particular coin.

The paper by Coleman was selected as a typical example of a mathematical model that takes social contagion into account. It seems to us that this type of analysis will play an increasing role in the social sciences, and we urge the reader to consider carefully the logical structure of Coleman's paper even if the mathematics seems somewhat difficult. Perhaps the best procedure is to start with the numerical example with which the paper ends. He has small groups of varying size, and for each set of groups he has available the number of people who voted for a certain candidate in a union election. The votes are by no means normally distributed: indeed, the number of groups in which either very many or very few people voted for a given candidate is quite large. Exactly such a distribution can be expected if we assume that people are more likely to vote for a man who already has many partisans. The general idea is the following: a sequence of time intervals is imagined for which the distribution of votes in one interval depends in a probabilistic way upon the distribution in the preceding interval. The model implies a final distribution of the votes over a large number of groups, and the test of the model consists in comparing this hypothetical distribution with the actual distribution found in a survey.

We can best underscore the importance and the limitations of this procedure by discussing it in still another context. We do know the actual distribution of accidents. It is possible to make alternative assumptions: after a person has had an accident he either becomes more cautious or more nervous and the probability of his having another accident either decreases or increases. Empirical statistics as to the number of people who have none, one, two, or more accidents permit us to decide which of the two models is the correct one: whether one should assume that one accident tends to increase or decrease the probability of another. In this sense the mathematical analysis is equivalent to the building of dynamic theories that *can* be tested, but a third alternative complicates the situation: it could be that people begin with different degrees of accident proneness, which never change; then the manifest distribution reflects only this original disposition. We can make the choice from among one or another of these models only if we have some repeated observations of the same sample. Coleman's paper shows how the building of substantive theory, mathematical formalization, and empirical research must eventually become more and more intertwined.

The final paper in this section shows what could be done if we did have repeated observations on the behavior of groups. To explain the general idea, think of the following situation: In the United States the country votes every four years for a President, and for all practical purposes only two parties are serious contenders. The country is divided into about three thousand counties, and each county at each election can be classified as having either a Republican or a Democratic majority. Some of these counties, for historical reasons, have remained in the same camp over many elections, while others have swung back and forth. Can one assume that there is any large-scale bandwagon effect? By this we mean to ask whether, at a given election, the oscillating counties are either positively or negatively affected by the *total* distribution of county decisions at the previous election. The paper by Kreweras shows how one might analyze the effect of preceding upon subsequent election returns. His basic assumption is to divide the voters into two groups, those who always stay with the same party and those who have no convictions. The latter are the ones whose probable vote is affected by how the entire population voted the time before. (We shall find this "stayer-mover" idea again in the paper by Blumen, Kogan, and McCarthy in Section Five.) This assumption leads to a matrix of transition probabilities that has remarkable mathematical properties, which enable us to draw substantive conclusions as to what would happen if various combinations of convinced and undecided voters are present.

For the time being this remains a purely mathematical formulation, and no actual data are available. As a matter of fact, the inference from manifest to latent data is not even clarified. The paper is important, however, because it, together with the two preceding ones, indicates the general direction in which this kind of research is moving. The Kemeny-Snell model deals with the behavior of individuals in groups. Coleman's paper deals with the equilibrium distribution of many groups, but it has to make hypothetical assumptions about how this distribution comes about. The Kreweras model shows what could be done if we had available both sets of data: the formation of groups and a number of repeated observations on them.

More Complex Aggregates

For this section we selected problems involving more than one "status." For example, the piece from Harrison White's book, in which he formalizes anthropological thinking on kinship systems, has some similarity to the sociometric paper that introduced the preceding section. From a formal point of view he uses the same kind of matrix to indicate who may marry whom as Luce and Perry used to indicate who likes whom. But here we have to consider two matrices: a second one indicates to what clan children will be assigned. The combination of *two* operations — the marriage matrix and the child matrix — permits deductions of much greater efficiency than the graphic methods traditionally used by anthropologists. Obviously the axiomatic system with which White starts reflects only a segment of reality, but the implications are numerous and useful. Here again the reader is urged to explore further in the monograph from which this paper was taken.

Marschak's paper deals not with the various members of a family, but with the various parts of an organization, especially its central office and its regional representative. We have included it in this section although its primary application is to a business decision. The mathematics is simple, but an important aspect of the decentralization problem is articulated: If people of minor authority have only partial information (or ability), how much is gained if this information is centrally coordinated (with the danger that the presumably greater but rarer ability of the "director" may be exhausted by too many decisions)?

Marschak argues that three factors have to be considered: the probability distribution of external events; the costs in salaries, talent, and the like that various organizational forms entail; and the "pay-offs" that can be expected from the possible combinations of events and organizational form. Such a conceptualization is obviously influenced by the term *game theory*, used to describe the mathematization of the different ways in which parts of a larger system can "act" in regard to each other. This newly developed branch of mathematics received its impetus from problems in economics; its application to other social sciences is still much under debate. We decided to include the paper by Shubik because it offers an elementary introduction together with a survey of possible applications. He has edited a collection of papers on specific applications of game theory to social behavior, which shows that other scholars have indeed begun to realize parts of his general program.

The relation between parts of social systems can be looked upon in still another way: How are the "activities" of a lower level combined into structures of a higher level? A good example is provided in the paper by March. He first summarizes the literature concerned with a well-known aspect of certain election systems. If two parties compete in a large number of constituencies, then a small increase in the popular vote obtained by the majority leads to a sharp increase in the number of majority seats in the legislative bodies. March next discusses various mathematical formulations in the light of empirical evidence and then offers his own ideas. The basic element is the variability of the popular vote between constituencies and the specific form of the distribution it takes on. The paper suggests that the size of the regional vote depends upon the number of compromises each party has to make with its supporters and the amount of competitiveness that exists between the two parties. The two factors can vary independently, and their combination accounts for the distribution of the number of seats the victorious party obtains.

The relation of popular vote to the number of seats is only a special case of a more general problem: How can individual choices be aggregated so as to represent a collective decision? The logic of this issue and its many ramifications form the topic of the last selection in this section. Guilbaud starts with the classical problem of how a set of individual preferences can be combined into an aggregate one. Take, for example, three candidates A, B, C and fourteen voters, of whom six have the preference $A > B > C$ while four each have the preference $B > C > A$ and $C > B > A$, respectively. If only the top choice is counted, obviously A is the winner. But if we make fourteen comparisons between A and B, six are in favor of A and eight in favor of B. Thus if the individual choices are reduced to their simplest elements, the collective decision is clearly challenged.

Guilbaud formulates what he calls the Condorcet paradox in full generality. Given individual choices that are subject to certain rules (transitivity, for example), can they be combined so that the collective decision does not violate these rules? (The arithmetic mean of integers, for example, violates such a restriction because it is not necessarily an integer.) The paper presents certain situations in which such composition rules can be found and others in which they do not exist. Among the former we have the case in which the objects of choice possess a natural order that at least partially affects the individual choices. This situation is quite similar to the well-known Guttman scale. The insoluble case is the one studied by K. J. Arrow. The author shows in passing how problems such as that raised by Quételet's concept of the "average man" are special cases of the general problem of composition.

We have not included in this section a group of papers that are usually called general systems theory and that, mathematically, reduce to classical systems of differential equations. Because applications of their use can be found in many textbooks, we felt that it was less urgent to include them here. The paper by Rapoport, briefly discussed at the end of Section Four, is a good introduction to this general area.

Models Analyzing Processes

The last section elaborates on some of the themes raised in the preceding sections and, at the same time, enlarges the range of substantive application. Goodman's paper deals with the effect of birth control on the actual sex ratio in a population. Suppose that in a certain society parents prefer to have boys. The vague notion of "preference" needs precision, however, in terms of what decisions parents might make after the birth of a boy or of a girl. Goodman distinguishes three cases: in Type I, parents stop after the birth of the first boy because they are satisfied; in Type III, parents stop after the first girl because they are afraid that their chances for a boy are small; Type II is mixed and somewhat more difficult to describe briefly. The key idea in the article concerns unanticipated consequences of the individual intentions. In Type I, for example, the effect of the parents' desire for a boy makes for a sex ratio unfavorable to males in the total population. The model implies that the smaller the probability of a male birth, the greater the number of children a family is likely to have. From there on it is easy to show that the proportion of male births will be smaller than if the parents had no policy at all and hence the number of children and the proportion of male births were uncorrelated.

One should notice the formal differences between Goodman's model and the one discussed in the section by Coleman. In both cases choices are made that are influenced by previous events — in the one case by the preceding distribution of choices in a group, in the other by the sex of the preceding birth in an individual family. Thus Goodman studies the effect on the "actor" of his own experience, whereas Coleman studies the effect of his social environment on him. As a consequence the latent parameters of Coleman's model involve the changing sizes of groups, whereas Goodman's model introduces individual latent parameters. In both cases, however, the latent parameters are not really computed. An important contribution has already been achieved by showing how variations in these latent rates — strong desire for a male heir or great suggestibility to majority opinion — affect our observable actions.

The second paper in this section extends the use of Markov chains, which played a role in several previous selections, especially in the model formalizing the Asch experiments. The authors had available data that told how, over a period of time, a group of workers shifted their employment from one industry to another. A simple transition matrix did not fit the actual changes, primarily because the proportion of workers retaining employment in the same group after a series of turnovers remained much too large when compared with the mathematical model. The first modification introduced consisted of dividing the workers into "stayers" and "movers," where transition matrices were applied only to the latter. The proportion of stayers is not known, being a latent characteristic of the population, just as are the sizes of the latent classes in the models discussed in the papers by Gibson and Lazarsfeld. The proportion of stayers can, however, be computed from the manifest data. In their original monograph the authors proposed procedures for estimating the transition probabilities of the mover-stayer model. In our adaptation we were satisfied with the demonstration of how the additional assumptions affect the model, and so omitted the rather complicated estimation procedure. This more general model was modified still further. Only the category to which the workers belong at the beginning and end of each quarter is known, and some of them might have changed several times during the quarter. Hence additional latent parameters are introduced: the probabilities of such intermediate moves.

The distinction between stayers and movers is an idea applicable to other process models. Thus Kemeny and Snell showed that the model of the Asch experiment underestimated the number of subjects who never made a wrong choice, even while under continued pressure by the rest of the group. They also proceeded to alter their model and derived from the manifest observations the proportion of latent stayers, or persons who were one hundred percent immune to pressure.

The second aspect of this model — the idea of hypothetical moves between actual turnover observations — bears on the following dilemma. In applying Markov chains to the study of opinion change, repeated observations can be made only at discrete points, often separated by rather long intervals. The "true" changes, on the other hand, may occur much more frequently, almost continuously. Anderson, in his classic introduction to the problem, reported as one of the annotated items at the end of this section, accepted the actual periods of observation as the basis for his analysis. Coleman, in *Introduction to Mathematical Sociology,* takes the opposite position, considering changes continuous in time. Our selection on labor mobility represents a compromise approach, in which changes take place at discrete points that are fixed neither in number nor in time.

All the process models discussed so far are closed systems in the sense that the variables introduced do account for the movement from one period to the next without any "exogenous" variables playing a role. The next selection, by Bush and Mosteller, introduces a new idea. In mathematical learning theory the probability of making some decision at a point in time also depends — at least partly — on the corresponding probabilities at preceding points in time. But something new intervenes: whether the preceding response was rewarded or punished. This is a factor that the experimenter can control at will; it thus comes from outside the system of variables that characterizes the behavior of the subject. Two equations are therefore necessary to link the parameters pertinent to two consecutive observations. The literature on mathematical learning theory is vast, and it seemed best to present a selection that compares several models with regard to a given set of data.

Finally, the paper by Mandelbrot in this section plays about the same role as the paper by Shubik in the preceding section. The author considers mathematical formalization of linguistics one of the main developments in our field, placing the notions of randomness and of "information," and the levels of language from letters to sentences in a fresh perspective. Closest to the purpose of this volume is the literature on word frequencies because it is a paradigm for a large number of problems. The distributions of income and city size show a regularity quite similar to the distribution of word frequencies within a given text: the number of times a word occurs is approximately inversely proportional to its rank order when all the words of a given text are listed according to their frequency. Mandelbrot first discusses the substantive part of the story and then, in a series of appendixes requested by the editors, sketches the main mathematical derivations.

Two aspects are especially relevant. One is the conversion of probabilities into rank orders as explained in Appendix B-1. The second is the idea of "cost" of letters sketched in Appendix B-2. Here the parallel to other models in this volume is apparent. The decision to add another letter to a word is formally equivalent to the decision to add another child to a family or to forsake one opinion for another. Although the reader must consult the references at the end of Mandelbrot's paper, especially the work of Chomsky and Miller, for a more complete introduction to mathematical linguistics, at least he will be aware of formalization in another substantive area.

On the Teaching of Mathematical Social Science

A "reader" is not a textbook; rather, it makes available to instructor and student alike a collection of studies that have been organized with certain points of similarity or continuity in mind, which are explained in the editorial introductions. Much is still left to do.

On the one hand, the instructor should supply additional information on the substantive studies on which the mathematical works are based: the Festinger paper from which Simon quotes and the Asch and Cohen studies from which Kemeny and Snell start are examples. On the mathematical side two suggestions seem appropriate. Not all students will know all the mathematics used in the reader, and additional sources will be needed. But such subsidiary mathematics teaching should be done with close reference to the social sciences. Thus a better understanding of various probability distributions and processes can be gained from Chapters 6 and 17 of Feller's book, but in many cases the teacher can add substantive illustrations from the social sciences. For example, permutations may be so illustrated as to lead to derivations of Mandelbrot's rank-frequency law for words, under broader conditions. Gibson gives a very brief summary of how the basic latent structure equations can be solved, but the instructor might introduce the more detailed computations in the Anderson article referred to by Gibson. And although Simon takes it for granted that the reader knows how to analyze the equilibrium state of a system of differential equations, this may not be the case in a course for social scientists. Any textbook on this topic, such as Apostol, Volume II, will provide the necessary supplementary information.

Often the papers in this volume carry out an argument from a deductive point of view, whereas in teaching it is more advisable to consider the students' reaction. Thus, for example, Goodman states in the latter part of his paper how the expected number of children can be computed from his model. In the case of parents who stop having children after the first boy, the probability is p of having one child (a boy); pq of having two children (a girl followed by a boy); pq^2 of having three; and so on. The expected number of children in such a family is evidently

$$p + 2pq + 3pq^2 + \ldots = p \sum_{n=0}^{\infty} (n+1)q^n = p/(1-q)^2 = 1/p.$$

Once this is established, it is easy to compute the expected sex ratio for the whole population. Goodman, in an effort to relate his work to previous publications, first gives the sex ratio formula, which thus appears in a somewhat mysterious way. In discussing derivations such as this, the instructor may do well to try to follow the intuition of the student rather than the editorial sophistication of the trained mathematician.

In many of the other papers opportunities exist for the instructor to present an alternative derivation or to add more details to a proof. It will often be valuable to exploit these opportunities, whether the students are well prepared in mathematics or not. In addition, the students should be urged to move deeper into any topic that attracts them. The annotated articles, the reference books in mathematics and in mathematical social science, and, of course, the papers referred to in the articles themselves should provide sufficient material for students of diverse backgrounds to dip into profitably.

The editors of this volume have taught mathematical social science to a variety of students. Invariably, at some point one question comes up: What's it all good for? Some mathematically trained participants suggest that they aren't learning enough new techniques; some substantively oriented social scientists wonder whether the formalizations add enough to the empirical findings. We have tried to indicate our answers to these questions in the first pages of this Introduction. We doubt whether one can give these students stronger answers, however, until they themselves have gone further into the subject.

Although the topics introduced in this volume have engaged quite a broad following, at present they remain in a state of flux. Most of our authors acquired their reputations elsewhere, in mathematics or a substantive area, and look on their contributions as "noble experiments" in a new field. The editors are convinced that this field is here to stay and to expand, and they hope that the present volume will help to recruit new workers who will in turn increase the scope and utility of the mathematical approach to the social sciences.

We would like to thank a number of people who helped us to prepare this book, beginning, of course, with the authors whose papers are reprinted herein. In particular, our thanks to G. Rasch, whose paper was written specifically for this volume; G. Kreweras, who rewrote his paper and aided in its translation; and B. Mandelbrot, who also modified his paper to make it more suitable to the needs of the reader and prepared the new Appendixes. Advice on what should be included came from many quarters, and was greatly appreciated even when not followed. We mention in particular the members of the Columbia University Seminar on Mathematical Methods in the Social Sciences. B. Lecuyer and A. Stoetzel helped us prepare the translations from the French.

Finally, we thank Samy Friedman of the Social Science Division of UNESCO for his encouragement in the initial development of the reader and for his continued interest; Clara Shapiro and the administrative staff of the Bureau of Applied Social Research for their assistance in carrying out the project; and Bruce Harlow and Goddard Winterbottom, our editors at SRA.

Paul F. Lazarsfeld
Neil W. Henry
Bureau of Applied Social Research, Columbia University

Selected Mathematics Texts for Supplementary Study

APOSTOL, T. M. *Calculus.* 2 vols. New York: Blaisdell, 1961 and 1962.

FELLER, WILLIAM. *An Introduction to Probability Theory and Its Applications.* 2d ed. New York: Wiley, 1957. Vol. I.

GOLDBERG, SAMUEL. *Introduction to Difference Equations.* New York: Wiley, 1958.

HOHN, FRANZ. *Elementary Matrix Algebra.* 2d ed. New York: Macmillan, 1964.

KEMENY, JOHN G., and others. *Finite Mathematical Structures.* Englewood Cliffs, N.J.: Prentice-Hall, 1959.

MCGINNIS, ROBERT. *Mathematical Foundations for Social Analysis.* Indianapolis: Bobbs Merrill, 1965.

MOOD, ALEXANDER M., and GRAYBILL, F. A. *Introduction to the Theory of Statistics.* New York: McGraw-Hill, 1963.

Section Two Problems of Measurement

The Relation of Test Score
to the Trait Underlying the Test

Frederic M. Lord   *Educational Testing Service*

In any consideration of the nature of the metric provided by the raw score on a mental test, one is likely to be faced with the fact that the raw score units of measurement cannot ordinarily be considered as "equal." If we administer two tests of the same trait or ability, the two tests having different distributions of item "difficulty," to the same group of examinees, we will obtain two different shapes of raw score distributions from the two tests, as illustrated in Figure 1, for

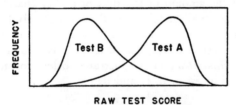

RAW TEST SCORE

Fig. 1. Distributions of Test Scores

example. Since there is no reason to prefer one of these distributions over the other, and since the two distributions cannot both simultaneously represent the shape of the distribution of the trait or ability in the group tested, we conclude that neither distribution gives a true representation of the shape of the distribution of the trait or ability in the group tested and that the raw score scale does not provide equal units of measurement in the case of either test.

In considering such matters, one is usually involved, either implicitly or explicitly, in the assumption that underlying the raw score of the test there is a trait or ability that it is desired to "measure." The present discussion is concerned with a line of argument to demonstrate a number of significant conclusions that can be reached regarding the nature of scores on certain kinds of tests without making any assumptions other than that it is not sheer nonsense to talk about "measuring" ability. Attention will be restricted to tests composed of certain types of items. Within the limits of this restriction, the argument is intended to be compelling rather than merely suggestive.

The reader may, within certain limits, define the scale on which "ability" is to be measured in whatever way he chooses. The conclusions reached will be valid for the types of tests under consideration irrespective of the way in which the "ability" scale is defined.

The Single Assumption

Explicitly, *it is assumed that the trait or ability under discussion can be thought of as an ordered variable represented numerically in a single dimension.* This means that the examinees may be considered as existing on a linear continuum in such a way that the amount of the trait or ability characteristic of each examinee may be represented quantitatively by his position on the continuum, although in practice the exact amount of ability possessed by each examinee is usually actually unknown. This situation is illustrated below for four hypothetical examinees, a, b, c, and d:

ABILITY

If there exists a naturally unique metric for expressing the amount of the trait or characteristic numerically, then the ability continuum will of course be considered to be expressed in terms of this metric. If, as seems likely, there exists no such naturally unique metric, the reader is at liberty to choose his own arbitrary metric. The choice of metric will not affect the conclusions reached here, provided that the same metric (except for a possible linear transformation) is always used for the same trait or ability, irrespective of the particular set of items used to test for this trait or ability.

Restrictions

The restrictions that will be imposed here may all be considered as restrictions on the type of test items to be considered rather than restrictions on the nature of the group of examinees to which the items are administered.

I. Consideration will be limited to tests composed of items that are scored either 0 or 1. If the score on item i is denoted by x_i, we may write

$$x_i = 0 \text{ or } 1. \tag{1}$$

For convenience, the item responses will hereafter be spoken of as either "right" or "wrong" and in general the terminology appropriate for tests of "ability" will be used. The conclusions reached will often be applicable to certain other types of tests, however.

II. Consideration will be limited to tests on which the raw score (s) is taken to be the number of items answered correctly. If there are n items in the test, we have

$$s = \sum_{i=1}^{n} x_i. \tag{2}$$

III. Let us look at the proportion of correct answers given to item i by all those examinees who fall at some specified point along the ability continuum. (We will consider the theoretically possible number of examinees at any specified ability level to be so large that sampling fluctuations may be ignored; consequently the terminology appropriate to a whole population of examinees will be used here and hereafter.) This proportion will be some unknown function of ability, such as is represented by any one of the three curves in Figure 2. Lazarsfeld (7) calls such a curve the "trace line" of the item; here we will follow Tucker's (13) terminology and call it the *item characteristic curve*.

It is important to point out that the shape of the item characteristic curves can be determined from empirical item analysis data for actual items to as close an approximation as desired, provided the test administered is sufficiently reliable (i.e., sufficiently long). It is thus possible to verify whether or not any given set of test data conforms to the restrictions here imposed. This statement will be proved and a procedure briefly described in the subsequent section titled "Determining Whether a Given Set of Items Meets the Original Restrictions."

The line of reasoning that will be followed throughout the present paper can be applied equally well to any items having any shape of item characteristic curve. In order conveniently to illustrate the line of reasoning and to reach specific conclusions, however, it is necessary to restrict present consideration to tests composed of items whose characteristic curves present some broadly specifiable common features. Attention will therefore be

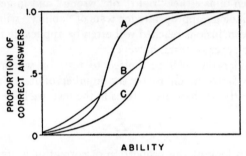

FIG. 2. Item Characteristic Curves

limited to tests composed of items whose characteristic curves have the following general features:

i. If examinees at a sufficiently low ability level are considered, the proportion of correct answers given by such examinees to any specified item will be close to zero. This restriction merely implies that it is at least theoretically possible to imagine examinees whose ability is so low that they cannot in general answer the item correctly.

ii. If examinees at a sufficiently high ability level are considered, the proportion of correct answers given by such examinees to any specified item will be close to 1.00.

iii. The proportion of correct answers increases as the ability level of the examinees increases.

iv. The characteristic curve is smooth and has only one point of inflection.

The foregoing general type of curve was chosen because it is fairly typical of empirical curves obtained for actual aptitude and achievement test items when the proportion of correct answers to an item is plotted as a function of actual test score. The fact that the scale used to measure ability may be stretched and squeezed at the whim of the reader should materially decrease the stringency of the foregoing restrictions on the shape of the characteristic curve.

It should be noted, however, that requirement III-i is likely to rule out of consideration any items that can be answered correctly by guessing, unless guessing is somehow minimized, at least among examinees of low ability. Appropriate alternative restrictions on the shape of the characteristic curves can be made, if desired, to cover the situation where the items may be answered correctly by guessing, and the approach illustrated in the present paper may then be used to reach conclusions about tests composed of such items.

The relation of the item characteristic curve to the item difficulty and to the item discriminating power may be noted briefly at this point. Difficult items have characteristic curves that, broadly speaking, lie further to the right on the ability continuum than do the easier items. Highly discriminating items have characteristic curves that slope steeply at some point; poorly discriminating items have characteristic curves without steep slopes.

It is important to note that the shape of the item characteristic curve is totally unrelated to the shape of the distribution of ability in the group tested. This fact is obvious when it is considered that the proportion of correct answers to an item among examinees at a given ability level is theoretically unrelated to the number of examinees found at that level in the group tested.

IV. Consideration will be restricted to tests that are *homogeneous* in the following sense: A homogeneous test is for present purposes defined as a test composed of items such that, *within any group of examinees all of whom are at the same ability level*, the responses given to any item are statistically independent of the responses given to the remaining items. In other words, those examinees at a given ability level who answer a given item correctly are no more likely to answer other items correctly than are those examinees at the same ability level who answer the given item incorrectly. This restriction has been used by Tucker (13, 14, 15) and Lazarsfeld (7); our "ability continuum" is virtually the same as Lazarsfeld's "latent continuum."

It may be well to note that the foregoing definition does *not* by any means imply that homogeneous items are uncorrelated in the group of examinees as a whole. On the contrary, the more able examinees will tend to answer the items correctly and the less able examinees will tend to answer them incorrectly, so that the items will definitely be correlated in the total group. It is only within a group of examinees at a fixed ability level that the items are considered to be uncorrelated.

It is important to point out the reasonableness—almost the necessity—of this restriction. Some sort of restriction is obviously necessary to rule out of consideration all tests that are composite measures of two or more abilities. We would not want to consider, for example, a test that was composed half of verbal items and half of mathematics items. Suppose restriction IV were not imposed. In this case we would give consideration to tests that contained two or more items that were correlated with each other even when the ability with which we are concerned was held constant. But these two or more items together would of necessity be measuring something other than the ability with which we are concerned. Consequently, restriction IV is necessary to rule out of consideration such tests.

A rough approximation to restriction IV in factorial terms would be the restriction that the matrix of the intercorrelations of the test items must be of rank one. This allows each item to have its own specificity and error variance, but rules out the existence of more than one common factor among the items. The definition of homogeneity given in a preceding paragraph is a better definition than could be given in the language of factor analysis because of the fact that the former definition requires complete independence, whereas factor analysis can only require that certain product-moment correlations shall be zero. The two definitions will not be identical, for example, unless all the regressions involved are rectilinear. Because of its familiarity, however, the terminology of factor analysis is frequently helpful in understanding the problems under discussion. It is often helpful as an approximation, for example, to think of the ability continuum simply as representing the common factor of the item correlations.

A procedure for actually verifying whether or not a set of actual test data conforms to restriction IV will be briefly outlined in the subsequent section titled "Verification of the Validity of the Original Restrictions."

Deductions

The Distribution of Test Scores in a Group of Examinees at a Fixed Ability Level

According to restriction IV, the responses to two items are independent within a group of examinees at a fixed ability level. Let $P_{i \cdot c}$ and $P_{j \cdot c}$ be the proportion of correct answers given by examinees at a fixed ability level (c) to items i and j, respectively. The probability that an examinee will answer both items correctly is therefore $P_{i \cdot c} P_{j \cdot c}$, the product of the independent probabilities. If we consider for a moment a test that is composed of only two items, the probability that any examinee at ability level c will obtain a raw score of 2 may therefore be written

$$\text{Prob}(s = 2 \mid c) = P_{i \cdot c} P_{j \cdot c}. \tag{i}$$

(The vertical line in the parentheses is used to indicate that the ability, c, is fixed.) Similarly, if we write $Q_{i \cdot c}$ for $1 - P_{i \cdot c}$, and $Q_{j \cdot c}$ for $1 - P_{j \cdot c}$, the probability that an examinee at ability level c will obtain a score of 0 on this 2-item test will be

$$\text{Prob}(s = 0 \mid c) = Q_{i \cdot c} Q_{j \cdot c}. \tag{ii}$$

The probability that an examinee will answer item i correctly and item j incorrectly is $P_{i \cdot c} Q_{j \cdot c}$, and the probability that he will answer item i incorrectly and item j correctly is $Q_{j \cdot c} P_{j \cdot c}$. Since these are the two ways that an examinee can obtain a score of 1 on the 2-item test, we have for the probability that he will obtain a score of 1

$$\text{Prob}(s = 1 \mid c) = P_{i \cdot c} Q_{j \cdot c} + Q_{i \cdot c} P_{j \cdot c} . \qquad \text{(iii)}$$

It will perhaps clarify matters if we examine equations (i), (ii), and (iii) for the special case where $P_{i \cdot c} = P_{j \cdot c}$ for all values of c, i.e., the case where both items have identical characteristic curves. Such items will hereafter be referred to as *equivalent items*. In this case, dropping the subscript i and using an asterisk to indicate that we are dealing with the special case of equivalent items, we have

$$\left. \begin{array}{l} \text{Prob}^*(s = 2 \mid c) = P_{\cdot c}^2 \\ \text{Prob}^*(s = 1 \mid c) = 2 P_{\cdot c} Q_{\cdot c} \\ \text{Prob}^*(s = 0 \mid c) = Q_{\cdot c}^2 \end{array} \right\} .$$

These equations represent the frequency distribution of raw score at a given ability level, for the special case of equivalent items. It is immediately seen that this distribution is the usual binomial distribution. The conditional frequency distribution of raw test score represented by the probabilities in (i), (ii), and (iii) for the case of nonequivalent items is a generalization of the binomial distribution.

An extension of the foregoing argument leads readily to the conclusion that the conditional distribution of raw scores at a given ability level on a test composed of n equivalent items is the usual binomial. Using $f_{s \cdot c}$ to denote the frequency of s for fixed c, this conditional distribution may be written

$$f_{s \cdot c}^* = \binom{n}{s} P_{\cdot c}^s Q_{\cdot c}^{n-s}, \qquad (3')$$

where $\binom{n}{s}$ is the usual binomial coefficient. The corresponding generalized binomial for the case of nonequivalent items may be written

$$f_{s \cdot c} = \sum_{\Sigma x_i = s} \prod_{i=1}^{n} P_{i \cdot c}^{x_i} Q_{i \cdot c}^{1-x_i}, \qquad (3)$$

where $\prod$ indicates a product taken over all values of i, and where the summation is over all combinations of values of x_i

such that $\sum_{i=1}^{n} x_i = s$. It should be remembered here that x_i equals 0 or 1 so that one of the two exponents in (3) will always vanish.

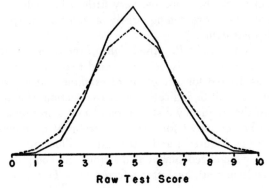

Row Test Score

Fig. 3. Binomial (– – – –) and Generalized Binomial (————) Frequency Polygons for Scores at a Fixed Ability Level

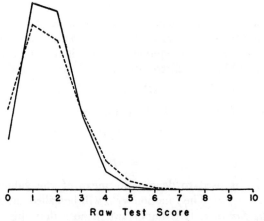

Row Test Score

Fig. 4. Binomial (– – – –) and Generalized Binomial (————) Frequency Polygons for Scores at a Fixed Ability Level

The generalization of the binomial represented by (3) is a somewhat awkward function to bear in mind, and it is for this reason that the special case of equivalent items has been intro-

duced, as represented by (3'). In the cases most commonly encountered in practice, the shape of the generalized binomial of
(3) is not appreciably different from that of the usual binomial
of (3'), except that the variance of (3) is less than that of (3').
The reader will therefore lose very little if he wishes to follow
the present line of reasoning largely in terms of the special case
of equivalent items.

Since the values of $P_{i \cdot c}$, the height of the item characteristic
curves, can theoretically be determined to as close an approximation as desired for any group of examinees at a given level
of ability, as will be indicated in a later section, the numerical
values of the frequency distribution of raw scores on an actual
test can be computed for any such group of examinees from
equation (3). Figures 3 and 4 present for illustrative purposes
two such generalized binomial distributions computed for an
actual 10-item test[1], hereafter referred to as Test h, and superimposed on these for purposes of comparison, the corresponding
ordinary binomial distributions having the same means. Figure
3 presents distributions of test scores for examinees at an ability
level such that their average score is 5.0. Each distribution in
Figure 4, on the other hand, has an average score of 1.7.

The mean ($M^*_{s \cdot c}$, say) of the conditional distribution of test
scores for the case of equivalent items is of course the usual
mean of a binomial distribution:

$$M^*_{s \cdot c} = n P_{\cdot c}. \tag{4'}$$

The mean of the generalized binomial is

$$M_{s \cdot c} = \sum_i P_{i \cdot c} \tag{4}$$

$$= n \bar{P}_{\cdot c},$$

where $\bar{P}_{\cdot c}$ is used to denote the mean of the values of $P_{i \cdot c}$
($i = 1, \cdots, n$). The function $n\bar{P}_{\cdot c}$ will be called the *test characteristic function*. It is important to note that this function,

---

[1] The 10-item test under discussion was composed of rather valid free-response
mathematics-achievement items having the following item difficulties (proportion of
correct answers) for the group tested: .16, .18, .20, .27, .34, .43, .44, .47, .57, and .87.
The method used to obtain the item characteristic curves was not identical with that
suggested in the present paper, but this fact does not affect the usefulness of the data
for illustrative purposes.

like the item characteristic function, remains the same irrespective of the shape of the distribution of ability in the group tested.

Similarly, the standard deviation of test score at a given ability level is represented by

$$\sigma_{s \cdot c}^{*} = \sqrt{n P_{\cdot c} \mathcal{Q}_{\cdot c}},$$ (5')

$$\sigma_{s \cdot c} = \sqrt{\sum_i P_{i \cdot c} \mathcal{Q}_{i \cdot c}}.$$ (5)

The Regression of Test Score on Ability

The mean test score at a fixed level of ability may be thought of as the mean of a column of a scatterplot between test score and ability. Consequently the *test* characteristic curve, represented by (4), is the regression curve of test score on ability.

It is seen from (4') that in the case of equivalent items the regression curve of test score on ability is identical in shape with the *item* characteristic curve, for n is a constant, and $P_{\cdot c}$ is the ordinate of the item characteristic curve. *In the general case, it is seen from (4) that the regression curve of test score on ability is identical in shape with the average of the item characteristic curves.* In the case of typical tests it is commonly found that this average curve looks much like any single characteristic curve except that its slope tends to be lower than that of the individual curves.

Figure 5 presents for illustrative purposes the regression curve or test characteristic curve for Test h. (The metric used for representing ability in this diagram is arbitrarily chosen on the basis of considerations external to the present discussion.)

It may seem disturbing to find that the regression of test score on ability is in general not linear. Actually, however, it would *in general* be quite unreasonable to consider this regression to be strictly linear, as will now be shown.

The metric on the base line of Figure 5, to be sure, can be stretched and squeezed in such a way as to change the regression curve for the particular test represented there into a straight line. However, supposing this to have been already done, consider a new test of the same ability but more discriminating than Test h, and consider the regression line for the new test to be plotted on the transformed Figure 5 along with that of Test *h*. If the new test is sufficiently discriminating, the slope of its regression will, for some ability levels, be greater than the slope of the straight regression line produced by transforming the base line in Figure 5. If the regression for the new test were a straight line with such a higher slope, the straight line would of geometrical necessity cut, and would project beyond, either the base line or the "ceiling" line of the

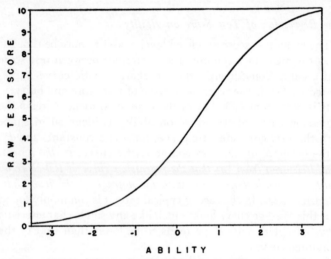

Fɪɢ. 5. The Test Characteristic Curve, i.e., the Regression Curve of Test Score on Ability

transformed Figure 5, or both. This result, however, would represent a prediction that examinees at certain ability levels will obtain negative or more-than-perfect scores, which of course would be absurd. We are forced, therefore, to conclude that the new test will not have a linear regression when the transformation selected for Test *h* is applied to the ability metric.

The transformation in question was a transformation especially designed for a specific test and will not in general rectify the regression curves of other tests of the same ability. Such a transformation of the ability metric might conceivably be legitimate for the practical worker who is concerned with only a single test; it is neither reasonable nor desirable, however, for purposes of theoretical discussion. For such purposes, as already pointed out, the ability metric chosen should remain unchanged while different tests of the same ability are considered, in order to provide an adequate frame of reference with the aid of which the different tests can be compared. We therefore conclude that the *regression of test score on ability must for general theoretical purposes be considered as nonlinear.* This conclusion means, furthermore, that *if we choose the metric for ability in such a way that we are willing to consider it as providing "equal" units of measurement, then the units of measurement provided by the raw score scale must necessarily be considered as "unequal."*

In spite of the fact that the regression of test score on ability is in most cases markedly curvilinear, it may frequently happen that the curvilinearity encountered in actual practice is wholly negligible. This situation will occur whenever the examinees in the particular group tested all lie in a range of ability within which the regression is for all practical purposes linear. Certain investigations (8, §B8) suggest that *effective* linearity may actually be rather closely approximated in most testing situations provided a) the test is near the difficulty level appropriate to the group tested so that the average examinee answers about half the items correctly, and b) the item intercorrelations are not unusually high (note that high item intercorrelations may result either from the use of highly disciminating items or from an unusually large range of ability in the group tested).

True Scores

The true score of an examinee is commonly defined as the average of the scores that he would obtain on an infinite number of equivalent tests. Now for any individual examinee this average will be the same as the average of the scores on the given test obtained by the theoretically infinite number of examinees at the same ability level. This statement may be proved by showing that any alternative assumption will lead to a contradiction; for if some examinees were to obtain higher average scores on an infinite number of equivalent tests than did the average examinee at the same ability level, then the items in these tests would be positively intercorrelated within this group of examinees. Since this conclusion is in contradiction to restriction IV, the assumption leading to this conclusion must be rejected. The conclusion that all true scores fall on the regression curve of raw scores on ability, i.e., on the test characteristic curve, may therefore be accepted as proven.

This conclusion may be rephrased to provide some important generalizations:

1. *The relation of true score to ability is in general curvilinear; consequently true score and ability are not identical concepts.*

2. *If the units chosen for the measurement of ability are to be considered "equal," then the units in which true score is measured must be considered "unequal."* The units of measurement at the extremes of the true score range are in general larger than those near the middle of the range. This fact is really obvious when it is considered that true scores cannot go below zero or above n, whereas for most tests the ability of the examinees to whom the test might conceivably be administered ordinarily ranges far below the ability level at which a true score of approximately zero would be obtained and far above the ability level at which a practically perfect true score would be obtained.

Since there is no scatter of true scores about the regression. it is seen that

3. *There is a perfect curvilinear correlation between true score and ability.*

4. *There exists a one-to-one transformation that will transform true scores into "ability scores"—the ability scale can be obtained from the true score scale by a stretching and squeezing process.*

A further conclusion can be deduced at this point. Let us consider the relation between true scores on two different n-item tests of the same ability. Since both true scores have a perfect curvilinear correlation with the same ability, it follows that the two true scores have a perfect curvilinear correlation with each other. It is of interest to determine under what conditions the relationship between these two scores will be rectilinear.

If the relation of t_1 to t_2 is linear, we have

$$t_2 = at_1 + b,$$

where a and b determine the slope and intercept of the line of relation. Now by restriction III i and ii, it is known that when c is sufficiently large all the item characteristic curves will differ from 1.00 by only a small amount and that when c is sufficiently low, the curves will differ from 0 by only a small amount. Since the regression of test score on ability is by (equation 4) simply n times the average of the item characteristic curve ordinates, it follows that when c is either large or small, the regression curves and hence the values of t_1 and t_2 will be close to n or 0 respectively. Since for such values of c, t_1 and t_2 can differ very little from each other, it follows that a must be approximately equal to 1 and b, to 0; and hence that t_1 and t_2 must be approximately equal for examinees at all ability levels. The conclusion is that

5. *True scores on two tests of the same ability can have a linear relation only if the tests are so similar that each examinee has virtually the same true score on both tests.* Tests of the same ability that differ in the average difficulty level or discriminating power of their component items will necessarily have true scores that are not linearly related.

The Curvilinear Correlation of Test Score on Ability

A curvilinear correlation coefficient is not affected by any transformation of the independent variable. Since the true score scale can be considered as a transformation of the ability scale, the curvilinear correlation of test score on ability is equal to the correlation of test score on true score. Now the regression of test score on true score is actually linear; consequently the "curvilinear" correlation of test score on true score is equal to the product-moment correlation between these two variables, which itself is well known to be equal to the square root of the test reliability. We thus have the conclusion that *the curvilinear correlation of test score on ability is exactly equal to the square root of the test reliability.*

The Standard Error of Measurement

Since all true scores fall on the curve of regression of actual scores on ability, it follows that the deviation of an examinee's actual score from this regression curve is the same as its deviation from the examinee's true score. Since an error of measurement is defined as the difference between the actual score and the true score, these deviations are actually the usual errors of measurement. The standard deviation of these errors of measurement at a fixed ability level is of course the same thing as the standard deviation of the test scores at the same ability level. This standard deviation is appropriately called the standard error of measurement at a fixed ability level (or at a fixed level of true score). Equation (5) provides a formula for this

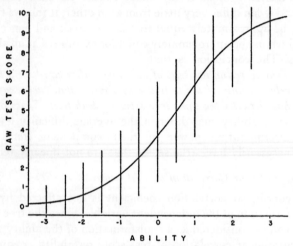

FIG. 6. Standard Errors of Measurement (Vertical Lines) at Selected Ability Levels

standard deviation. The "standard error of measurement" most commonly referred to in the literature is simply an average value for the foregoing standard deviation taken over all examinees in the group tested.

First of all we note from equation (5) that *the standard error of measurement is in general different at different ability levels.* Furthermore, if the ability level is sufficiently low, all values of $P_{i \cdot e}$ will be close to o (restriction III i); if the level is sufficiently high, all values of $Q_{i \cdot e}$ will be close to o (restriction III ii). Consequently, it is seen from equation (5) that *at extreme levels of ability, the standard error of measurement will be very small*. It is worth noting that this small standard error of measurement does *not* indicate that the test has high discriminating power for examinees at extreme levels of ability; actually the test's discriminating power for such examinees will be very poor since examinees in a wide range of very low ability levels will all get scores of zero or approximately zero, and those in a wide range of very high ability levels will all get perfect or near-perfect scores.

In Figure 6 the standard errors of measurement at selected levels of ability for Test *h* are indicated for illustrative purposes by vertical lines, the length of each line being equal to four times the corresponding standard error.

The Bivariate Distribution of Test Score and Ability

The frequency distribution of test scores ($f_{s\cdot c}$) for examinees at a fixed ability level has already been shown (equation 3) to be a generalized binomial. If the frequency distribution of ability were known, which it usually is not, the bivariate frequency distribution of test score and ability could be readily written down. Denoting the distribution of ability by f_c and the desired bivariate distribution by f_{cs}, we have

$$f_{cs} = f_c f_{s\cdot c} \, . \tag{6}$$

Table 1 presents for illustrative purposes the scatterplot that would be obtained if Test *h* were administered to a group of examinees in which ability is normally distributed with zero mean and unit standard deviation. The cell frequencies shown in Table 1 are obtained from equation (6) by numerical integration.

Errors of Measurement

As already pointed out, the deviation of an examinee's score from the regression curve of test score on ability is actually the error of measurement, as this term is usually used. The mean error of measurement for examinees at any given ability level is zero, and the standard deviation of the errors of measurement at a given ability level is given by equation (5). The frequency distribution of the errors of measurement at a given ability

TABLE 1

Scatterplot between Test h Scores and Ability for a Hypothetical Group of 10,000 Examinees in Which Ability Is Normally Distributed

Score	\-4.0 to \-3.5	\-3.5 to \-3.0	\-3.0 to \-2.5	\-2.5 to \-2.0	\-2.0 to \-1.5	\-1.5 to \-1.0	\-1.0 to \-0.5	\-0.5 to 0.0	0.0 to 0.5	0.5 to 1.0	1.0 to 1.5	1.5 to 2.0	2.0 to 2.5	2.5 to 3.0	3.0 to 3.5	3.5 to 4.0	f_s
																Ability	
10										3	18	44	47	28	7	2	149
9									3	25	92	116	66	17	2		321
8								2	17	115	199	143	39	1			519
7								7	94	263	259	96	11				731
6							2	54	261	385	213	35	2				952
5						2	23	200	450	376	106	2					1163
4					1	13	129	427	516	236	26						1350
3				1	9	87	352	573	381	84	3						1490
2			1	9	69	277	530	459	161	13	1						1520
1		2	10	63	209	396	386	180	27	3							1276
0	2	9	37	92	153	145	75	15	2								530

level is a generalized binomial distribution identical with equation (3) except that the mean error of measurement is zero.

The most important of these conclusions may be summarized:

1. *The errors of measurement are not normally distributed, but instead have a generalized binomial distribution which is symmetrical only in a special case.*

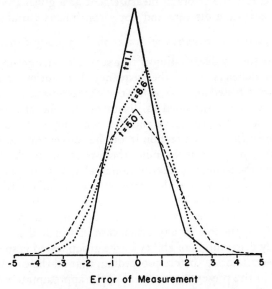

Error of Measurement

Fig. 7. Frequency Polygons of Errors of Measurement for Three Groups of Examinees at Specified Levels of True Scores (t)

2. *The errors of measurement are not independent of true score (or of ability); as the true score deviates from the neighborhood of n/2, the distribution of the errors of measurement becomes less and less variable and more and more skewed.*

3. Since the mean error of measurement at any given ability or true-score level is always zero in the universe of examinees, the regression line passing through these means is horizontal, and *the product-moment correlation between errors of measurement and true score is always zero.*

Although it is common to assume that the errors of measurement are *independent* of true score, this assumption is not necessary to the proof of the basic formulas of test theory—these formulas require merely that the errors of measurement shall have a zero product-moment correlation with true score.

For illustrative purposes, Figure 7 shows the frequency distributions of the errors of measurement for examinees at three different levels of true score on Test h. It may be noted that for an actual test the errors of measurement at a given true score level constitute a discrete and not a continuous variable.

The Frequency Distribution of Scores on Very Long Tests

The frequency distribution of true scores for any group tested of course depends (a) on the frequency distribution of ability in the group tested and (b) on the test characteristic curve. The present section is intended to illustrate the relations between the test characteristic curve and the frequency distribution of true scores. In this one section it will be convenient for purely illustrative purposes to examine these relations in the special case when the frequency distribution of ability in the particular group of examinees tested happens to be a normal distribution. The procedure that will be applied to derive the true score distribution from the test characteristic curve in this special case is equally applicable in any other case in which the shape of frequency distribution of ability in the group tested is specified.

It is worth noting, before proceeding, that all the conclusions reached in the present section will apply approximately to the distribution of actual test scores provided the actual test is sufficiently lengthy, since on sufficiently long tests the actual score will differ from the true score by only a small amount.

In Figure 8 is shown the characteristic curve of a rather discriminating hypothetical test of appropriate difficulty for the group tested, so that the average examinee answers half the items correctly. Such a test might, for example, be composed of items all of which had characteristic curves just like the curve shown, which is fairly typical of the curves found for good free-response items in cognitive tests; or the test might be composed of a variety of items having characteristic curves whose average value would be represented by the test characteristic curve shown.

In Figure 8 the normal frequency distribution of ability is

indicated by the (inverted) normal curve on the base line. The base line has been calibrated in standard deviation units for this normal curve. For illustrative purposes the curve will be considered to have been replaced by the histogram shown superimposed on it. True scores are expressed on the vertical axis in terms of proportion of items answered correctly, so that the possible true score range is from o to 1.

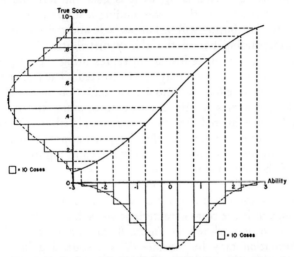

FIG. 8. Derivation of the Distribution of True Scores for a Test of
Moderate Difficulty and Average Discriminating Power

It is assumed for convenience that the total number of examinees in the group tested is 1,000. Our present purpose is to derive the true score distribution from the ability distribution by means of the characteristic curve. Consider the 197 cases that lie between −0.25 and +0.25 on the base line of Figure 8. These cases are represented by the area of the corresponding bar of the histogram. Now, the true scores for all these cases must fall on the regression curve shown, i.e., all their true scores must lie between .45 and .55 (the ordinates of the regression curve when ability is −0.25 and +0.25, respectively). These 197 cases may therefore be represented by a bar in a histogram of true scores, as shown on the left side of the figure. This new bar is constructed so that its area (the area actually covered on the printed page) is equal to the area of the original bar on the ability axis.

Since the actual slope of the regression curve is close to 1 for these 197 cases, the base and height of the histogram bar that represents them in the true score distribution is practically the same as in the ability distribution. However, when the slope of the regression is ½, as it is near the left and right margins of the figure, the corresponding histogram bar in the true score distribution will be half as wide and twice as high as the corresponding bar in the ability distribution.

In this way an entire histogram representing the frequency distribution of true scores may be constructed. The test characteristic curve in effect imposes a transformation on the ability scale that converts it into the true score scale. It should of course be remembered that the true score distribution is actually a smooth curve to which the histogram approximates. The appropriate smooth curve is actually shown in Figure 8 and in some of the subsequent figures.

If the test difficulty is appropriate to the group tested, so that the average examinee has a true score of 50 per cent correct answers, and if the test characteristic curve has a typical ogive shape, such as is shown in Figure 8, the main effect of this transformation may be considered as a squeezing in of the ability scale at the extremes. If the distribution of ability is normal in the group tested, the distribution of test scores will therefore be somewhat platykurtic. The effect is not great for most tests in actual practice; however, for a number of years Dr. L. R Tucker has pointed out that the numerous test score distributions that he has occasion to see are usually platykurtic. Confirmatory empirical results are contained in papers by Mollenkopf (10) and Lord (8).

Figure 9 may be thought of as showing the true score distribution of a test that has rather low discriminating power. Actually, the test shown in Figure 9 may be thought of as the same test as is shown in Figure 8, the difference being due to a difference in the range of ability in the groups of examinees tested. Exactly such a difference would be produced if the group of examinees in Figure 8 had a standard deviation on ability

2½ times that of the group of examinees in Figure 9, i.e., if the arbitrary unit used to measure ability in Figure 8 were 2½ times as large as the unit used in Figure 9.

In order to keep the figure to manageable size, the area used to represent one case in the frequency curves and histograms of Figure 9 has been chosen to be one-half the area used in Figure 8. This change of scale merely reduces the height of the frequency distributions; it is totally unrelated to the size of the unit used to measure ability, discussed in the preceding paragraph.

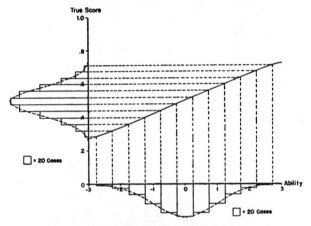

Fig. 9. Derivation of the Distribution of True Scores for a Test of Moderate Difficulty and Poor Discriminating Power

Since the characteristic curve in Figure 9 is virtually straight over the range of ability in which the examinees are found, its effect is virtually that of a linear transformation of the ability scale. The true scores are therefore virtually normally distributed, since a linear transformation of the ability scale will leave the shape of the distribution unchanged. A group of examinees having a normal distribution of ability will obtain a normal distribution of test scores if and only if the test characteristic curve is straight over the range of ability in the group tested. As previously mentioned, the characteristic curve may be nearly straight over the required range when (a) the test is at an appropriate difficulty level for the group tested and (b) the item intercorrelations are not unusually high.

It is worth noting that the true scores in Figure 9 effectively cover only about half the possible range from 0 to 1. This is the obvious result to be expected when the characteristic curve has a low slope, i.e., when the test has low discriminating power. Such a test will yield a relatively low standard deviation of test scores, and will accordingly tend to be unreliable.

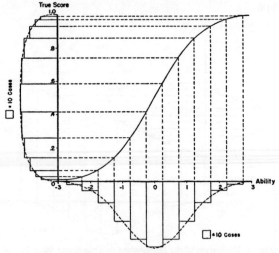

Fig. 10. Derivation of the Distribution of True Scores for a Test of Moderate Difficulty and Very High Discriminating Power

Figure 10 shows the distribution of true scores for a test that is much more discriminating than the test shown in Figure 8; or, alternatively, for the same test as shown in Figure 8 when administered to a very heterogeneous group of examinees. The true scores here have a very platykurtic, almost rectangular distribution with a relatively large standard deviation.

Figure 11 completes the sequence by showing the situation when the test is so discriminating as to produce a U-shaped distribution of true scores. Ferguson and Jackson (3, 4) have pointed out the importance of obtaining actual score distributions shaped like those in Figures 10 and 11 for any situation where it is desired to set a cutting score near the median of the group tested. In such a situation, it is desirable to have as few examinees as possible with scores near the cutting score—a goal that is more nearly achieved with a U-shaped or rectangular than with a bell-shaped distribution of test scores. Unfortunately, the items at present available in practice for use in most cognitive tests do not seem to be sufficiently discriminating to produce anything but a bell-shaped score distribution when administered to typical groups of examinees.

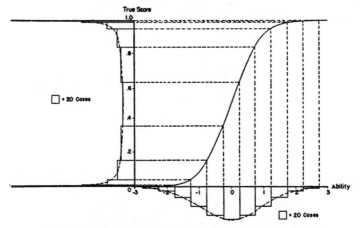

Fig. 11. Derivation of the Distribution of True Scores for a Test of Moderate Difficulty and Extremely High Discriminating Power

From the foregoing sequence of illustrations we may draw the following broad generalizations:

1. Since the test characteristic curve is in general nonlinear, *the test score distribution will not in general have the same shape as the distribution of ability; in particular, if the ability distribution is normal, the score distribution in general will not be strictly normal.*

2. *U-shaped and roughly rectangular score distributions can be produced provided sufficiently discriminating test items can be found.*

3. *Typically, if a test is at the appropriate difficulty level for the group tested, the more discriminating the test, the more platykurtic the score distribution.*

Figure 12 shows the distribution of true scores for a test just like the test in Figure 8 only considerably more difficult; or, alternatively, for the same test as in Figure 8 when administered to a less competent group of examinees. The characteristic curve shown in Figure 12 is simply an extension of the curve in Figure 8. The resulting true score distribution is markedly skew, as would be expected, since most examinees do not know the answers to most of the items. If skewness is

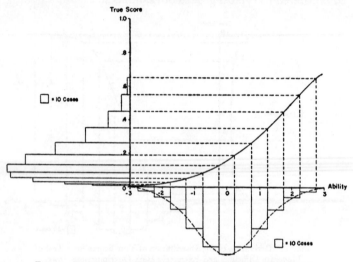

FIG. 12. Derivation of the Distribution of True Scores for a Difficult Test of Average Discriminating Power

measured in the customary fashion on a scale ranging from high negative skewness through zero skewness to high positive skewness, the following generalization may be made:

4. *The skewness of the test score distribution typically tends in a positive direction as the test difficulty is increased above the level appropriate for the group tested; in a negative direction as the test difficulty is decreased below that level.*

The validity of this generalization is apparent when one considers the extreme case where most examinees obtain a score of zero (or perfect) on the test, thus producing a marked positive (or negative) skewness of the distribution of scores.

In Figures 13 and 14, we will consider the peculiar case of a test composed of highly discriminating items, half of which are quite easy and half of which are quite difficult. We will suppose that each of the easy items has the characteristic curve shown by the broken line in Figure 13, and that each of the difficult items has the curve shown by the dotted line. The average of these curves, shown by the solid line lying halfway between them, is proportional to the characteristic curve of the total

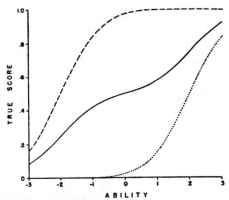

Fig. 13. Characteristic Curves of an Easy Subtest (– – – –), a Difficult Subtest (····), and the Combined Test (———)

test. Unlike the curves for the individual items, the test characteristic curve in this peculiar case has three points of inflexion.

It may be noted that, at any given ability level, the test characteristic curve slopes less steeply than does one of the other two curves, so that at no point does the test characteristic curve attain the maximum slope attained by the curves of which it is an average. We may make the following generalization:

5. *A test composed of items of equal discriminating power but of varying difficulty will not be as discriminating in the neighborhood of any single ability level as would a test composed of similar items all of appropriate difficulty for that level.*

Figure 14 shows the true score distribution for the test composed half of easy and half of difficult items. The effect of the item characteristic curve here, considered as a transformation imposed on the frequency distribution of ability, is to squeeze together the cases that are near the middle of the ability distribution, thus producing a leptokurtic true score distribution. Empirical evidence confirming this result is found in (8, 10).

.Using the graphical method illustrated here, the reader can, if he wishes, readily determine the true score distributions that will be produced by other shapes of test characteristic curves.

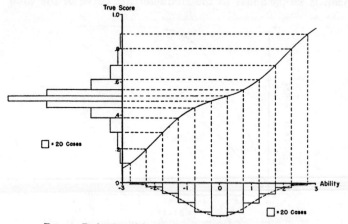

FIG. 14. Derivation of the Distribution of True Scores for a Test Composed Half of Easy Items and Half of Difficult Items

Determining Whether a Given Set of Items Meets the Original Restrictions

Restrictions I and II simply require the use of certain standard scoring methods. Restriction III imposes certain broad limits on the shape of the characteristic curves of the items to be considered. Restriction IV requires that the item responses shall all be independent when ability is held constant.

If we can prepare and administer a sufficiently reliable (i.e., a sufficiently long) test, we can obtain test scores that approximate as closely as desired to the true scores. Ignoring the small difference between our obtained scores and the desired true scores, we can compute the proportion of examinees at a given score level who answer a given item correctly. Let us plot the values of this proportion for a single item on a graph, using test score as abscissa. Since the true score scale is simply a transformation of the ability scale, a curve connecting the plotted points is simply a transformation of the item characteristic curve.

Let us plot all such transformed item characteristic curves on the same graph and try to find a way to stretch and squeeze the scale on the abscissa so that all the characteristic curves simultaneously will meet the broad restrictions imposed on their shape. Actually, if the correct answers are not ordinarily obtained by guessing, no transformation may be needed, or at worst a number of items may need to be discarded from the test, since most item characteristic curves in the cognitive area seem to have the general shape required.

If restriction III can be shown to have been met by the foregoing procedure, we may now examine the data for conformity to the more stringent restriction IV. We can take all examinees at a given score level and apply a chi-square test (or, if the number of cases is small, an exact test) to determine if their responses to any pair of items, or to any set of items, are independent. Values of chi-square obtained at different score levels may be added and the resulting total chi-square may be tested for significance.

In case the entire test fails to produce an insignificant chi-square, it must be concluded that the test is not homogeneous and does not meet restriction IV; however, even in such a case, it may frequently be possible to break down such a test into homogeneous subtests with which work can be carried forward. For example, a mathematics achievement test might be found to be composed of relatively homogeneous subtests in the areas of algebra, geometry, trigonometry, etc.

As will have been noted, the foregoing procedures, while theoretically simple, would be extremely arduous in practice in view of the large number of items required. Practical approximations may suggest themselves to reduce the labor involved. The main point, however, is not that this procedure should be carried out in common practice, but that it is possible, at least theoretically, to determine whether or not a set of items conforms to the restrictions imposed.

Summary

Since two different tests of the same ability will not in general yield the same shape of frequency distribution of raw scores, or of true scores, when administered to a single group of examinees, it is obvious that neither the raw score scale nor the true score scale accurately represents the distribution of "ability" in the group. (The terminology of achievement and aptitude testing is used here, although the results will apply to certain other kinds of tests also.) Since we are usually really concerned with "ability" and not with the particular raw score scale provided by a particular test, it is helpful to determine what may be rigorously deduced about the relation of the raw score scale of a given test to the underlying ability. Since the relation of the raw score scale to ability is determined by the particular characteristics of the items of which the test is composed, some light will thereby be thrown on the question of how the test items should be selected in order to obtain certain desirable relations between test score and ability.

The only assumption made in the present argument is that the underlying ability is an ordered variable that can be thought of as represented numerically in a single dimension. The choice of a metric to be used for measuring ability is considered to be a purely arbitrary choice; no such metric is specified here, the the choice of metric being left to the whim of the reader.

The following four restrictions are imposed on the test items to be considered:

I. Items are scored o or 1.

II. The raw test score is the number of items answered correctly.

III. The item characteristic curves have the general shape typical of cognitive items that are not answered correctly by guessing.

IV. The items are homogeneous in a certain specified sense.

It is theoretically possible to determine whether or not a set of items conforms to these restrictions.

The conclusions deduced include the following:

1. The regression of test score, and of true score, on ability must in general be considered as curvilinear. (The practi-

cal effect of this curvilinearity will often be so small as to be negligible, however, since there is usually a limited range of ability within which the regression curve is virtually linear.)

2. If an ability metric has been chosen by the reader so as to provide units of measurement that he is willing to consider as "equal," then the raw score units, and also the true score units, must in general be considered as "unequal." The raw score and true score units at the extremes of the score range tend to be larger than those near the middle.

3. The regression of test score on ability is identical in shape with the average of the characteristic curves of the test items.

4. There is a perfect curvilinear correlation between true score and ability; hence the true score scale may be considered as a transformation of the ability scale.

5. If two tests of the same ability differ in the average difficulty level or discriminating power of their component items, the true scores on the two tests, although perfectly correlated, will necessarily have a curvilinear relation to each other.

6. The curvilinear correlation of test score on ability is always equal to the square root of the test reliability.

7. The standard error of measurement varies for examinees at different ability levels; it is smallest for examinees who would be expected to obtain near-perfect or near-zero scores.

8. The errors of measurement are not normally distributed, but rather have a "generalized binomial" distribution which is symmetric only in special cases.

9. Although *uncorrelated* with ability and with true score in the product-moment sense, the errors of measurement are not *independent* of ability or of true score, since the standard deviation and the skewness of the errors vary with the ability level.

10. The test score distribution will not in general have the same shape as the distribution of ability; in particular, if ability is normally distributed, the raw scores in general

will not be normally distributed. (In practice, however, the degree of non-normality will often be negligible.)

11. U-shaped and rectangular distributions of raw scores can be obtained if sufficiently discriminating test items can be found.

12. Typically, if a test is at the appropriate difficulty level for the group tested, the more discriminating the test, the more platykurtic the score distribution.

13. The skewness of the test score distribution typically tends to become positive as the test difficulty is increased, negative as the difficulty is decreased.

14. A test composed of items of equal discriminating power but of varying difficulty will not be as discriminating in the neighborhood of any single ability level as would a test composed of items of the same discriminating power but all of appropriate difficulty for that level. A "peaked" test, composed of items all of approximately equal difficulty, should therefore be used whenever the sole purpose of the test is to divide examinees into "passing" and "failing" groups.

It has been possible rigorously to deduce a number of significant conclusions from the single assumption and the four restrictions stated. More specific, additional conclusions can be reached if some mathematical form can be specified for the item characteristic curve, as has been done by Carroll (1), Cronbach and Warrington (2), Lawley (5, 6), Lazarsfeld (7), Lord (8, 9), Mosier (11, 12), and Tucker (13, 14, 15).

REFERENCES

1. Carroll, J. B. "Problems in the Factor Analysis of Tests of Varying Difficulty." *American Psychologist*, V (1950), 369. (Abstract.)

2. Cronbach, L. J. and Warrington, W. G. "Efficiency of Multiple-Choice Tests as a Function of Spread of Item Difficulties." *Psychometrika*, XVII (1952), 127–148.

3. Ferguson, G. A. "Item Selection by the Constant Process." *Psychometrika*, VII (1942), 19–29.

4. Jackson, R. W. B. and Ferguson, G. A. "A Functional Approach in Test Construction." EDUCATIONAL & PSYCHOLOGICAL MEASUREMENT III (1943) 23–28.

5. Lawley, D. N. "On Problems Connected with Item Selection and Test Construction." *Procedures of the Royal Society of Edinburgh*, 1943, 61-A, Part 3, 273–287.
6. Lawley, D. N. "The Factorial Analysis of Multiple Item Tests." *Procedures of the Royal Society of Edinburgh*, 1944, 62-A, Part I, 74–82.
7. Lazarsfeld, P. F. (with S. A. Stouffer, et al). *Measurement and Prediction*, Vol. 4 of *Studies in Social Psychology in World War II*. Princeton: Princeton University Press, 1950, Chapters 10 and 11.
8. Lord, F. M. "A Theory of Test Scores." *Psychometric Monographs*, (1952), No. 7.
9. Lord, F. M. "An Application of Confidence Intervals and of Maximum Likelihood to the Estimation of an Examinee's Ability." *Psychometrika*, XVIII (1953), 56–76.
10. Mollenkopf, W. G. "Variation of the Standard Error of Measurement." *Psychometrika*, XIV (1949), 189–229.
11. Mosier, C. I. "Psychophysics and Mental Test Theory: Fundamental Postulates and Elementary Theorems." *Psychological Review*, XLVII (1940), 355–366.
12. Mosier, C. I. "Psychophysics and Mental Test Theory. II. The Constant Process." *Psychological Review*, XLVIII (1941), 235–249.
13. Tucker, L. R. "Maximum Validity of a Test with Equivalent Items." *Psychometrika*, XI (1946), 1–13.
14. Tucker, L. R. "A Method for Scaling Ability Test Items in Difficulty Taking Item Unreliability into Account. *American Psychologist*, III (1948), 309–10. (Abstract)
15. Tucker, L. R. "A Level of Proficiency Scale for a Unidimensional Skill." *American Psychologist*, VII (1952), 408. (Abstract).

Three Multivariate Models:
Factor Analysis, Latent Structure Analysis,
and Latent Profile Analysis*

W. A. Gibson†   *Queens College of the City University of New York*

The factor analysis model and Lazarsfeld's latent structure scheme for analyzing dichotomous attributes are derived to show how the latter model avoids three knotty problems in factor analysis: communality estimation, rotation, and curvilinearity. Then the latent structure model is generalized into latent profile analysis for the study of interrelations among quantitative measures. Four latent profile examples are presented and discussed in terms of their limitations and the problems of latent metric and dimensionality thereby raised. The possibility of treating higher order empirical relations in a manner paralleling their various uses in the latent structure model is indicated.

At an early point in *Multiple-Factor Analysis* ([18], p. 70), Thurstone remarks:

> It would be unfortunate if some initial success with the analytical methods to be described here should lead us to commit ourselves to them with such force of habit as to disregard the development of entirely different constructs that may be indicated by improvements in measurement and by inconsistencies between theory and experiment.

This paper is an attempt to take that statement to heart.

First the derivation of the factor analysis model will be sketched, noting three inherent conceptual and procedural problems: (i) how to estimate communalities in the event that only shared variance is to be analyzed, (ii) how to resolve rotational indeterminacy, and (iii) what to do with the extra linear factors that are forced to emerge when nonlinearities occur in the data. Some recent concepts for the multidimensional analysis of qualitative data— the latent structure model of Lazarsfeld [15]—are considered, with special reference to their handling of the trouble spots in factor analysis. Next these new concepts are generalized to produce an alternative way of analyzing the interrelations among quantitative measures. This is the latent profile model.

All three of these models are discussed strictly from the point of view of sample statistics. The problem of generalizing to a population of which the

---

*The latter model is anticipated in an earlier paper by Green [12].

†The major portion of this paper was completed at the Center for Advanced Study in the Behavioral Sciences. The opinions expressed are those of the author and are not to be construed as reflecting official Department of the Army policy.

sample may be considered representative is not taken up for any of the three models.

Four examples of the latent profile model are given. Two of them are fictitious but their form closely parallels the corresponding two empirical examples. These examples are discussed from the viewpoint of the further work they suggest concerning the metric and dimensionality of the latent space. The use of higher order empirical relations for testing fit and for further particularization of the latent profile model is briefly discussed, and the possibility of close parallelism between developments in the latent structure and latent profile models is pointed out. The paper concludes with a plea for continued flexibility in the choice of multivariate models as new and improved ones appear.

Some Problems in Factor Analysis

The fundamental postulate of factor analysis ([18], p. 63) is expressed in the simple linear equation

$$(1) \qquad Z_{ij} = a_{j1}Z_{i1} + a_{j2}Z_{i2} + \cdots + a_{jq}Z_{iq} .$$

Z_{ij} is the standard score of individual i on test j. Z_{i1}, Z_{i2}, $\cdots$, Z_{iq} are the standard scores of individual i on a hypothesized set of q statistically independent traits or factors. (This does not preclude subsequent conversion to correlated factors in any given analysis. The algebra of correlated factors will not be introduced here, however, for that would only complicate the discussion without changing the arguments.) The a's in (1) are a set of weights descriptive of test j and invariant for individuals.

Straightforward summational algebra and the independence of factors lead directly from (1) to the basic equation of factor analysis ([18], p. 78):

$$(2) \qquad r_{jk} = a_{j1}a_{k1} + a_{j2}a_{k2} + \cdots + a_{jq}a_{kq} .$$

Thus r_{jk}, the correlation between tests j and k, is expressed as a simple bilinear function of the a's for those two tests. These a's, also known as factor loadings, are interpretable as correlations between tests and factors.

The essential task in the factor analysis of a battery of s tests is to solve for the a's in the system of $s(s - 1)/2$ bilinear equations resulting from (2). The number of factor loadings is sq, q for each of the s tests. These loadings can be obtained by a wide variety of techniques that have been developed over the years. Most of these methods attempt to account for the intercorrelations in terms of a minimum number of factors. Perfect accounting for the intercorrelations by the factors is seldom demanded because of sampling error and the frank expectation of at least minor disagreements between model and data. Some nonvanishing "residual" correlations are permitted, so long as they are small and show no systematic pattern.

One troublesome feature of the factor model is the problem of how to deal with those elements in the correlation matrix that have repeated sub-scripts—the diagonal r_{ii}'s. To take these as perfect self-correlations of unity would amount to trying to analyze all of the variance of every test, including the unreliable part. To insert the test reliabilities into the diagonal cells would imply an interest in analyzing all of the "true" or repeatable variance of the tests, including that specific to each test and unrelated to other tests in the battery. More commonly preferred among factor analysts is to attempt to analyze only that part of a test's variance—its communality—that is shared with other tests in the battery. Communalities could be defined alternatively as those portions of the self-correlations accounted for by the factors that suffice to account for the between-test correlations. In any event, the com-munalities are not empirically given and yet are needed at the start for maxi-mum efficiency of solution. In principle the communalities could be determined by certain operations (cf. [18], pp. 294–307) applied to the empirically given side entries in the correlation matrix, but these operations are usually so time consuming that a successive approximations approach is often sub-stituted. Rough communality estimates are used to obtain an initial factorial solution, which in turn provides improved estimates for a second cycle of the same kind, and so on until the communalities are sufficiently "stabilized." It fortunately happens that with large test batteries little or no iterating of this kind is needed, but for small batteries several cycles may be required before the communality problem is adequately resolved.

A second and more important problem in factor analysis is the inherent partial indeterminacy of the a's that is known as the rotational problem. It is most easily understood in terms of q-dimensional geometry. The a's for any test j may be thought of as the projections of a point j on a set of co-ordinate axes in q-space. The table of factor loadings for the s tests then defines a configuration of s points in terms of their projections on a q-di-mensional reference frame. But the equations of factor analysis, by themselves, do not indicate *which* position of the reference frame, among an infinite number of possibilities in the same q-space, is to be preferred. Only the origin of the coordinate system is fixed, so that the reference frame can be rotated freely from any position to any other without distortion of the configuration of points defined by it. Naturally the a's change with such rotations, but always in such a way as to preserve the spatial interrelations among the points they define. Many ways of resolving this rotational indeterminacy have been proposed. Probably the most notable is the simple structure principle ([18], pp. 181–193), which strives to simplify the factorial structure of the tests by maximizing the number of near-zero factor loadings. Many of these proposals (especially those centering around the simple structure principle) involve heavy computing loads, relatively rare geometric intuition, or both; many are debated or debatable; all are in the nature of afterthoughts that are not built into the equations defining the model.

Another perplexing problem in the factor analysis model is the paradox of difficulty factors [2, 4, 13, 20]. If factor analysis is applied to a battery of tests varying widely in difficulty but quite obviously measuring but one underlying trait, the result is not one but several "factors"—one for each level of difficulty. This is generally attributed to curvilinear relations among tests markedly different in difficulty, such curvilinearity being forced by the differential skewness of the score distributions. Note, however, that it is only the relations between tests and factors, as indicated by (1), that the factor model explicitly restricts to linear form.

The record of empirical fruitfulness (or lack thereof) of factor analysis is not at issue here. Nor are misapplications of it pertinent to this discussion. The other two models to be discussed here are meant to be put to much the same use, and they may very well suffer the same kind of misuse.

Some New Concepts: Latent Structure Analysis

Only one variety of latent structure analysis—that known as the discrete class model—is discussed here.

Latent structure analysis [15] is Lazarsfeld's technique for analyzing the interrelations among dichotomous attributes, such as the item responses on a survey questionnaire. It is based on linear recruitment equations of the following kind:

$$
\begin{aligned}
n &= n_1 + n_2 + \cdots + n_q \,, \\
n_j &= n_1 p_{1j} + n_2 p_{2j} + \cdots + n_q p_{qj} \,, \\
n_{jk} &= n_1 p_{1jk} + n_2 p_{2jk} + \cdots + n_q p_{qjk} \,, \\
n_{jkl} &= n_1 p_{1jkl} + n_2 p_{2jkl} + \cdots + n_q p_{qjkl} \,, \quad \text{etc.}
\end{aligned}
$$

(3)

The quantities on the left are empirically given or *manifest* data. They indicate the number of people in the entire sample, n, the number endorsing a single item, n_j, the number endorsing any pair of items, n_{jk}, and so on. The quantities on the right are the underlying or *latent* parameters of the model. The number of terms on the right is q, the number of mutually exclusive and exhaustive subgroups (*latent classes*) into which the analysis will divide the total sample. The number of people in latent class 1 is n_1, and so on. The *latent probability* p_{1j} is the proportion of the members of latent class 1 who endorse item j, p_{1jk} is the proportion of class 1 members who endorse both items j and k, and so on. Equations (3) merely show how the manifest joint endorsements are recruited from the latent classes. It may be noted, in passing, that equations (3), being a set of recruitment equations, are intrinsically linear, while the initial equation of factor analysis is linear only because it was made so.

The manifest-latent distinction that is so prominent in latent structure theory is of course central in factor analysis as well. There the tests and their intercorrelations are manifest, and the factors and the loadings thereon are latent. The same distinction also appears in the latent profile model to be discussed later.

The preceding recruitment equations are equally valid for any method of classification and for any number of latent classes. The next step is to invoke a pertinent basis for classification. This is the core of the latent structure model. It is quite relevant to require that each latent class exhibit homogeneity with respect to any underlying dimensions that may be responsible for the manifest interrelations. Perfect homogeneity is not crucial, so long as deviations from the class norm are random. Such random deviations are of course uncorrelated within the class. Thus it is sufficient to require that each latent class be homogeneous enough, with respect to any and all such latent dimensions, so that all item responses *within the class* are independent in the coin-tossing sense. This intraclass independence is expressed in the following equations.

$$
(4) \quad
\begin{aligned}
&p_{1jk} = p_{1j}p_{1k} , \qquad p_{2jk} = p_{2j}p_{2k} , \cdots , p_{qjk} = p_{qj}p_{qk} , \\
&p_{1jkl} = p_{1j}p_{1k}p_{1l} , \qquad p_{2jkl} = p_{2j}p_{2k}p_{2l} , \cdots , p_{qjkl} = p_{qj}p_{qk}p_{ql} , \quad \text{etc.}
\end{aligned}
$$

The substitution of (4) into (3) yields the basic equations of latent structure analysis ([15], p. 385).

$$
(5) \quad
\begin{aligned}
n &= n_1 + n_2 + \cdots + n_q , \\
n_j &= n_1 p_{1j} + n_2 p_{2j} + \cdots + n_q p_{qj} , \\
n_{jk} &= n_1 p_{1j}p_{1k} + n_2 p_{2j}p_{2k} + \cdots + n_q p_{qj}p_{qk} , \\
n_{jkl} &= n_1 p_{1j}p_{1k}p_{1l} + n_2 p_{2j}p_{2k}p_{2l} + \cdots + n_q p_{qj}p_{qk}p_{ql} , \quad \text{etc.}
\end{aligned}
$$

Thus all of the manifest joint frequencies are accounted for in terms of $(q + sq)$ latent parameters, q class sizes and q latent probabilities (p_{1j} , p_{2j} , $\cdots$, p_{qj}) for each of the s items. The successive levels of manifest frequencies (n, n_j , n_{jk} , etc.) number, respectively, 1, s, $s(s-1)/2$, etc., the coefficients in the binomial expansion $(a + b)^s$. These add up to 2^s, the number of equations relating manifest to latent data in this model.

The task here, as in factor analysis, is to solve the basic equations for the unknown latent parameters. Several latent structure solutions already exist. The most recent of these [1, 7] avoid the use of any joint frequencies with repeated subscripts (n_{jj} , n_{jjk} , n_{jjj} , n_{jjkl} , etc.). In latent structure analysis these are treated as analogous to the communalities of factor analysis, in not being manifest. To interpret them as equivalent to the corresponding lower order joint frequencies without repeated subscripts (i.e., $n_{ii} = n_i$, $n_{iik} = n_{ik}$, $n_{iii} = n_i$, etc.) would be analogous to the use of unit self-correlations in factor analysis. Instead, the latent structure model usually treats these elements with repeated subscripts as stemming from, rather than leading to, the latent parameters of the model that suffices to account for the manifest data *without* repeated subscripts.

The Anderson latent structure solution and an earlier one by Green [11] eliminate the latent structure analogue of the rotational problem through the use of manifest data with more than two subscripts, such as n_{ikl} . (A cursory investigation indicates that it might be self-contradictory for the factor model to make use of manifest interrelations among more than two variables at a time. This is because at least some of the joint distributions among factor scores would have to exhibit asymmetries that could easily destroy the basic linear postulate of factor analysis.)

These higher order data select, from the infinite number of rotational solutions accounting for lower order manifest frequencies equally well, the *one* that fits *themselves* best. Another early latent structure solution [5, 6, or 8] effects a partial (often severe) reduction of rotational indeterminacy without the expense of obtaining higher order data. This is accomplished by capitalizing on the simple fact that the latent parameters, being probabilities, can be neither negative nor greater than unity.

Earlier it was indicated that the artifact of difficulty factors arises in factor analysis when curvilinearities are present. Note that the derivation of the latent structure model embodies no restriction on curvilinear relations, either among the manifest attributes or between them and the latent dimensions.

The latent structure model has already shown promise in empirical research [cf. 14, 17]. Only its restriction to the analysis of dichotomous attributes prevents it from being a feasible alternative to the factor analysis of quantitative variables. The latent profile model to be taken up next is the generalization of latent structure analysis to the case of quantitative manifest variables [cf. 12].

Some Linear Recruitment Equations for Quantitative Manifest Variables

A reasonable question to ask is whether the natural linearity of recruitment equations could not provide a basis for analyzing interrelations among manifest variables that are quantitative rather than qualitative. This section will display such a system of recruitment equations.

Suppose there is available a set of s quantitative measures, such as test scores, on a sample of n people. On some basis let every sample member be assigned to one, and only one, of q subgroups. Then the size, sums of scores, and sums of score products for the entire sample are related to corresponding subgroup statistics in the following simple way.

$$n = n_1 + n_2 + \cdots + n_q ,$$

(6)
$$\sum^n X_{ij} = \sum^{n_1} X_{ij} + \sum^{n_2} X_{ij} + \cdots + \sum^{n_q} X_{ij} ,$$

$$\sum^n X_{ij}X_{ik} = \sum^{n_1} X_{ij}X_{ik} + \sum^{n_2} X_{ij}X_{ik} + \cdots + \sum^{n_q} X_{ij}X_{ik} ,$$

$$\sum^n X_{ij}X_{ik}X_{il} = \sum^{n_1} X_{ij}X_{ik}X_{il}$$

$$+ \sum^{n_2} X_{ij}X_{ik}X_{il} + \cdots + \sum^{n_q} X_{ij}X_{ik}X_{il} , \quad \text{etc.}$$

All summations in (6) are over individuals. The summations on the left are over the entire sample, while those on the right are over the members of the various subgroups. X_{ij} is the score of individual i on test j, and it may be in raw, deviational, standard, or any other derived units. The same is true of X_{ik}, X_{il}, etc.

It is convenient to designate the various summations in (6) by the letter m with appropriate subscripts. Thus m_j and m_{jk} represent, respectively, the sum of scores on test j and the sum of products of scores on tests j and k, each sum being for the entire sample. m_{1j} and m_{1jk}, on the other hand, stand for the same things in subgroup 1 only, and so on. Equations (6) then become

(7)
$$n = n_1 + n_2 + \cdots + n_q ,$$

$$m_j = m_{1j} + m_{2j} + \cdots + m_{qj} ,$$

$$m_{jk} = m_{1jk} + m_{2jk} + \cdots + m_{qjk} ,$$

$$m_{jkl} = m_{1jkl} + m_{2jkl} + \cdots + m_{qjkl} , \quad \text{etc.}$$

The m's in (7) will be referred to as *product moments* of various orders. The product moments in the third line, involving two tests, will be said to be of second order, while those for three tests are of third order, and so on. For consistency, the m's involving only one test j will be called first-order product moments, and n, the sample size, could be called the zero-order product moment for the sample. The m's on the left in (7) will be called sample product moments, while those on the right are subgroup product moments.

It should be stressed that (6) and (7) in no way restrict either the empirical data or the method of classification into subgroups. It will be the burden of the next two sections to establish a basis for grouping that will convert these recruitment equations into a mathematical model.

The Fundamental Theorem of Latent Profile Analysis

Consider now a two-dimensional joint distribution in which the score of every person in the sample on test k is plotted against his score on test j.

Such a scatterplot is pictured in Figure 1. The unit of measurement for both tests is entirely arbitrary here. The ellipse in Figure 1 indicates only one of the possible shapes that the total configuration of points could have. The circle represents a subgroup t, of size n_t, *within* which the correlation between

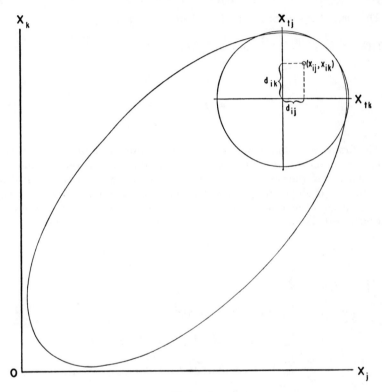

FIGURE 1
A Hypothetical Scatter Diagram

tests j and k is zero. The two lines labeled X_{tj} and X_{tk} in Figure 1 indicate the means of subgroup t on tests j and k. They intersect in what is called the *centroid* of the points comprising subgroup t. The point corresponding to individual i, a member of subgroup t, is shown with the coordinates (X_{ij}, X_{ik}), his scores on the two tests. The two distances, d_{ij} and d_{ik}, are the deviations of individual i from the j and k means of his subgroup. A property of such deviations is that their sum, over all members of the subgroup, is zero.

The j and k scores of individual i may be expressed in terms of his subgroup means and his deviations from those means, as follows:

$$(8) \qquad X_{ij} = X_{tj} + d_{ij} ,$$

$$(9) \qquad X_{ik} = X_{tk} + d_{ik} .$$

Then m_{tj}, the sum of j scores for subgroup t, is given by

$$(10) \qquad m_{tj} = \sum^{n_t} X_{ij}$$
$$= \sum^{n_t} (X_{tj} + d_{ij})$$
$$= \sum^{n_t} X_{tj} + \sum^{n_t} d_{ij}$$
$$= n_t X_{tj} .$$

The first term in the third line simplifies because X_{tj} is the same for every member of the subgroup. The last term in the third line vanishes because it is a sum of deviation scores. Thus the j scores for any subgroup t contribute to the sum of all j scores *as if* the members of the subgroup were concentrated at their mean for test j. This result (by no means a new one) will next be generalized, in an appropriate way, to the second-order product moment, m_{tjk}, for subgroup t.

By definition and with the help of (8) and (9), m_{tjk} becomes

$$(11) \qquad m_{tjk} = \sum^{n_t} X_{ij} X_{ik}$$
$$= \sum^{n_t} (X_{tj} + d_{ij})(X_{tk} + d_{ik})$$
$$= \sum^{n_t} (X_{tj} X_{tk} + X_{tj} d_{ik} + X_{tk} d_{ij} + d_{ij} d_{ik})$$
$$= \sum^{n_t} X_{tj} X_{tk} + X_{tj} \sum^{n_t} d_{ik} + X_{tk} \sum^{n_t} d_{ij} + \sum^{n_t} d_{ij} d_{ik}$$
$$= n_t X_{tj} X_{tk} .$$

The first term in the fourth line of (11) simplifies because X_{tj} and X_{tk} are the same for all members of the subgroup. The second and third terms in that line vanish because they contain sums of deviations. The last term vanishes because it is the numerator of the formula for the correlation, within the subgroup, between tests j and k. The subgroup was earlier defined as having that correlation equal to zero. Thus the second-order product moment, m_{tjk}, is the same as it would be if all members of subgroup t were concentrated at their centroid. This holds for any subgroup within which tests j and k are uncorrelated.

A further distinction in terminology needs to be made here. The quantity

m_{tjk} is a sum of products of horizontal and vertical distances from the origin in Figure 1. It will therefore be called a *product moment about the origin*. Another kind of product moment in (11) is the last term in line 4, the sum of products of horizontal and vertical distances of a set of points from their own centroid. Such a quantity is appropriately called a *product moment about the centroid* of the set of points that is involved. The geometric interpretation of scores and deviations as distances makes it clear that the point of reference (origin, centroid, or some other point) of a product moment must always be specified in some way. Naturally this holds for all orders of product moments. Up to now, with four exceptions, all product moments have had the origin as their point of reference. The four exceptions are the last term in line 3 of (10) and the summations in the last three terms of line 4 in (11), which have the centroid of subgroup t as their point of reference.

The results of (10) and (11) can be generalized to higher order product moments by imposing additional restrictions on subgroup t. Not only must that subgroup be defined as having all pairs of tests j, k, and l uncorrelated within it, but, let it also have, for those three tests, a vanishing third-order product moment about its centroid. With these restrictions its third-order product moment about the origin, m_{tjkl} , becomes

(12) $$m_{tjkl} = n_t X_{tj} X_{tk} X_{tl} .$$

This result is, in form and mode of development, a third-order analogue of the final step in the previous two equations. The fourth-order equivalent is obtained by analogous higher order restrictions, and so on.

Since in all of this discussion the origin could have been placed at any point 0, it now becomes possible to state the fundamental theorem of latent profile analysis.

> The g-order product moment, about any point O, of n_t points having zero product moments of order g and less about their centroid, is equal to the g-order product moment, about the point O, of n_t points placed at that centroid.

The Basic Equations of Latent Profile Analysis

The foregoing theorem provides a basis for grouping in the recruitment equations introduced previously. The close analogy with latent structure analysis will be obvious. Each subgroup or latent class should be homogeneous in whatever underlying dimensions are necessary to account for the observed interrelations. The homogeneity need not be complete, so long as deviations from the class averages are random, i.e., independent.

In the statistics of dichotomous attributes (as employed in coin-tossing experiments, for example), the notion of independence has usually applied to all orders of joint occurrence, and not just to pairs of events. This is the case in latent structure analysis, where within-class independence is *defined* as pertaining not only to all pairs of items but also to all triplets, all quadruplets, and so on. (It is easily shown by example that higher order independence among dichotomous attributes is *not* a mere logical consequence of uncorrelatedness between all pairs of such attributes.)

The concept of uncorrelatedness among quantitative measures, on the other hand, has more often been restricted, at least among psychometricians, to pairs of such measures. (A statistically oriented prepublication reviewer has pointed out that the two kinds of independence being discussed here are known to statisticians as *pair-wise* and *mutual* independence.) This is not an intrinsic or logical difference between qualitative and quantitative statistics. It is rather only a historical accident that the question of higher order independence among quantitative measures has less often arisen in psychometrics. That question arises here, for it turns out that the proper definition of such independence is crucial for this model.

In the previous section the within-class uncorrelatedness between pairs of tests was shown to be synonymous with vanishing second-order product moments about the centroid of the class. This is because such product moments are the numerators of the formulas for the corresponding correlations. Purely by analogy, higher order within-class independence may be equated with the vanishing of higher order product moments about the centroid of the class. (The failure of such product moments to vanish would allow, for example, a positive correlation between tests j and k among class members with high scores on test l, accompanied by a compensating negative correlation between the same two tests among class members having low scores on test l. This could happen in spite of zero correlations between all pairs of the three tests within the class as a whole. If correlational patterns can differ within subdivisions of a class, then the class is not homogeneous even from a commonsense point of view.) Therefore let the within-class independence of the present model be *defined* as applying to all orders of interrelations, and as expressing itself in the vanishing of product moments of all orders about the centroid of the class. Then the fundamental theorem applies with full force to the product moments of each class, so that the results of equations (10), (11), and (12) can be used to transform (7) into the basic equations of latent profile analysis:

(13)
$$n = n_1 + n_2 + \cdots + n_q ,$$
$$m_j = n_1 X_{1j} + n_2 X_{2j} + \cdots + n_q X_{qj} ,$$
$$m_{jk} = n_1 X_{1j} X_{1k} + n_2 X_{2j} X_{2k} + \cdots + n_q X_{qj} X_{qk} ,$$
$$m_{jkl} = n_1 X_{1j} X_{1k} X_{1l} + n_2 X_{2j} X_{2k} X_{2l} + \cdots + n_q X_{qj} X_{qk} X_{ql} , \quad \text{etc.}$$

Thus for s tests the 2^s manifest product moments (including n) are accounted for in terms of $(q + sq)$ latent parameters—the q latent class sizes and the

q class averages for each of the s tests. Each latent class is therefore character-ized by its size and its profile of s test averages, its *latent profile*.

The latent profile equations and those of latent structure analysis turn out to be identical in form, as can be seen from a comparison of (5) and (13). This means that all algebraic latent structure solutions [1, 7, 11] are directly applicable to the latent profile equations. Hence the latent profile equations have a solution that can be obtained without the involvement of communality analogues (m_{ii}, m_{iik}, m_{iii}, etc.), and that is, in general, rotationally unique. (A conversation with Robert P. Abelson at Yale University has clarified the fact that, when deviational scores are used, the m_{ii} are the between-groups variances.) Nor do the latent profile equations restrict the occurrence of curvilinear relations among tests or between tests and underlying dimensions. Thus the dilemma of difficulty factors is avoided in this model.

Two Special Cases of Latent Profile Analysis

In the development of the latent profile equations the score units were entirely arbitrary. There are, however, two kinds of test scores that deserve special attention. Consider first the case where the manifest variables are, as in latent structure analysis, dichotomous attributes. Let the presence and absence of each such attribute be designated by scores of one and zero, respectively. In this case the manifest latent profile m's become identical with the manifest latent structure n's, and the class averages of latent profile analysis become the latent probabilities of latent structure analysis. The latent class sizes mean the same thing in both models. Thus the latent structure model is interpretable as the special case of latent profile analysis in which the manifest variables are dichotomous.

A second special result is obtained by using standard scores and by dividing the latent profile equations through by n, the number of people in the sample. The latent profile equations then assume their standard form:

$$
\begin{aligned}
1 &= p_1 + p_2 + \cdots + p_q , \\
0 &= p_1 Z_{1j} + p_2 Z_{2j} + \cdots + p_q Z_{qj} , \\
r_{jk} &= p_1 Z_{1j} Z_{1k} + p_2 Z_{2j} Z_{2k} + \cdots + p_q Z_{qj} Z_{qk} , \\
r_{jkl} &= p_1 Z_{1j} Z_{1k} Z_{1l} + p_2 Z_{2j} Z_{2k} Z_{2l} + \cdots + p_q Z_{qj} Z_{qk} Z_{ql} , \quad \text{etc.}
\end{aligned}
$$

(14)

The p's are the proportionate class sizes, and of course their sum is unity. The Z's are the average standard scores of classes on tests. Their weighted sum for any test (in the second line) vanishes because it is the mean of all standard scores on that test. The r_{jk}, being average products of pairs of standard scores, are the same correlations for which factor analysis attempts to account. The r_{jkl} are, analogously, average triple products, and so on.

The latent profile equations in standard form have the advantage of dealing with magnitudes that are independent of sample size and of arbitrary score units. It is in standard form that the equations will be applied to the examples in the next four sections.

Latent Profile Example I: A Fictitious Two-Class Case

The fictitious manifest data in Tables 1 and 2 will serve as a first latent profile example. Imagine the data as resulting from the administration of four alternate forms of the same test (such as arithmetic) to a sample of, let us say, a hundred people. Suppose, further, that all six intercorrelations turn out to be .50, so that every two-dimensional scatter diagram, with scores plotted in standard units, has the appearance of an ellipse twice as long as wide, centered on the origin, and tilted at an angle of 45 degrees. There are four three-dimensional scatter diagrams. Each is approximately egg-shaped, and, being symmetric about the origin, yields a third-order manifest product moment of zero.

Tables 1 and 2 display the necessary manifest data in a convenient way. The upper left entry in Table 1 is the first term in the first line of (14), the latent profile equations in standard form. The other entries in row and column 0 of Table 1 are the means of standard scores for each of the four tests—the left-hand term in the second line of (14). The remaining cells of Table 1 contain the test intercorrelations—the manifest data in the third line of (14).

Table 2 summarizes the manifest data of first, second, and third order. The upper left entry is the sum of the four means of standard scores. Each of the other entries in row or column 0 is the sum of the four correlations (including r_{ii}) involving the associated test. Every other cell in Table 2 contains the sum of the four third-order manifest product moments (including r_{iik} and r_{ikk}) for the corresponding pair of tests.

For convenience of exposition in both fictitious examples in this paper, all elements with repeated subscripts (such as r_{ii}, r_{iik}, and r_{iii}) are treated as known. Their values are, in fact, easily inferred from the simple form of the manifest data, but this would not be true generally, even for all sets of fictitious data. In this first example, all r_{ii} are .50, all r_{iik} are zero, and all r_{iii} are zero.

Tables 1 and 2 have been labeled R and R_1 respectively. This is convenient notation for any such display of manifest data, and it will be used in all examples. In any latent profile solution, a distinction must be made between the given and the fitted R and R_1, the latter pair of tables indicating what the former should be in order to be completely accounted for by the solution. In both fictitious examples in this paper, the given and the fitted manifest data, the latter computed from the solution by means of (14), are identical and hence need not be compared. In the two empirical examples,

TABLE 1

R for a Fictitious Two-Class Case

Test No.	Test Number				
	0	1	2	3	4
0	1.00	.00	.00	.00	.00
1	.00		.50	.50	.50
2	.00	.50		.50	.50
3	.00	.50	.50		.50
4	.00	.50	.50	.50	

TABLE 2

R_1 for a Fictitious Two-Class Case

Test No.	Test Number				
	0	1	2	3	4
0	.00	2.00	2.00	2.00	2.00
1	2.00	.00	.00	.00	.00
2	2.00	.00	.00	.00	.00
3	2.00	.00	.00	.00	.00
4	2.00	.00	.00	.00	.00

TABLE 3

Latent Profile Solution for a Fictitious Two-Class Case

	Test No.	Latent Class	
		I	II
Class Means	1	-.71	.71
	2	-.71	.71
	3	-.71	.71
	4	-.71	.71
Class Sizes		.50	.50

TABLE 4

Given Correlations for Nine Reading Tests

Test No.	Test Number									
	0	1	2	3	4	5	6	7	8	9
0	1.00	.00	.00	.00	.00	.00	.00	.00	.00	.00
1	.00		.72	.41	.28	.52	.71	.68	.51	.68
2	.00	.72		.34	.36	.53	.71	.68	.52	.68
3	.00	.41	.34		.16	.34	.43	.42	.28	.41
4	.00	.28	.36	.16		.30	.36	.35	.29	.36
5	.00	.52	.53	.34	.30		.64	.55	.45	.55
6	.00	.71	.71	.43	.36	.64		.76	.57	.76
7	.00	.68	.68	.42	.35	.55	.76		.59	.68
8	.00	.51	.52	.28	.29	.45	.57	.59		.58
9	.00	.68	.68	.41	.36	.55	.76	.68	.58	

TABLE 5

Approximate Latent Profile Solution for Nine Reading Tests

	Test No.	Latent Class	
		I	II
	1	-.80	.80
	2	-.81	.81
	3	-.47	.47
	4	-.41	.41
Class Means	5	-.68	.68
	6	-.90	.90
	7	-.85	.85
	8	-.66	.66
	9	-.84	.84
Class Sizes		.50	.50

however, the comparison will be made when possible in order to appraise the adequacy of the solution.

The latent profile solution for the present example, obtained by applying the algebra of the latent structure solution of Green [11], is shown in Table 3. Each of the two latent classes is defined in terms of its relative size and its latent profile—the complete set of average test scores for its members. Apparently Class I consists of those who are poor at arithmetic, while Class II contains the good arithmetic students.

A fruitful way to visualize this latent profile solution is in terms of the regressions of the tests on the latent continuum of arithmetic ability. Such a graph of mean test score, Y, against position along the latent continuum, X, is shown in Figure 2. Here the regressions of all four tests on the latent

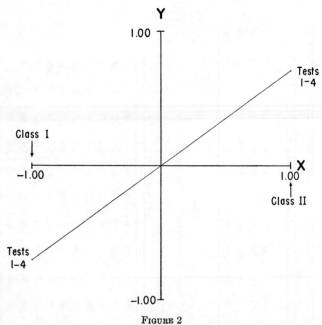

FIGURE 2

Regression of Tests on Latent Continuum for A Fictitious Two-Class Case

continuum are identical. In Figure 2 both Y and X are expressed in standard units, so that the slope of the regression line is also the correlation between Y and X. This is a correlation between test and "factor," and for the linear regressions of the present example, these correlations turn out to be exactly the same ($\sqrt{2}/2$) as the factor loadings that would result from a factor analysis of the correlations in Table 1. This simple correspondence between the two models will vanish, however, as soon as any of the regressions become nonlinear.

Latent Profile Example II: *An Empirical Two-Class Case*

As a second latent profile example, consider the given R in Table 4. That table is a simple modification of a table of intercorrelations among nine reading tests previously reported by Davis [3]. The only modification was to border Davis' table with the 0 column and row. The intercorrelations were based on 421 cases.

A letter from Davis has indicated that the raw scores that would be needed for the computation of R_1 are no longer available. In the absence of higher order data which would provide a unique solution, it was necessary here to adapt some factoring and rotational procedures that were involved in an early approximate latent structure solution [5, 6, or 8] in order to obtain an approximate latent profile solution. For this purpose a factorization of the Davis data by Thurstone [19] was used. Thurstone's analysis indicated that one factor was sufficient to account for the data, all but three of the discrepancies between given and fitted correlations being less than .04, and the largest being .07. It is with exactly these same discrepancies that the present latent profile solution accounts for the intercorrelations.

An approximate latent profile solution for the Davis data is shown in Table 5. This solution is obtainable by resolving the rotational problem with any one of the following three assumptions:

(i) that the two latent classes are equal in size;

(ii) that the two latent profiles are identical except for reversed algebraic sign; or

(iii) that the given R_1 , if available, would be like that of Example I in having nonzero entries only in its 0 column and row.

The solution in Table 5 generates, by means of (14), a fitted R_1 having the form indicated in assumption 3.

The regressions for this solution are pictured in Figure 3. Again both axes are in standard units, so that the slopes of the regressions are identical with the factor loadings reported by Thurstone. Although the present latent profile solution is not rotationally unique, it can fairly readily be shown to possess an important kind of invariance, namely, that *the slopes of the regressions, when both axes are in standard units, remain constant regardless of how the rotational indeterminacy is resolved*. This is but one illustration of the fact that the factor analysis and latent profile models are mutually complementary when the assumptions of both models are not violated.

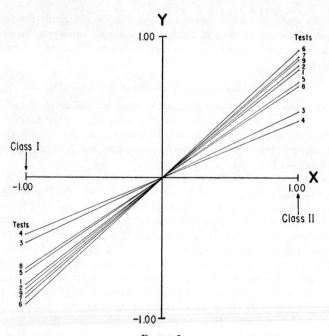

FIGURE 3

Regressions of Tests on Latent Continuum for Nine Reading Tests

Latent Profile Example III: A Fictitious Three-Class Case

The fictitious R and R_1 in Tables 6 and 7 will provide a first illustration of how latent profile analysis handles the problem of difficulty factors. Imagine tests 1 and 2 as being two easy vocabulary tests, tests 4 and 5 as two hard vocabulary tests, and 3 as a vocabulary test of intermediate difficulty. Again assume the data are based upon a hundred cases.

Before proceeding to the latent profile analysis of this fictitious data, it will be instructive to examine the results of a factor analysis of the correlations in Table 6. The simple structure factor analytic solution with correlated factors is given in Table 8. The entries in that table are the correlations between the five tests and the two factors, A and B. The correlation between the two factors, r_{AB}, is .33. If the usual rules for interpreting factors were followed unquestioningly here, the conclusion would be that the two factors are knowledge of easy words, A, and knowledge of hard words, B, and that the two abilities are relatively independent. This is absurd.

The unique, perfectly fitting latent profile solution for this example, again obtained from R and R_1 by the same algebra as is used in the latent

TABLE 6

R for a Fictitious Three-Class Case

Test	Test Number					
No.	0	1	2	3	4	5
0	1.00	.00	.00	.00	.00	.00
1	.00	.75	.75	.50	.25	.25
2	.00	.75	.75	.50	.25	.25
3	.00	.50	.50	.50	.50	.50
4	.00	.25	.25	.50	.75	.75
5	.00	.25	.25	.50	.75	.75

TABLE 8

Simple Structure Factor Analysis
Solution for Correlations in Table 6

Test	Factors	
No.	A	B
1	.82	.00
2	.82	.00
3	.41	.41
4	.00	.82
5	.00	.82

$r_{AB} = .33$

TABLE 7

R_1 for a Fictitious Three-Class Case

Test	Test Number					
No.	0	1	2	3	4	5
0	.00	2.50	2.50	2.50	2.50	2.50
1	2.50	-2.50	-2.50	-1.25	.00	.00
2	2.50	-2.50	-2.50	-1.25	.00	.00
3	2.50	-1.25	-1.25	.00	1.25	1.25
4	2.50	.00	.00	1.25	2.50	2.50
5	2.50	.00	.00	1.25	2.50	2.50

TABLE 9

Latent Profile Solution for
a Fictitious Three-Class Case

	Test	Latent Class		
	No.	I	II	III
	1	-1.50	.50	.50
Class	2	-1.50	.50	.50
Means	3	-1.00	.00	1.00
	4	- .50	-.50	1.50
	5	- .50	-.50	1.50
Class Sizes		.25	.50	.25

structure solution of Green [11], is shown in Table 9. Figure 4 shows, in standard units, the regressions implied by Table 9 and by the assumption of equal spacing of the latent classes along the single latent continuum of vocabulary knowledge.

The contour of the various regressions in Figure 4 is exactly what would be expected on the basis of the relative difficulty of the tests. The easy tests (1 and 2) discriminate only at the lower end of the latent continuum. The hard tests (4 and 5) differentiate only at the upper end. Test 3, of medium difficulty, discriminates throughout the range.

Latent Profile Example IV: *An Empirical Three-Class Case*

The data in Table 10 will provide a final latent profile example. Aside from its 0 column and row, that table is merely a rounded version of a table of subtest intercorrelations reported by Ferguson ([4], p. 328) to illustrate the occurrence of difficulty factors. Ferguson took single items from a Moray-House verbal intelligence test and combined them into six subtests that were reasonably homogeneous in content but that increased in difficulty from subtest 1 to subtest 6. The correlations were based on a sample of 108 children, age 11.

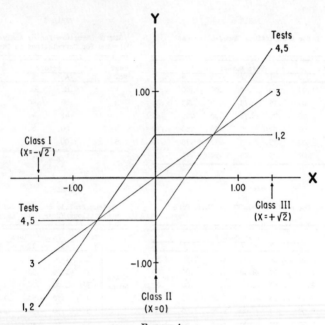

FIGURE 4
Regressions of Tests on Latent Continuum for A Fictitious Three-Class Case

The simple structure correlated factor solution for the Ferguson example is shown in Table 12. That solution was obtained by a rotation of the factorization reported by Ferguson ([4], p. 328). Here again it would be absurd to conclude, according to the usual rules, that the data must be thought of in terms of two relatively independent factors—high-level and low-level verbal intelligence.

A letter from Ferguson has indicated that the raw scores are no longer available for the computation of higher order manifest product moments. It therefore was necessary to approximate the latent profile solution by means of procedures similar to those used in the Davis example. For this purpose Ferguson's factorization of his correlations was used. His two factors accounted for the correlations with discrepancies not exceeding .03, and the present latent profile solution fits the correlations in exactly the same way.

The rotational indeterminacy here was resolved in two stages. The first step was to rotate Ferguson's factorization, with attention being given only to subtests 1 and 6, into maximum correspondence with the initial factorization for the first and last tests in Example III. The latter factorization was a part of the latent profile solution for that example. In Example III the unique solution was obtained by applying, to the initial factorization

TABLE 10

Given Correlations for Six
Verbal Intelligence Sub-Tests

Test No.	Test Number						
	0	1	2	3	4	5	6
0	1.00	.00	.00	.00	.00	.00	.00
1	.00	...	.86	.81	.81	.61	.37
2	.00	.86	...	.80	.82	.68	.47
3	.00	.81	.80	...	.87	.80	.67
4	.00	.81	.82	.87	...	.80	.68
5	.00	.61	.68	.80	.80	...	.78
6	.00	.37	.47	.67	.68	.78	...

TABLE 12

Simple Structure Factor Analysis
Solution for Correlations in Table 10

Test No.	Factors	
	A	B
1	.86	.00
2	.75	.15
3	.55	.43
4	.57	.42
5	.30	.64
6	.00	.81

$$r_{AB} = .43$$

TABLE 11

Fitted R_1 for Six Verbal Intelligence Sub-Tests

Test No.	Test Number						
	0	1	2	3	4	5	6
0	.00	4.31	4.49	4.80	4.84	4.47	3.77
1	4.31	-4.42	-3.93	-2.98	-3.07	-1.74	-.24
2	4.49	-3.93	-3.37	-2.30	-2.39	-1.02	.45
3	4.80	-2.98	-2.30	-.99	-1.08	.33	1.75
4	4.84	-3.07	-2.39	-1.08	-1.16	.26	1.70
5	4.47	-1.74	-1.02	.33	.26	1.52	2.71
6	3.77	-.24	.45	1.75	1.70	2.71	3.57

TABLE 13

Approximate Latent Profile Solution
for Six Verbal Intelligence Sub-Tests

	Test No.	Latent Class		
		I	II	III
	1	-1.64	.51	.62
	2	-1.56	.36	.84
Class	3	-1.38	.07	1.24
Means	4	-1.41	.09	1.23
	5	-1.05	-.20	1.44
	6	-.60	-.48	1.56
Class Sizes		.25	.50	.25

of R, a rotation completely specified by the higher order data in R_1. The second rotational stage in the present approximate solution was to imitate the Example III solution by using exactly the same rotation. The consequences of this rotational solution are the following.

(i) The relative class sizes are the same as in Example III.

(ii) The regressions of all six subtests on the latent continuum are ascending.

(iii) Assuming equal spacing of the classes along the latent continuum, the regressions of subtests 1 and 6 have curvatures that are approximately equal but opposite in direction.

(iv) The form of the fitted R_1 is similar to that of the given and fitted R_1 of Example III.

The resulting approximate latent profile solution is given in Table 13, and the regressions, again in standard units, and assuming equal spacing of the three classes along the latent continuum, are shown in Figure 5. The progression of curvatures from the easiest to the hardest subtest is just what it ought to be. This progression was found to be quite invariant over a wide range of alternative approximate solutions. Several such solutions were

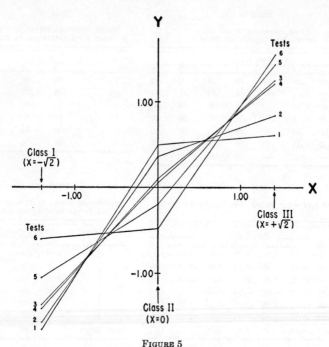

FIGURE 5

Regressions of Subtests on Latent
Continuum for Six Verbal Intelligence Subtests

computed in order to study the nonuniqueness of this latent profile solution. Only one restriction applied to all of the alternative solutions that were tried, namely, that the resulting regressions be ascending for all subtests. Within this restriction large changes in class sizes and in class averages could be brought about, but never in such a way as to alter the ordering of curvatures among the regressions. It should be added that only with very strained assumptions about the spacing of the three classes along the latent continuum could the regressions of both subtests 1 and 6 be made to curve in the same direction.

Table 11 shows the fitted R_1 implied by the approximate solution in Table 13. A comparison of Tables 7 and 11 will reveal the similarities between the fitted higher order manifest data for the two three-class latent profile examples.

Discussion

There are two limitations to the foregoing latent profile examples that should be discussed explicitly. These are in addition to the indeterminacy produced by the absence of higher order manifest data in the case of the two empirical examples. The first is the lack of a scale of measurement for the latent continuum. For two classes this is unimportant, for it leaves only an arbitrariness as to the origin and the distances of the two classes from that origin. The problem of the relative distances between classes cannot arise when there is only one such distance. With three-class solutions, however, the problem of relative spacing is a critical one. Without some resolution of it the regressions of tests on the latent continuum could not be drawn. Nor could the shape of the distribution of positions along the latent continuum be ascertained. In both of the present three-class solutions, the problem was resolved by the *arbitrary* assumption of equal spacing of the classes along the latent continuum. The regressions were drawn on that basis, and on the same basis the latent distribution in each case became symmetric and approximately normal. Other assumptions about the underlying metric would have led to different regressions and to different latent distributions. A separate paper [9], stemming from some recent developments in latent structure analysis [16], deals further with this metric problem. It indicates one way in which, with the aid of manifest product moments of still higher order, a metric for the latent continuum can be made to emerge as an integral part of the latent profile solution.

A second limitation of all latent profile examples in the present paper is their unidimensionality. It will be recalled that nothing in the development of the latent profile equations restricts the number of underlying dimensions within which the latent classes lie. Of course the two-class examples here can be understood in terms of a single continuum, for that would be true of any two-class case. The present three-class examples, however, are unidimensional because of the special nature (homogeneous in content but graded in difficulty) of the tests involved in them. Many three-class examples would require two underlying dimensions for an adequate understanding of their psychological meaning. In general, a q-class solution could require as many as $(q - 1)$ underlying dimensions for its interpretation. Subsequent work [cf. 10] will deal with such multidimensional examples and with the problems of dimensionality and metric that arise in their interpretation.

The reader may have noticed that in all four latent profile examples no mention was made of a need for manifest data of order higher than the third. Even for the two empirical examples a unique solution would not have required the use of such higher order manifest data. These higher order data therefore constitute a means for testing the assumption of higher order within-class independence. This could be done by comparing the given higher order data with the corresponding fitted values as generated from the latent parameters by subsequent lines of equations (13) or (14). Alternatively it could be argued that, if the solution never requires data above third order, there is no need to postulate within-class independence beyond that order. From this parsimonious viewpoint, the latent profile equations need extend no higher than third order, and it would be inappropriate to think of using higher order data to test the fit of the model. However, it might then be more important to test the adequacy of the solution by relating it to variables not included in the original analysis. (An empirical example in [8] gives an illustration of how this could be carried out in latent structure analysis, where the very same argument over the use or non-use of higher order equations not needed in a particular solution can be made.)

The latent profile equations that have been derived and illustrated here are analogous to only one form of latent structure analysis—that known as the discrete class case. The analysis divides the sample into a small number of discrete classes possessing second- and third-order within-class independence, and stops there. Other varieties of latent structure analysis, one of which has already been referred to, have gone further in stipulating the algebraic form of the regressions (the so-called *trace lines* [cf. 15] of latent structure analysis) or of the set of class sizes, or of both. Always, however, the postulate of within-class independence is retained. Usually these further restraints require within-class independence of higher than third order, so that the corresponding higher orders of manifest data become directly involved in the solution. Most of these variants of latent structure analysis are readily translated into latent profile terms. In fact, the analogy between the two models is so close that almost whatever progress is made in the various solutions for one model is convertible into a corresponding advance for the other.

Conclusion

After outlining the derivation of the factor analysis and latent structure models, this paper has shown how the latter can be generalized for analyzing the interrelations among quantitative measures in a way that avoids some of the troublesome problems of factor analysis. The resulting latent profile model is applied to some simple fictitious and empirical data to illustrate its use. Because such applications may seem to show some promise, it is perhaps appropriate and not premature to conclude this paper merely by broadening the reference for the admonition ([18], p. 70) with which it began.

> It would be unfortunate if some initial success with the analytical methods . . . described here should lead us to commit ourselves to them with such force of habit as to disregard the development of entirely different constructs that may be indicated by improvements in measurement and by inconsistencies between theory and experiment.

References

1. ANDERSON, T. W. "On Estimation of Parameters in Latent Structure Analysis," *Psychometrika*, 1954, **19**, 1–10.
2. CARROLL, J. B. "The Effect of Difficulty and Chance Success on Correlations Between Items or Between Tests," *Psychometrika*, 1950, **10**, 1–19.
3. DAVIS, F. B. "Fundamental Factors of Comprehension in Reading," *Psychometrika*, 1944, **9**, 185–87.
4. FERGUSON, G. A. "The Factorial Interpretation of Test Difficulty," *Psychometrika*, 1941, **6**, 323–29.
5. GIBSON, W. A. "Applications of the Mathematics of Multiple-Factor Analysis to Problems of Latent Structure Analysis," in P. F. LAZARSFELD *et al., The Use of Mathematical Models in the Measurement of Attitudes.* (Res. Memo. No. 455.) Rand Corp., 1951.
6. ———. "Latent Structure and Positive Manifold," *British Journal of Statistical Psychology*, 1962, **15**, 149–60.
7. ———. "An Extension of Anderson's Solutions for the Latent Structure Equations," *Psychometrika*, 1955, **20**, 69–73.
8. ———. "Multiple Factors and Latent Structure." Unpublished manuscript.
9. ———. "Nonlinear Factor Analysis, Single Factor Case," *American Psychologist*, 1955, **10**, 438. (Abstract.)
10. ———. "Nonlinear Factors in Two Dimensions," *Psychometrika*, 1960, **25**, 381–92.
11. GREEN, B. F. "A General Solution for the Latent Class Model of Latent Structure Analysis," *Psychometrika*, 1951, **16**, 151–66.
12. ———. "Latent Structure Analysis and Its Relation to Factor Analysis," *Journal of the American Statistical Association*, 1952, **47**, 71–76.
13. GUILFORD, J. P. "The Difficulty of a Test and Its Factor Composition," *Psychometrika*, 1941, **6**, 67–77.
14. LAZARSFELD, P. F. "The Interpretation and Computation of Some Latent Structures," in S. A. STOUFFER *et al., Measurement and Prediction.* Princeton: Princeton Univ. Press, 1950. Chap. 11.
15. ———. "The Logical and Mathematical Foundation of Latent Structure Analysis," in S. A. STOUFFER *et al., Measurement and Prediction.* Princeton: Princeton Univ. Press, 1950. Chap. 10.
16. ———. "Some New Results and Problems in Latent Structure Analysis." Unpublished manuscript.
17. ———. "Latent Structure Analysis," in S. KOCH (ed.), *Psychology: A Study of a Science.* New York: McGraw-Hill, 1959.
18. THURSTONE, L. L. *Multiple Factor Analysis.* Chicago: Univ. of Chicago Press, 1947.
19. ———. "Note on a Reanalysis of Davis' Reading Tests," *Psychometrika*, 1946, **11**, 185–88.
20. WHERRY, R. J., and GAYLORD, R. H. "Factor Pattern of Test Items and Tests as a Function of the Correlation Coefficient: Content, Difficulty, and Constant Error Factors," *Psychometrika*, 1944, **9**, 237–44.

Latent Structure Analysis and Test Theory

Paul F. Lazarsfeld   *Columbia University*

Section 1

The foundations of test theory can be put in the following form. A sample of testees has answered a test consisting of n dichotomous items. A score s has been assigned to any respondent with s correct answers. There is, however, assumed to exist a perfect test that would assign each testee a "true score" t if he gave t correct answers. The score values s and t form a bivariate distribution. The conditional distribution of s given a fixed value of t is assumed to be due to errors of measurement. One important purpose of test theory is to infer the position of a testee on the t-axis when his position on the s-axis is known. This can, of course, be done only if we make some mathematical assumptions about the bivariate s-t distribution. In some models additional assumptions are made relating the covariance of the "true" items to the average covariance between the items actually observed. Often special attention is given to the marginal distribution of t-scores.

Thus any test theory model can essentially be described in terms of three considerations:

1. How many empirical data are used? Usually one will find only $(n+1) + n + \dfrac{n(n-1)}{2}$ empirical data used. This would happen if the model considered the $n+1$ frequencies of the marginal s-distribution; the n "item difficulties" or proportions of correct responses; and the $\dfrac{n(n-1)}{2}$ covariances between items. Often much less actual information is used.

2. What axioms or mathematical assumptions are introduced into the theory?

3. Which characteristics of the bivariate s-t distribution can be deduced from 1 and 2?

Questions 2 and 3 are obviously related. The more we put into the model under 2, the more will we be able to pull out under 3, given the same amount of empirical information actually used. As a matter of fact, test theory, like any measurement model, is really a theory of stochastic transformation, in this case from the s-axis to the t-axis.

The material on which this brief statement is based was ably summarized by Frederic Lord in his presidential address [2] to the Psychometric Society, September 1959. I omit certain variations which come up if it is assumed that the "true" and the actual tests can consist of a different number of items; this leads to the introduction of percent scores and requires further assumptions on the sampling of items.

Section 2

Latent structure analysis (LSA) can be looked upon as a generalization of test theory models. Using the preceding three aspects, the differences are as follows:

1. LSA starts with the full joint distribution of all dichotomous items. This is called the manifest space and corresponds to the marginal distribution of s-scores in test theory, sometimes supplemented by item difficulties and covariances. LSA uses 2^n pieces of information.

2. It assumes that the testees can be arranged in a latent space which will have much fewer dimensions than the n-dimensional manifest space. The latent axes may have a continuous or discontinuous metric. The mathematical assumptions of the model are held together by an axiom of local independence to be explained presently.

3. Because of the richer input of manifest data, the number of model parameters that can be computed is very large. We do end up with a distribution of people over the latent space which corresponds to the marginal distribution of "true scores" and with a set of conditional distributions which correspond to the "error of measurement." However, the LSA model is much more complex and any test theory model can be derived from it as a special case.

I shall first elaborate on this overcondensed statement and then give a concrete example.

Section 3

LSA is then based on the following ideas:

(a) An intended (latent) continuum is assumed.*

(b) A number of dichotomized manifest items are introduced. Each item, i, has a probability p_i^x to be answered "positively" at any point x of the latent continuum.

(c) The function $p_i^x = f_i(x)$ is called operating characteristic (o.c.) in test theory and traceline in LSA. We shall hereafter use the term (o.c.), although I prefer mine as more descriptive and colloquial.

---

*For the sake of simplicity we shall think of it as unidimensional. This restriction will be removed in Section 7.

(d) A *principle of local independence is assumed:* At a fixed point x the probabilities for joint occurrence are products of the separate probabilities.

(e) To facilitate the subsequent discussion I shall use the term "the signature σ of a response pattern." This means the sequence of (+) and (−) responses given in a specific case. If a negative response probability is designated by a barred index ($p_{\bar{\imath}} = 1 - p_i$), then the principle of local independence can be written in the form

$$(1) \qquad f_\sigma = f_i f_j f_k \ldots,$$

where σ is a sequence of indices, e.g., 1, 2, 3, 4, 5 . . ., etc.

(f) Equation 1 is the o.c. (traceline) of the response pattern σ. It indicates the probability of getting a response pattern of signature σ at any point of the latent continuum. A set of items which satisfies the principle of local independence can be called a *pure test.*

(g) To any response pattern σ there correspond *recruitment probabilities.* This is a function which indicates the reversed probabilities that the response σ was given by a respondent at point x.

(h) To compute these recruitment probabilities (Rec. Pr.) we have to introduce into the model a latent (unknown) density distribution $\phi(x)$. It indicates the proportion of people at point x; no assumption is made that $\phi(x)$ be normal.

(i) The reversed probabilities are represented by the function

$$(2) \qquad \psi_\sigma(x) = \frac{f_\sigma(x) \cdot \phi(x)}{\int f_\sigma(x) \cdot \phi(x)\ dx} = \frac{f_\sigma \phi}{p_\sigma}.$$

Obviously p_σ is the *manifest* proportion of respondents giving the response σ. But f_σ and ϕ are unknown (latent).

(j) To each response pattern we can give scores by adding an additional convention. It can be, for instance,

$$(3) \qquad S_\sigma = \frac{\int x\, f_\sigma(x) \phi(x)\, dx}{p_\sigma},$$

that is, the expected (average) recruitment place. Or it can be the most likely place; that is, the point x at which $\psi_\sigma(x)$, as defined by Equation 2, has a maximum. Or it can be the place where 50 percent of the respondents have a higher and 50 percent a lower Rec. Pr.

(k) It is very important to realize the implications of the three points just made. Every response pattern can come from anywhere on the latent continuum but with different probabilities. Therefore, to each σ there corresponds a complete distribution of reversed probabilities. A score is some kind of average position, with these probabilities as weights; which average to choose is a matter of convention. Scores can be developed for any combination of items, including a single item, and not only for an ultimate response pattern (where a positive or negative response is recorded for each item). This corresponds to the fact that we can write down an operating characteristic for any combination of items. The traditional score of test theory will be discussed in Section 5.

Section 4

Against this general background, LSA proceeds in the following steps:

(a) It investigates models with algebraically specified o.c.'s, e.g., polynomials with undetermined coefficients but assumed degree. The distribution might be algebraically prescribed [e.g., $\phi(x) = \dfrac{1}{B(a+1, b+1)} x^a (1-x)^b$, $0 \leqslant x \leqslant 1$] or left completely free.

(b) LSA then develops the conditions of reducibility. This means the restrictions imposed upon manifest data in case a chosen model were applicable.

(c) A given set of data is examined to see whether they could "reasonably" come from the chosen model. (Sampling problems will not be discussed in this paper.)

(d) If the chosen model is eligible, its latent parameters are computed.

(e) If not, a new model is tested.

To give a very simple example, we pick a test of work satisfaction answered by 876 employees of a company (see Table 1). We now go through the four steps just mentioned.

(a) We chose linear tracelines $f_i = a_i + b_i x$. The distribution $\phi(x)$ is free. It is required, however, that $\phi(x) = 0$ wherever $f_i(x) < 0$ or $f_i(x) > 1$.

(b) One of the reducibility conditions of this model is as follows: The matrix of the expressions $p_{ij} - p_i p_j = [ij]$ has to have rank one. Other conditions are that $\dfrac{p_k p_{kij} - p_{ki} p_{kj}}{p_{ij} - p_i p_j}$ be the same for a given k irrespective of choice of i and j.

(c) The matrix of $[ij]$ has a reasonably good fit to rank 1. The original matrix and the residuals from a fitted matrix are given in Tables 2 and 3. In this model the latent parameters can be computed from second- and first-order data. We therefore at first do not worry about higher-order data.

(d) It can be shown that $a_i = p_i$ and $b_i = \sqrt{\dfrac{[ig]\,[ih]}{[gh]}}$, which is modelwise invariant against changes of g and h.

For $\phi(x)$ we cannot compute the first two moments and therefore arbitrarily set the mean of the distribution at zero and its variance as one. The third moment turns out to be

$$(4) \qquad M_3 = \frac{p_{ijk} - p_i p_j p_k}{b_i b_j b_k} - \sum_{g=i,j,k} \frac{p_g}{b_g}.$$

(Obviously M_3 has to have the same value whatever three items i, j, k we choose; this is the reducibility condition mentioned before but appearing in different form. Actually we compute M_3 by forming the mean of all possible equations (4).) It turns out that $M_3 = -.011$, $M_4 = 1.57$, $M_5 = 5.47$. We shall discuss these values presently.

Table 1.

Question	Positive Response	p_i
1. Are there any things about your job that you particularly like?	"A lot of things"	.34
2. Are there any things about your job that you particularly dislike?	"None" and "not many"	.57
3. How often do you look forward with some pleasure to your day on the job?	"Every day" and "almost every day"	.62
4. If someone asked you about getting a job like yours, which of the following would you be inclined to do? Encourage her? Discourage her? Neither?	"Encourage her"	.48
5. Do you ever feel you would like to quit and get a job with some other company?	"Never"	.38
6. Do you feel that you would like to get a transfer from your present job to some other kind of job in your department?	"Seldom" and "never"	.58

Table 2. **Cross-Product Matrix**

	1	2	3	4	5	6
1	—	041	062	069	057	029
2	041	—	080	088	077	050
3	062	080	—	107	088	054
4	069	088	107	—	103	061
5	057	077	088	103	—	058
6	029	050	054	061	058	—

Table 3. **Matrix of Residuals**

	1	2	3	4	5	6
1	—	−006	005	005	002	−004
2	−006	—	002	−001	001	005
3	005	002	—	−001	−005	−002
4	005	−001	−001	—	−002	−002
5	002	001	−005	002	—	003
6	−004	005	−002	−002	003	—

(e) To get an idea of the fit of the model, we compute the fifth-order frequencies as they derive from the model and compare them with the manifest data (see Table 4). The results are not too bad.

Table 4. **Actual and Fitted Joint Frequencies of Item Quintuplets**

Combination of Items	Actual Joint Frequencies	Joint Frequencies Required by Model
12345	.127	.129
12346	.132	.134
12356	.113	.115
12456	.112	.103
13456	.119	.114
23456	.174	.178

To get a graphic picture of the o.c.'s for the six items, we draw Figure 1.

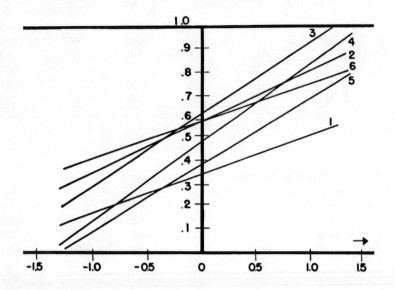

Figure 1.

To get a better picture of the distribution, we assimilate to the five known moments three discrete located classes. We find that 99.9 percent of all cases fall about equally at the points $x_1 = -1.03$ and $x_2 = .96$. A few cases fall far out to the right into a highly satisfied group. This reflects the fact that M_3 nearly vanishes, while M_5 is quite high. Another way of representation would be to find the proper Pearson types for these moments.

Section 5

In traditional test theory a person's score is the number of items he answers positively. Such a score has an o.c. which can be derived by simple probability calculus if the o.c. of each single item is known. For three items, for example, the score 2 can be obtained from the following patterns:

$$+ + - \qquad + - + \qquad - + +.$$

The probability for a respondent to return any of these patterns is obviously

(5) $$f_s = \Sigma f_i f_j \, (1 - f_k),$$

where the sum is taken over all possible combinations of the three items. This point has been made by Tucker [3], Lord [1], and others, to which I shall refer as the "Princeton tradition."

Once it is clear that a manifest test score has an o.c. of the type of Equation 5, all the rest of the statements in Section 3 apply automatically. Especially important is the fact that *to a manifest test score* s *there corresponds a whole distribution of latent recruitment probabilities.* A latent (or, if you please, true) score can only be established after we have decided whether we mean by it the expected, the most likely, or another "average" latent position.

Suppose, to fix our ideas, we choose the expected latent position of people who have a manifest score s. We can then raise the question of how s is mathematically related to this "true" score. This will of course be different for each model and is usually a very involved mathematical form. Even for such a simple model as the one with linear o.c.'s it is too long to write down. Just to give an idea of the numerical relations, we have chosen two items from our example and have graphed the o.c.'s for the four response patterns $++, +-, -+, --$. The graph gives the o.c.'s for the four response patterns and the latent scores.

$$\mu_{46} = .835; \; \mu_{4\bar{6}} = .441; \; \mu_{\bar{4}6} = -.433; \; \mu_{\bar{4}\bar{6}} = -.859.$$

They are the mean (expected) values for the reversed probability distribution, $\psi_\sigma(x) = \dfrac{f_\sigma(x)\phi(x)}{p_\sigma}$. The latter cannot be fully graphed because we know only a few moments of $\phi(x)$. (See Fig. 2.)

To compute the latent position for the traditional test score, we have to combine for $s = 1$ the pattern $+-$ and $-+$. It can be easily seen that this is

$$s_1 = \frac{p_{\bar{4}6}\mu_{\bar{4}6} + p_{4\bar{6}}\mu_{4\bar{6}}}{p_{\bar{4}6} + p_{4\bar{6}}} = .008.$$

Obviously

$$s_2 = \mu_{46} = .835$$

$$s_0 = \mu_{\bar{4}\bar{6}} = -.859.$$

While in this case the distances $(s_2 - s_1)$ and $(s_1 - s_0)$ are fairly similar, they are not equal. In more complex situations a Pearson correlation between traditional score and latent score would be far from one.

For each test score there exists a recruitment probability function ψ_s the properties of which can be examined. For example, one may square out the values of $\int x^2 \psi_s(x)dx$ and so decide which score has the highest probability to locate a person within a given interval from the expected position, which could well be called the reliability of this specific score s.

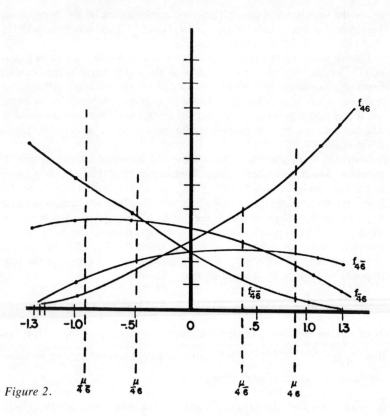

Figure 2.

Section 6

When I developed the mathematics of LSA during the war, I was not aware of the paper by Tucker [3]. I have since come to the conviction that as far as application to test theory goes there are great similarities between LSA and the Princeton tradition. The differences consist mainly in a broader algebraic formulation of LSA, which does not require normality for $\phi(x)$ and permits the investigation of any kind of operating characteristics (tracelines). A collateral advantage is a greater emphasis on the reverse probability functions $\psi(x)$, which should be studied in their own right.

I see only one disagreement, which might be based on a misunderstanding. In the Princeton tradition the latent probabilities p_i^x of a given item i are not directly linked to the underlying continuum. For each item an additional latent element z_i is introduced; this, in turn, is correlated with the latent continuum, x. There are, so to say, $n+1$ latent variables, one for each of the n items and one for the intended general classification. These n-specific variables, z, seem to me mere ghosts. I have the impression that all papers in the Princeton tradition could be simplified by defining directly for any item i

$$p_i = \int f_i(x)\phi(x)\,dx,$$

without going through the n additional latent abilities z_i which determine whether a person can or cannot answer the item i correctly. But I raise that more as a question because I might misunderstand the purpose of the Princeton assumption.

Section 7

Polynomial o.c.'s of any degree and the moments of a free $\phi(x)$ can be completely determined. This permits in one special case to exemplify the problem of latent dimensionality. Suppose we want to decide for a special set of data whether the appropriate model is unidimensional with quadratic tracelines:

$$(\text{Model A}) \qquad f_i(x) = a_i + b_i x + c_i x^2,$$

or two-dimensional with a linear trace surface:

$$(\text{Model B}) \qquad f_i(u,v) = a_i + b_i u + c_i v,$$

where now u and v are two latent continua.

It can be shown that the two models have a large number of reducibility conditions in common. For example, the matrix of cross-products in both cases has rank 2. Certain ratios of determinants formed from joint frequencies on various levels are constant and equal for both levels. Only if one forms a so-called ascending determinant that includes fourth-order frequencies does a difference appear. A typical example is as follows:

$$A = \begin{vmatrix} 1 & p_1 & p_2 & p_{12} & p_{13} & p_{23} \\ p_4 & p_{14} & \cdot & \cdot & \cdot & p_{234} \\ p_5 & \cdot & & & & \cdot \\ p_{45} & \cdot & & & & \\ p_{46} & \cdot & & & & p_{2346} \\ p_{56} & p_{156} & \cdot & \cdot & \cdot & p_{2356} \end{vmatrix}$$

Such a determinant vanishes in the case of the one-dimensional quadratic model but does not vanish if the appropriate model has two latent dimensions and a linear trace surface. Obviously the sampling problem of such a decision is very serious. Professor T. W. Anderson, of Columbia University, and one of his students have made progress on the sampling aspect, but it will not be discussed here.

References

1. LORD, F. M. "The Relation of a Test Score to the Trait Underlying the Test," *Educational and Psychological Measurement*, 1953, **13**, 517–49.*
2. _____. "An Approach to Mental Test Theory," *Psychometrika*, 1959, **24**, 283-302.
3. TUCKER, L. R. "Maximum Validity of a Test with Equivalent Items," *Psychometrika*, 1946, **11**, 1–13.

*[EDITORS' NOTE: This article appears as the first selection in this volume.]

An Individualistic Approach to Item Analysis

Georg Rasch *University of Copenhagen*

1. Introduction

Traditionally the properties of a psychological test are defined in terms of variations within some specified population. In practice such populations may be selected in various reasonable ways, and accordingly the properties referred to—for example, the reliability coefficient—are not specific to the test itself but may vary according to how the population is defined. Similarly, the evaluation of a subject is usually linked up with a population by a standardization of some kind and is therefore not specific to the subject per se. Our aim is to develop probabilistic models in the application of which the population can be ignored. It was a discovery of some mathematical significance that such models could be constructed, and it seemed remarkable that data collected in routine psychological testing could be fairly well represented by such models.

In a previous study (2) an attempt was made to build up a general framework within which the models of an earlier study (3) appear to be special cases, and some properties of this general framework were recognized. But only recently it has become quite clear that this model is in fact *the complete answer to the requirement that statements about the parameters and adequacy of a discrete probabilistic model be objective in a sense to be fully specified.*

At present, at least, the theory leading to this result is rather involved, and it is not going to be a main topic for this paper. However, it is intended that the following discussion on one of the models in the earlier study (3), the model for item analysis in case of only two possible answers, should demonstrate the nature of the type of objectivity we are aiming at, thus pointing to the more general problem to be treated elsewhere.

2. Data

The kind of situation to be considered is the following, in which a fairly large number of subjects were given an intelligence test. Two subtests, N (completing numerical sequences) and F (analyzing geometric figures), are of particular interest. The time allowed for N was chosen so that very few of the subjects could be expected to achieve an appreciably larger number of correct answers even with unlimited time. (This fact was ascertained by independent experimental evidence.) Therefore items that were not answered were counted as incorrect, and one of the two responses, correct (+) or incorrect (−), was recorded for each item. Test F was scored in a similar way.

3. Model

The model to be suggested is based on three assumptions:

1. To each situation of a subject (ν) having to solve a test item (i), there corresponds a probability of a correct answer which we will write in the form

$$(3.1) \quad p\,\{+\mid \nu,\, i\} = \frac{\lambda_{\nu i}}{1 + \lambda_{\nu i}}\,,\ \lambda_{\nu i} \geqslant 0.$$

2. The situational parameter $\lambda_{\nu i}$ is the product of two factors,

$$(3.2) \quad \lambda_{\nu i} = \xi_\nu \epsilon_i,$$

ξ_ν pertaining to the subject, ϵ_i to the item.
3. All answers, given the parameters, are stochastically independent.

Each of these assumptions calls for some comments.
    1. For description of observations two apparently antagonistic types of models are available, deterministic models (such as the law of gravitation) and stochastic models (such as Mendel's laws of heredity). However, the choice of one type or the other does not imply that the phenomena observed *were* causally determined or that they *did* occur by chance.
    Even if it were believed that certain phenomena could be "explained causally" (whatever such a phrase may mean), a stochastic model may be preferable (as in thermodynamics).
    Although adopting a probabilistic model for describing responses to an intelligence test, we have taken no sides in a possible argument about responses being ultimately explainable in causal terms.
    2. In many psychophysical threshold experiments a subject is exposed to the same stimulus a large number of times. Assuming that the repetitions do not affect the judgments of the subject, this procedure gives the opportunity of estimating each $\lambda_{\nu i}$ separately and hence of studying directly how the situational parameter varies with subject and with strength of stimulus. In such a situation we may or may not observe the multiplicative rule laid down in 3.2.
    For the intelligence tests we shall deal with, experience has shown that

on one repetition the results are usually somewhat improved. A large number of repetitions have not been tried, mainly because the questions are such that it seems almost certain that several of them will easily be recognized after a few repetitions. Therefore the possibility of a direct approach to the estimation of response probabilities seems remote.

To compensate, we have recourse to an assumption that may seem rather bold, possibly even artificial, namely that λ_{vi} can be factored into a subject parameter and an item parameter. This, combined with the two other assumptions, produces a model that turns out to have rather remarkable properties, some of which even lead to the possibility of examining how well the model represents the data (see Section 6).

Provided the two kinds of parameters can be operationally defined, they also have a clear meaning, as seen by inserting 3.2 into 3.1:

$$(3.3) \qquad\qquad p\{+ \mid v, i\} = \frac{\xi_v \epsilon_i}{1 + \xi_v \epsilon_i}.$$

Thus, if the same person is given items with ϵ_i approaching 0, then his probability of giving a correct answer approaches 0 while his probability of giving an incorrect answer tends toward unity. And that is true for every person, provided the model holds. Similarly, when ϵ_i gets large, the probability of $+$ tends toward 1 and the probability of $-$ toward 0. Since with increasing ϵ_i the items become easier, we may call ϵ_i *the degree of easiness* of item i.

On the other hand, giving the same item to persons with ξ_v approaching 0, we get probabilities of correct answers tending toward 0, while if ξ_v increases indefinitely the probability tends toward 1. This holds for every item. Thus we may colloquially call ξ_v *the ability of subject v* with respect to the kind of items in question.

In the definition of ξ_v and ϵ_i there is an inherent indeterminacy. In fact, if $\xi_v, v = 1, \ldots, N$ and $\epsilon_i, i = 1, \ldots, k$ is a set of solutions to the equations

$$(3.4) \qquad\qquad \xi_v \epsilon_i = \lambda_{vi}$$

then, if ξ_v', ϵ_i' is another set of solutions, the relation

$$(3.5) \qquad\qquad \xi_v' \epsilon_i' = \xi_v \epsilon_i$$

must hold for any combination of v and i. Thus

$$(3.6) \qquad\qquad \frac{\xi_v'}{\xi_v} = \frac{\epsilon_i}{\epsilon_i'}$$

must be a constant, say, and accordingly the general solution is

$$(3.7) \qquad \xi'_\nu = \alpha \xi_\nu, \ \epsilon'_i = \frac{1}{\alpha}\epsilon_i, \ \alpha > 0 \text{ arbitrary.}$$

The indeterminacy can be removed by the choice of one of the items, say $i = 0$, as the *standard item* having "a unit of easiness," in multiples of which the degrees of easinesses of the other items are expressed.

By this choice, or an equivalent one, the whole set of ξ'_ν's and ϵ'_i's is fixed. In particular

$$(3.8) \qquad \xi_\nu = \lambda_{\nu 0},$$

that is, the parameter of a subject is a very simple function of *his probability of giving a correct answer to the standard item,*

$$(3.9) \qquad \lambda_{\nu 0} = \frac{p\{+ \mid \nu, 0\}}{1 - p\{+ \mid \nu, 0\}}$$

being the "betting odds" on a correct answer. Now we may be able to find a person who has in fact his $\xi = 1$. We may refer to him as a *standard subject* ($\nu = 0$). And then *the item parameter*

$$(3.10) \qquad \epsilon_i = \lambda_{0i}$$

is the same simple function of *the probability that the standard person gives a correct answer to this item.*

3. To some psychologists the assumption of stochastic independence at first sight appears to be rather startling, since it is well known that usually quite high correlation coefficients between responses to different items are found.

Correlated items are, however, a consequence of the assumption. With moderate variation of ξ, say from 0.1 to 10, we will obtain quite high correlation coefficients. But, of course, if ξ is the same, or nearly the same, for all individuals, the correlations become zero, or nearly zero. Under this model the interitem correlations do not represent intrinsic properties of the items, but are mainly determined by the variations in the person parameters.

Let $p\{(\substack{i \\ +})\}$ and $p\{(\substack{i \\ -})\}$ stand for a person's probabilities of a positive and negative response, respectively, to item i. Considering next his possible responses to two items, i and j, they can also be allotted probabilities: $p\{(\substack{i \\ +}), (\substack{j \\ +})\}$, and so on. Now our third assumption states, among other things, that his responses to i and j should be "stochastically independent." Technically this is expressed in the following relations:

$$(3.11) \qquad \begin{cases} p\{(^i_+), (^j_+)\} = p\{(^i_+)\}p\{(^j_+)\} \\ p\{(^i_+), (^j_-)\} = p\{(^i_+)\}p\{(^j_-)\} \text{ etc.} \end{cases}$$

If in the first of these equations we divide by $p\{(^j_+)\}$ and in the second by $p\{(^j_-)\}$, we get

$$(3.12) \qquad p\{(^i_+)\} = \frac{p\{(^i_+), (^j_+)\}}{p\{(^j_+)\}} = \frac{p\{(^i_+), (^j_-)\}}{p\{(^j_-)\}}.$$

The ratio (3.12) of the two probabilities is *the conditional probability of a + answer to* i, *given a + answer to* j. The notation is

$$(3.13) \qquad p\{(^i_+) \mid (^j_+)\} = \frac{p\{(^i_+), (^j_+)\}}{p\{(^j_+)\}}.$$

Thus the relations (3.12) can be written

$$(3.14) \qquad p\{(^i_+) \mid (^j_+)\} = p\{(^i_+) \mid (^j_-)\} = p\{(^i_+)\},$$

that is, *the probability of a plus answer to* i *is independent of whether the answer to* j *is* $+$ *or* $-$; it is just the probability of a plus answer to *i*.

And of course the same holds for a minus answer to *i*. This is a specification of the statement that the answers to *i* and *j* are *stochastically independent*.

Assumption 3 also requires that for each subject the answers to all questions be stochastically independent. Technically this is expressed in the equation

$$(3.15) \qquad p\{(^1_+),(^2_+), \ldots (^k_+)\} = p\{(^1_+)\} \, p\{(^2_+)\} \ldots p\{(^k_+)\}$$

and all its analogues. The content of this statement is that *the probability of a certain answer to an item or of a combination of answers to a set of items is unaffected by the answers given to the other items.*

4. Comparison of two items

As an introduction to the more general treatment of the model in Section 5 we will consider how two items can be compared.

According to 3.11 and 3.3, the probability of correct answers to both item *i* and item *j* is

$$(4.1) \quad \begin{cases} p\{(\tfrac{i}{+}),(\tfrac{j}{+}) \mid \xi\} = p\{(\tfrac{i}{+}) \mid \xi\} p\{(\tfrac{j}{+}) \mid \xi\} \\ \qquad = \dfrac{\xi^2 \epsilon_i \epsilon_j}{(1 + \xi \epsilon_i)(1 + \xi \epsilon_j)} \end{cases}$$

for a subject with the parameter ξ. Similarly,

$$(4.2) \quad p\{(\tfrac{i}{+}),(\tfrac{j}{-}) \mid \xi\} = \frac{\xi \epsilon_i}{(1 + \xi \epsilon_i)(1 + \xi \epsilon_j)},$$

$$(4.3) \quad p\{(\tfrac{i}{-}),(\tfrac{j}{+}) \mid \xi\} = \frac{\xi \epsilon_j}{(1 + \xi \epsilon_i)(1 + \xi \epsilon_j)},$$

$$(4.4) \quad p\{(\tfrac{i}{-}),(\tfrac{j}{-}) \mid \xi\} = \frac{1}{(1 + \xi \epsilon_i)(1 + \xi \epsilon_j)}.$$

With the notations

$$(4.5) \quad a_i = \begin{cases} 1 \text{ in case of answer} + \text{to item } i \\ 0 \text{ in case of answer} - \text{to item } i \end{cases}$$

and

$$(4.6) \quad a. = a_i + a_j,$$

the probabilities of $a. = 0$ and 2 are given by 4.1 and 4.4, while the probability of $a. = 1$ is the sum of 4.2 and 4.3:

$$(4.7) \quad p\{a. = 1 \mid \xi\} = \frac{\xi(\epsilon_i + \epsilon_j)}{(1 + \xi \epsilon_i)(1 + \xi \epsilon_j)}.$$

Now the conditional probability of $a_i = 1$ provided $a. = 1$ is — analogous to 3.13 — obtained by dividing 4.7 into 4.2. However, by that operation the common denominator and ξ in the numerators cancel and we are left with

$$(4.8) \quad p\{a_i = 1 \mid a. = 1, \xi\} = \frac{\epsilon_i}{\epsilon_i + \epsilon_j},$$

irrespective of the subject parameter ξ.

Considering, then, a number, n, of subjects, all of whom happened to have $a. = 1$, the probability that c of them have $a_i = 1$ (and thus $a_j = 0$) is given by the binomial law:

$$(4.9) \quad p\{c \mid n\} = \binom{n}{c} \left(\frac{\epsilon_i}{\epsilon_i + \epsilon_j}\right)^c \left(\frac{\epsilon_j}{\epsilon_i + \epsilon_j}\right)^{n-c}.$$

Accordingly, by the relation

$$(4.10) \qquad \frac{\epsilon_i}{\epsilon_i + \epsilon_j} \approx \frac{c}{n}$$

the ratio (ϵ_i/ϵ_j) is estimated *independently of the subject parameters*, the distribution of which is therefore irrelevant in this connection.

Furthermore, we may get a check on the model by first stratifying the subjects according to any principle — educational level or socioeconomic status or even randomly — and then applying 4.10 to each of the groups. For the model to hold, the ratio ϵ_i/ϵ_j should be the same in all of the groups and the variation of the estimates obtained should therefore concur with the binomial distributions 4.9.

The appropriate test for this constancy has a remarkable property. Denote the within-group c's and n's by c_g, n_g, with $g = 1, \ldots, h$, and their totals by $c.$ and $n.$ Since the groups could be collected into one group of size $n.$ to which 4.9 applies, we have

$$(4.11) \qquad p\{c. \mid n.\} = \binom{n.}{c.} \left(\frac{\epsilon_i}{\epsilon_i + \epsilon_j}\right)^{c.} \left(\frac{\epsilon_j}{\epsilon_i + \epsilon_j}\right)^{n.-c.}.$$

On the other hand, the joint probability of the numbers $c_1, \ldots, c_h$, due to their stochastic independence, is

$$(4.12) \qquad p\{c_1, \ldots, c_h \mid n_1, \ldots, n_h\} = \prod_{g=1}^{h} \binom{n_g}{c_g} \cdot \left(\frac{\epsilon_i}{\epsilon_i + \epsilon_j}\right)^{c_g} \left(\frac{\epsilon_j}{\epsilon_i + \epsilon_j}\right)^{n_g - c_g}$$

In consequence the conditional probability of $c_1, \ldots, c_h$ given the total $c.$, obtained by dividing 4.11 into 4.12, becomes independent of ϵ_i and e_j:

$$(4.13) \qquad p\{c_1, \ldots, c_h \mid c., n_1, \ldots, n_h\} = \frac{\prod_{g=1}^{h} \binom{n_g}{c_g}}{\binom{n.}{c.}}.$$

It follows that as far as the items i and j are concerned, *the testing of the model* can be carried out in a way that is *independent of all of the parameters.*

In the formal derivation of the fundamental relation 4.8, subjects and items can of course be interchanged. Thus the comparison of two subjects μ and ν by means of a single item with parameter ϵ leads to the conditional probability

$$(4.14) \qquad p\{a_\mu = 1 \mid a. = 1, \epsilon\} = \frac{\xi_\mu}{\xi_\mu + \xi_\nu},$$

where a_μ, a_ν, and $a.$ have a meaning similar to 4.5 and 4.6. Probability 4.14 is *independent of which item was used*.

In principle, therefore, it should be possible to estimate the ratio independently of the item parameters. In practice, however, this method does not work, because the number of items — in contrast to the number of subjects — usually is small.

5. Generalization to *k* items

In generalizing the results of the preceding section we will first consider the responses of an individual with parameter ξ to *k* items. With the notation 4.5 and the adaptation

$$(5.1) \qquad a. = a_1 + \ldots + a_k$$

of 4.5, we may condense 3.3 to

$$(5.2) \qquad p\{a_i \,|\, \xi\} = \frac{(\xi\epsilon_i)^{a_i}}{1 + \xi\epsilon_i}$$

and the generalization of 4.1 through 4.4 to

$$(5.3) \qquad \left\{ \begin{aligned} p\{a_1, \ldots, a_k \,|\, \xi\} &= p\{a_1 \,|\, \xi\} \ldots p\{a_k \,|\, \xi\} \\[2mm] &= \frac{\xi^{a.}\ \epsilon_1^{a_1} \ldots \epsilon_k^{a_k}}{\displaystyle\prod_{i=1}^{k} (1 + \xi\epsilon_i)}, \end{aligned} \right.$$

recalling that a_i is either zero or one. From this result we derive the probability that $a.$ takes on a specified value r. If $r = 0$, every $a_i = 0$, and thus

$$(5.4) \qquad p\{a. = 0 \,|\, \xi\} = \frac{1}{\gamma(\xi)},$$

where for short we write

$$(5.5) \qquad \prod_{i=1}^{k} (1 + \xi\epsilon_i) = \gamma(\xi).$$

We can obtain $r = 1$ in k different ways —

$$a_1 = 1,\ a_2 = \ldots = a_k = 0,$$
$$a_1 = 0,\ a_2 = 1,\ a_3 = \ldots = a_k = 0$$

(5.6)
$$-\ -\ -\ -\ -\ -\ -\ -\ -\ -\ -\ -\ -$$

$$a_1 = a_2 = \ldots = a_{k-1} = 0,\ a_k = 1$$

— with the probabilities

(5.7)
$$\frac{\xi \epsilon_1}{\gamma(\xi)},\ \frac{\xi \epsilon_2}{\gamma(\xi)},\ \ldots,\ \frac{\xi \epsilon_k}{\gamma(\xi)},$$

the sum of which is the probability

(5.8)
$$p\{a_. = 1 \mid \xi\} = \frac{\xi(\epsilon_1 + \ldots + \epsilon_k)}{\gamma(\xi)}.$$

We can obtain $r = 2$ in $\binom{k}{2}$ different ways, namely by taking any two of the a_i's to be 1, the rest of them being 0. The probabilities of these combinations are

(5.9)
$$\frac{\xi^2 \epsilon_1 \epsilon_2}{\gamma(\xi)},\ \frac{\xi^2 \epsilon_1 \epsilon_3}{\gamma(\xi)},\ \frac{\xi^2 \epsilon_2 \epsilon_3}{\gamma(\xi)},\ \ldots,\ \frac{\xi^2 \epsilon_{k-1} \epsilon_k}{\gamma(\xi)},$$

and the sum of them is

(5.10)
$$p\{a_. = 2 \mid \xi\} = \frac{\xi^2(\epsilon_1 \epsilon_2 + \ldots + \epsilon_{k-1} \epsilon_k)}{\gamma(\xi)}.$$

In general $a_. = r$ can be obtained in $\binom{k}{r}$ different ways, by taking any r out of the k a_i's to be 1, the rest of them being 0. The probabilities of these combinations being

(5.11)
$$\frac{\xi^r\ \epsilon_1 \ldots \epsilon_r}{\gamma(\xi)},\ \frac{\xi^r\ \epsilon_1 \ldots \epsilon_{r-1} \epsilon_{r+1}}{\gamma(\xi)},\ \ldots,\ \frac{\xi^r\ \epsilon_{k-r+1} \ldots \epsilon_k}{\gamma(\xi)},$$

the probability of $a_. = r$ becomes

(5.12)
$$p\{a_. = r \mid \xi\} = \frac{\gamma_r \xi^r}{\gamma(\xi)}$$

where, for short,

(5.13) $$\gamma_r = (\epsilon_1 \ldots \epsilon_r) + \ldots + (\epsilon_{k-r+1} \ldots \epsilon_k).$$

In particular for $r = k$, 5.13 contains only one term,

(5.14) $$\gamma_k = \epsilon_1 \epsilon_2 \ldots \epsilon_k.$$

If in 5.12 we let r pass through the values $0, 1, \ldots, k$, all possibilities have been exhausted and therefore the probabilities must add up to unity:

(5.15) $$\sum_{r=0}^{k} p\{a. = r \mid \xi\} = 1.$$

Hence

(5.16) $$\gamma(\xi) = \sum_{r=0}^{k} \gamma_r \xi^r,$$

that is, γ_r are the coefficients in the expansion of the product 5.5 in powers of ξ.* If the ϵ's were known, the γ_r's could be computed and it would be possible from an observed $a.$ to estimate ξ and to indicate the precision of the estimate—for example, in terms of confidence intervals. Thus $a.$ is what is called an *estimator* for ξ. How to compute an estimate from the estimator is not our concern at present, but as an estimator $a.$ has an important property.

On dividing 5.12 into 5.3 we obtain the conditional probability of the a_i's, given that their sum is r. Through this operation both the common denominator and the common power of ξ cancel and we get

(5.17) $$p\{a_1, \ldots, a_k \mid a. = r, \xi\} = \frac{\epsilon_1^{a_1} \ldots \epsilon_k^{a_k}}{\gamma_r},$$

which is *independent of ξ*, the parameter to be estimated.

In order to realize the significance of this result we can turn to an obvious but fundamental principle of science, namely, that *if we want to know something about a quantity*—for example, a parameter of a model—*then we have to observe something that depends on that quantity*, something that changes if the quantity varies materially. For the purpose of estimating the parameter ξ of a person, the observations $a_1, \ldots, a_k$ are available. On repetition of the experiment they would, according to our theory, vary at random in concord-

---

*In algebra they are known as elementary symmetric functions of $\epsilon_1, \ldots, \epsilon_k$.

ance with the distribution 5.3, which depends on ξ. Also a random variable is $a.$, the distribution of which 5.12 depends on ξ, and therefore it can be used for the estimation. But what 5.17 tells is that *the constellation of 0's and 1's* producing $a.$, which also varies at random, *has a distribution that does not depend on ξ*. From the fundamental principle it then follows that once $a.$ has been recorded, any extra information about *which of the items* were answered correctly is, according to our model, *useless as a source of inference about ξ* (but not for other purposes, as will presently be seen).

The capital discovery that such situations exist was made by R. A. Fisher in 1922, and following his terminology we shall call $a.$ a *sufficient statistic* — or *estimator* — for the parameter in question.

In the present situation, however, the sufficiency of $a.$ needs a qualification as being *relative*, since it rests upon the condition that the ϵ_i's are known. As long as such knowledge is not available, the sufficiency as such is not very helpful, but the important point of 5.17 then is that it depends solely upon the ϵ's, not on ξ.

From 5.17 we can therefore proceed, as we did from 4.8, to consider a collection of subjects that all happen to have $a. = r$. Specifying by a_{vi} the a_i of subject v and denoting by (a_{vi}), given v, the set of responses $a_{v1}, \ldots, a_{vk}$, that is,

$$(5.18) \qquad (a_{vi}) = (a_{v1}, \ldots, a_{vk}),$$

we can rewrite 5.17 in the form

$$(5.19) \qquad p\{(a_{vi}) \mid a_{v.} = r\} = \frac{\epsilon_1^{a_{v1}} \ldots \epsilon_k^{a_{vk}}}{\gamma_r}, \quad v = 1, \ldots, n.$$

The responses of the n persons being independent, their joint probability is obtained by multiplying the n probabilities of 5.19. Denoting for short the whole set of $n \times k$ responses by $((a_{vi}))$ — the double parentheses indicating variation over both v and i — we get

$$(5.20) \qquad p\{((a_{vi})) \mid (a_{v.} = r)\} = \frac{\epsilon_1^{a_{.1}} \ldots \epsilon_k^{a_{.k}}}{\gamma_r^n},$$

where

$$(5.21) \qquad a_{.i} = \sum_{v=1}^{n} a_{vi}.$$

Statement 5.20 implies that, as a consequence of the model, we have to deal with the total number of correct answers to each item for the n persons in question.

6. Separation of parameters

Let us finally consider the responses of n individuals with the parameters $\xi_1, \ldots, \xi_n$ to k items with the parameters $\epsilon_1, \ldots, \epsilon_k$. With the notation a_{vi} introduced in the last section, the model 5.2 now takes the form

$$(6.1) \qquad p\{a_{vi} \mid \xi_v, \epsilon_i\} = \frac{(\xi_v \epsilon_i)^{a_{vi}}}{1 + \xi_v \epsilon_i},$$

and on the assumption of stochastic independence of all of the responses a_{vi}, $v = 1, \ldots n$, $i = 1, \ldots k$, the joint probability of the whole set $((a_{vi}))$ of them becomes

$$p\{((a_{vi})) \mid (\xi_v), (\epsilon_i)\} = \prod_{v=1}^{n} \prod_{i=1}^{k} p\{a_{vi} \mid \xi_v, \epsilon_i\}$$

$$(6.2) \qquad\qquad = \frac{\prod\limits_{v=1}^{n} \prod\limits_{i=1}^{k} (\xi_v \epsilon_i)^{a_{vi}}}{\prod\limits_{v=1}^{n} \prod\limits_{i=1}^{k} (1 + \xi_v \epsilon_i)}.$$

In the numerator we notice that the parameter ξ_v occurs in k places, each time raised to a power a_{vi}, which all together makes $\xi_v^{a_{v\cdot}}$, and that the parameter ϵ_i occurs in n places, each time raised to a power a_{vi}, adding up to a total power of $a_{\cdot i}$. If furthermore the denominator is denoted by

$$(6.3) \qquad \gamma((\xi_v), (\epsilon_i)) = \prod_{v=1}^{n} \prod_{i=1}^{k} (1 + \xi_v \epsilon_i),$$

we can simplify 6.2 to

$$(6.4) \qquad p\{((a_{vi})) \mid (\xi_v), (\epsilon_i)\} = \frac{\prod\limits_{v=1}^{n} \xi_v^{a_{v\cdot}} \cdot \prod\limits_{i=1}^{k} \epsilon_i^{a_{\cdot i}}}{\gamma((\xi_v), (\epsilon_i))}.$$

This formula is the generalization of 5.3 to n persons, but in consequence of 6.4 we now have to derive the probability that $a_{1\cdot}, \ldots, a_{n\cdot}$ and $a_{\cdot 1}, \ldots, a_{\cdot k}$ take on two specified sets of values: $r_1, \ldots, r_n$ and $s_1, \ldots, s_k$.

In analogy to Section 5 — in particular the logical chain of 5.11 through 5.13 — we should find all possible ways of building up zero/one matrices $((a_{vi}))$ that have the same row totals $a_{v\cdot} = r_v$, $v = 1, \ldots, n$ and column totals $a_{\cdot i} = s_i$, $i = 1, \ldots, k$, state the probability of each realization, and add up all such probabilities to a total joint probability of the two sets of totals considered. However, this procedure is greatly simplified by the fact that all the probabilities to be added are equal, namely — according to 6.4 —

(6.5)
$$\frac{\prod_{\nu=1}^{n} \xi_\nu^{r_\nu} \cdot \prod_{i=1}^{k} \epsilon_i^{s_i}}{\gamma((\xi_\nu),(\epsilon_i))}.$$

Thus we have only to count the number of different ways in which it is algebraically possible to build up a zero/one matrix with the row totals of $r_\nu, \nu = 1, \ldots, n$ and the column totals of $s_i, i = 1, \ldots, k$.

Determining this number is a combinatorial problem that appears to be rather difficult, but at present we need nothing more than a notation. For this number we write

(6.6)
$$\begin{bmatrix} r_1, \ldots, r_n \\ s_1, \ldots, s_k \end{bmatrix} = \begin{bmatrix} (r_\nu) \\ (s_i) \end{bmatrix},$$

and then we have

(6.7) $\quad p\{(a_\nu = r_\nu),(a_i = s_i) \mid (\xi_\nu),(\epsilon_i)\} = \begin{bmatrix} (r_\nu) \\ (s_i) \end{bmatrix} \dfrac{\prod_{\nu=1}^{n} \xi_\nu^{r_\nu} \prod_{i=1}^{k} \epsilon_i^{s_i}}{\gamma((\xi_\nu),(\epsilon_i))}.$

This joint probability distribution of the row totals a_ν and the column totals a_i contains just as many parameters as observables, and the latter would therefore seem suitable for estimation purposes. How true this is becomes clear when we divide 6.7 into 6.4 — or 6.5 — to obtain the probability of the whole set of observations, *on the condition that the totals of rows and columns are given*. In fact, all parametric terms cancel, and we are left with a conditional probability

(6.8)
$$p\{((a_{\nu i})) \mid (a_\nu = r_\nu),(a_i = s_i)\} = \frac{1}{\begin{bmatrix} (r_\nu) \\ (s_i) \end{bmatrix}}$$

that is independent of all of the parameters.

Therefore, once the totals have been recorded, any further statement as regards *which of the items* were answered correctly by *which persons* is, according to our model, *useless as a source of information about the parameters*. (Another use that can be made of the $a_{\nu i}$'s will emerge at a later stage of our discussion.) Thus the row totals and the column totals are *not only suitable* for estimating the parameters; they *imply every possible statement about the parameters that can be made on the basis of the ob-*

servations $((a_{vi}))$. Accordingly we will, in continuation of the terminology introduced in Section 5, characterize the row totals $a_{v.}$, $v = 1, \ldots, n$ and the column totals $a_{.i}$, $i = 1, \ldots, k$ as a *set of sufficient estimators for the parameters* $\xi_1, \ldots, \xi_n$ and $\epsilon_1, \ldots, \epsilon_k$.

As 6.7 contains both sets of parameters, a direct utilization of this formula would apparently lead to a simultaneous estimation of both sets. However, in view of previous results (see the comments following 5.17) it would seem appropriate to ask whether it is possible—also in this general case—to estimate the item parameters independently of the person parameters and, if so, vice versa as well.

In order to approach this problem we will first derive the distribution of the row totals, appearing as exponents of the ξ's, irrespective of the values of the column totals, by summing 6.7 over all possible combinations of $s_1, \ldots, s_k$. During this summation the denominator $\gamma((\xi_v), (e_i))$ remains constant, as do the terms $\xi_v^{r_v}$, $v = 1, \ldots, n$ in the numerator. Thus, on introducing the notation

$$(6.9) \qquad \gamma_{.}(r_v)((\epsilon_i)) = \sum_{(s_i)} \begin{bmatrix} (r_v) \\ (s_i) \end{bmatrix} \epsilon_1^{s_1} \ldots \epsilon_k^{s_k}$$

we obtain

$$(6.10) \qquad p\{(a_{v.} = r_v) \mid (\xi_v), (\epsilon_i)\} = \frac{\gamma_{.}(r_v)((\epsilon_i)) \cdot \prod_{\nu=1}^{n} \xi_v^{r_v}}{\gamma((\xi_v), (\epsilon_i))};$$

from which it is seen that the ξ_v's might be estimated from the row totals *if the* ϵ_i's—and therefore also the polynomials 6.9—*were known*.

Similarly, we can sum 6.7 over all possible combinations of $r_1, \ldots, r_n$, keeping $s_1, \ldots, s_k$ fixed. Substituting, in 6.9, $\xi_1, \ldots, \xi_n$ for $\epsilon_1, \ldots, \epsilon_k$ and in consequence interchanging the r's and the s's, we get

$$(6.11) \qquad \gamma_{(s_i)}((\xi_v)) = \sum_{(r_v)} \begin{bmatrix} (s_i) \\ (r_v) \end{bmatrix} \xi_1^{r_1} \ldots \xi_n^{r_n},$$

where, by the way,

$$(6.12) \qquad \begin{bmatrix} (s_i) \\ (r_v) \end{bmatrix} = \begin{bmatrix} (r_v) \\ (s_i) \end{bmatrix}.$$

With this notation the summation yields on analogy to 6.10:

$$(6.13) \qquad p\{(a_{.i} = s_i) \mid (\xi_\nu), (\epsilon_i)\} = \frac{\gamma_{(s_i)}((\xi_\nu)) \cdot \prod_{i=1}^{k} \epsilon_i^{s_i}}{\gamma((\xi_\nu), (\epsilon_i))},$$

and accordingly the ϵ_i's might be estimated from the column totals *provided the ξ_ν's were known.*

Thus we might estimate the ξ's if the ϵ's were known, and the ϵ's if the ξ's were known! And both estimations would even be relatively sufficient. In fact, on dividing 6.10 into 6.7 to obtain the conditional probability of $a_{.i}$ for given $a_{\nu.}$, we get

$$(6.14) \qquad p\{(a_{.i} = s_i) \mid (a_{\nu.} = r_\nu), (\xi_\nu), (\epsilon_i)\} = \begin{bmatrix} (r_\nu) \\ (s_i) \end{bmatrix} \frac{\prod_{i=1}^{k} \epsilon_i^{a_{.i}}}{\gamma_{(r_\nu)}((\epsilon_i))},$$

which is independent of the parameters ξ_ν to be estimated. Similarly, the division of 6.13 into 6.10 gives

$$(6.15) \qquad p\{(a_{\nu.} = r_\nu) \mid (a_{.i} = s_i), (\xi_\nu), (\epsilon_i)\} = \begin{bmatrix} (r_\nu) \\ (s_i) \end{bmatrix} \frac{\prod_{\nu=1}^{n} \xi_\nu^{r_\nu}}{\gamma_{(s_i)}((\xi_\nu))},$$

which is independent of the ϵ's. But, of course, as long as neither set of parameters is known, these possibilities are of no avail.

It is one of the characteristic features of the model under consideration that this vicious circle can be broken, the instrument being a reinterpretation of the formulas 6.14 and 6.15. In fact, as 6.14 depends on the ϵ's but not on the ξ's, this formula gives the opportunity of estimating the ϵ's without dealing with the ξ's. Thus the objections to both 6.7 and 6.13 have been eliminated. The unknown ξ's in these expressions have been replaced with observable quantities: the individual totals $a_{\nu.}$. Similarly, in 6.15 the ϵ's of 6.7 and 6.10 have been replaced with the item totals $a_{.i}$, in consequence of which we can estimate the ξ's without knowing or simultaneously estimating the ϵ's. Thus the estimation of the two sets of parameters can be separated from each other.

In this connection we can return to 6.8, noting that this formula is a consequence of the model structure — 3.3 and the stochastic independence — irrespective of the values of the parameters of which the right-hand term is independent. Therefore, if from a given matrix $((a_{\nu i}))$ we construct a quantity that would be useful for disclosing a particular type of departure from the model, then its sampling distribution as conditioned by the marginals $a_{\nu.}$ and

$a_{,i}$ will be independent of all of the parameters. Thus the testing of the model can be separated from dealing with the parameters.

We will not consider here the question of how to perform such testing in practice and also that of turning the observed row and column totals into adequate estimates of the ξ's and the ϵ's.

In Chapter 6 of the earlier study (3) these questions were dealt with by simple methods which were taken to be acceptable approximations. In the case of subtest N the observations passed the test for the model satisfactorily, but the model failed completely in the case of subtest F (geometrical shapes). In the latter subtest the time allowance, for some technical reasons, had been cut below the optimal limit, but a reanalysis of the data (not reported here) has shown that when allowance is made for the working speed of each subject, the data fit the model just as well as for the numerical sequences.

However, from a theoretical point of view the method used to test the model was unsatisfactory (see Rasch [3], Chapter 10, in particular pp. 181 – 182). By now we are in the process of working out better methods, and therefore for the time being we shall leave the documentation of the applicability of the model with simply a reference to the earlier work.

7. Specific objectivity

As regards the basic formulas 6.14 and 6.15, we have already noted that when they are applied to the total set of data they enable us to separate the estimation of one set of parameters from that of the other. However, formula 6.15 can also be applied to any subgroup of the total collection of subjects having been exposed to the k stimuli. Thus the parameters of the subjects in the subgroup can be evaluated without regard to the parameters of the other subjects.

In particular, the parameters of any two subjects can be compared on their own virtues alone, quite irrespective of the group or population to which for some reason they may be referred. Thus, as indicated in Section 1, the new approach, when applicable, does rule out populations from the comparison of individuals.

Similarly, formula 6.14 can be applied to any subset of the k stimuli, and accordingly their parameters can be evaluated without regard to the parameters of the other stimuli. In particular, the parameters of any two stimuli can be compared separately.

With these additional consequences, the principle of separability leads to a singular objectivity in statements about both parameters and model structure. In fact, *the comparison of any two subjects* can be carried out in such a way that *no other parameters are involved than those of the two subjects* — neither the parameter of any other subject nor any of the stimulus parameters. Similarly, *any two stimuli can be compared independently of all other parameters than those of the two stimuli,* the parameters of all other stimuli as well as the parameters of the subjects having been replaced with observable numbers.

It is suggested that comparisons carried out under such circumstances be designated as "specifically objective." The same term would seem appropriate for statements about the model structure that are independent of all the parameters specified by the model, their unknown values being, in fact, irrelevant for the structure of the model.

Of course, specific objectivity is no guarantee against the "subjectivity" of the statistician when he chooses his fiducial limits or when he judges which kind of deviations from the model he will look for. Neither does it save him from the risk of being offered data marred by the subjective attitude of the psychologist during his observations. Altogether, when introducing the concept of specific objectivity, I am not entering upon a general philosophical debate on the meaning and the use of objectivity at large. At present the term is strictly limited to observational situations that can be covered by the stimulus-subject-response scheme, to be described in terms of a parametric model that specifies parameters for stimuli and for subjects.

What has been demonstrated in detail in the case of two response categories is *that the specified objectivity in all three directions can be attained insofar as the type of model defined herein holds.* Recently it has been shown that except for unimportant mathematical restrictions, the inverse statement is also true: if only two responses are available, the observations must conform to the simple model 3.3 if it is to be possible to maintain specific objectivity in statements about subjects, stimuli, and model.

8. Fields of application

The problems we have been dealing with in the present paper were formulated within a narrow field, psychological test theory. However, with the discovery of specific objectivity we have arrived at concepts of such generality that the original limitation is no longer justified. Extensions into other fields of psychology, such as psychophysical threshold experiments and experiments on perception of values, offer themselves, but the stimulus-subject-response framework is by no means limited to psychology. Thus in a recent publication (1) a Poisson model was employed in an investigation of infant mortality in Denmark in the period 1931–60. In each year the number of infant deaths (of all causes or of a particular cause) out of the number of boys and of girls, born in or out of wedlock, was recorded. In this case the years served as subjects, the combination of sex and legitimacy of the children as the stimulus, and the number of infant deaths out of the number of children born as the responses.

From economics we can take household budgets as an example. The families serve as subjects, income and expenditures – classified into a few types – as stimuli, and the amount earned and the amount spent as the responses.

These examples may indicate that the framework covers a rather large field within the social sciences. Delineating the area in which the models described here apply is a huge problem, the inquiry into which has barely started.

But already the two intelligence tests mentioned in Section 2 and discussed at the end of Section 6 are instructive as regards the sort of difficulties we should be prepared to meet. For one of them, the numerical sequences, the earlier analysis (3, Chapter 6) showed a perfectly satisfactory fit of the observations to the model – that is, in this case specific objectivity can be obtained on the basis of the response pattern for each subject. For the other test, the geometrical shapes, the analysis most unambiguously showed that the separability did not hold.

Neither did it hold for a different intelligence test, which was of the omnibus type, containing items that presumably called upon very different intelligence functions. In this case, therefore, the data could not be expected to allow for a description comprising only one parameter for each subject. The items in the numerical sequences were quite uniform in that they required the testee to recognize a logical structure in a sequence of numbers. According to the analysis, the items were sufficiently uniform – although of very different levels of difficulty – to allow for a description of the data by one parameter for each subject as well as for each item. The items of the geometric figure test were constructed just as uniformly as the numerical sequences, and therefore it was somewhat of a surprise that the results turned out quite adversely.

To this material I could add observations on two other tests, constructed with equal care. One was a translation of the idea of Raven's matrix test into letter combinations, at the same time substituting the multiple choice by a construction, on the part of the testee, of the answer. For this test the results were just as good as for the numerical sequences. The other test consisted of a set of verbal analogies where the number of answers offered was practically infinite, with the effect that the multiple choice was in fact eliminated. Here the results of the testing were just as disappointing as for the figure test.

This contrast, however, led to the solution of the mystery. The difference between the two pairs of tests was due not to construction principles but to the administration of the tests. For all four tests the adequate time allowance was determined by means of special experiments. On applying them to random samples of 200 subjects, it turned out that the number of correct answers formed a convenient distribution for the letter matrix test and for the numerical sequences, but verbal analogies and the figure test were too easy and the distributions showed an undesirable accumulation of many correct answers.

This happened in 1953, when only the barest scraps of the theory had been developed, and yielding to considerable time pressure the test constructor, consulting me on the statistical part of the problem, severely cut down the time allowances so as to move the distributions to the middle of the range. While succeeding in that, we spoiled the test, turning it into a mixture of a test for ability and a test for speed.

More recently, however, I have had the opportunity to reanalyze both sets of data, grouping the subjects primarily according to their working speed, as given by the number of items done, and applying to each group the technique of Chapter 6 of the earlier report (2). The result was startling: Within each speed group I found confirmation of the theory, and the relative difficulties of the items were independent of the working speed. Altogether, with speed as ancillary information, specific objectivity can be attained in regard to the properties which the tests really aimed at measuring.

Inverting the final statement, we get the moral of this story: *Observations may easily be made in such a way that specific objectivity, otherwise available, gets lost.* For instance, this can easily happen when qualitative observations with, say, five categories of responses for convenience are condensed into three categories. If the basic model holds for the five categories, it is mathematically almost impossible for the three-category model also to hold. Thus the grouping, tempting as it may be, will usually tend to slur the specific objectivity.

In concluding, therefore, I must point out that the problem of the relation of data to models is not only one of trying to fit data to an adequately chosen model from our inventory to see whether it works; it is also *how to make observations in such a way that specific objectivity obtains.*

References

1. MATTHIESSEN, P. C. *Infant Mortality in Denmark, 1931–60.* Copenhagen: Statistical Department, 1965.
2. RASCH, G. "On General Laws and the Meaning of Measurement in Psychology," in *Proceedings of the Fourth Berkeley Symposium on Mathematical Statistics and Probability* Vol. IV, 321-34, Berkeley; Univ. of California Press, 1961.
3. _____. *Probabilistic Models for Some Intelligence and Attainment Tests.* Copenhagen: Danish Institute for Educational Research, 1960.

Suggestions for Further Reading (Section Two)

COOMBS, CLYDE. *A Theory of Psychological Scaling.* (Bulletin No. 34.) Ann Arbor: Engineering Research Institute, Univ. of Michigan, 1952. Coombs formulates an axiom system for a theory of scaling. He supposes that there is some underlying basis for behavior, and that, although this latent variable is actually a ratio scale, the manifest behavior can be measured only in very crude ways, such as through dichotomous items, or preferences. The first three chapters form an excellent introduction to scaling problems.

GUTTMAN, LOUIS. "The Quantification of a Class of Attributes: A Theory and Method of Scale Construction," in PAUL HORST and others, *The Prediction of Personal Adjustment.* New York: Social Science Research Council, 1941. Guttman gives a solution to the problem of assigning weights to items, the responses to which are simple polytomies. No assumptions are made about the nature of the items or even about the relations between the items. The basic idea is that of "classification," both of respondents and of items, and this leads naturally to the desire to maximize certain quantities. The procedures involved are closely related to principal component analysis.

LAZARSFELD, PAUL F. "Latent Structure Analysis," in *Psychology: A Study of a Science,* ed. S. KOCH. Vol. III. New York: McGraw-Hill, 1961. Lazarsfeld introduces the basic concept of the latent structure models and details the steps required in the analysis of these models and of the data to which they may be applied. The linear traceline model is studied at length, and examples are given.

LUCE, R. DUNCAN. "A Probabilistic Theory of Utility and Its Relationship to Fechnerian Scaling," in *Measurement,* eds. C. CHURCHMAN and P. RATOOSH. New York: Wiley, 1959. Luce considers the problem of inferring a latent scale of values when the observed phenomena are the individual's choices on a set of pair comparisons; he devises an axiom system that describes the properties that such a scale should possess. The basic concepts are an individual's subjective probability of the various events and their subjective value (utility) to him. He shows that a scale satisfying his axioms will be a Fechner-type scale: that is, the probability of choosing one of a pair of alternatives will be a function of the difference between the scale values of the two alternatives. This probability will be an exponential function of the difference in the utility of the two alternatives.

SHEPARD, R. N. "Similarity of Stimuli and Metric Properties of Behavioral Data," in *Psychological Scaling,* eds. HAROLD GULLIKSEN and SAMUEL MESSICK. New York: Wiley, 1960. In many applications involving comparisons of stimuli, a matrix of similarities will arise. The scientist then has some desire to locate the stimuli in a "real" space, but may have no idea of the relation between the underlying real space and the manifest "psychological" space inferred from the similarity matrix. Shepard outlines a technique of multidimensional scaling of data in an unknown metric, an iterative procedure that attempts to squeeze the stimuli into a Euclidean space of a certain dimension. In later papers (*Psychometrika,* 1962, **27,** 125-40 and 219-46) Shepard describes a computer program to carry this out and gives several examples.

TORGERSON, WARREN S. "The Law of Comparative Judgment," in *Theory and Methods of Scaling.* New York: Wiley, 1958. Thurstone's law of comparative judgment in its most general form states that the difference between the scale values of two stimuli, $s_k - s_j$, is a function of the proportion of times stimulus k is judged greater than stimulus j; the discriminal dispersions of the two stimuli; and the correlation between the reactions to the two stimuli. Torgerson classifies the various special cases of the law for which solutions exist, describes the experimental method of paired comparisons, and gives an example of the analysis.

The Mathematical Study of Small Homogeneous Groups

A Method of Matrix Analysis of Group Structure

R. Duncan Luce *University of Pennsylvania*
Albert D. Perry

Matrix methods may be applied to the analysis of experimental data concerning group structure when these data indicate relationships which can be depicted by line diagrams such as sociograms. One may introduce two concepts, *n*-chain and clique, which have simple relationships to the powers of certain matrices. Using them it is possible to determine the group structure by methods which are both faster and more certain than less systematic methods. This paper describes such a matrix method and applies it to the analysis of practical examples. At several points some unsolved problems in this field are indicated.

1. Introduction

In a number of branches of the social sciences one encounters problems of the analysis of relationships between the elements of a group. Frequently the results of these investigations may be presented in diagrammatic form as sociograms, organization charts, flow charts, and the like. When the data to be analyzed are such that a diagram of this type may be drawn, the analysis and presentation of the results may be greatly expedited by using matrix algebra. This paper presents some of the results of an investigation of this application of matrices. Initial trials in the determination of group structures indicate that the matrix method is not only faster but also less prone to error than manual investigation.*

The second section of this paper presents certain concepts used in the analysis and associates matrices with the group in question. The third states the results obtained and the fourth gives illustrations of their application. Finally, section five contains a mathematical formulation of the theory and derivation of the results presented in section three.

2. Definitions

2.01. The types of relationships which this method will handle are: man *a* chooses man *b* as a friend, man *a* commands man *b*, *a* sends messages to *b*, and so forth. Since in a given problem we concern ourselves with one sort

---

*Some of these examples have been worked out by the Research Center for Group Dynamics, Massachusetts Institute of Technology, in conjunction with some of its research.

of relation, no confusion arises from replacing the description of the relationship by a symbol $=>$. Thus, instead of "man i chooses man j as a friend," we write "$i => j$." If, on the other hand, man i had not chosen man j, we would have written "$i \neq > j$," using the symbol $\neq >$ to indicate the negation of the relationship denoted by $=>$.

2.02. Situations such as mutual choice of friends or two-way communication would thus be indicated by $i => j$ and $j => i$, or briefly, $i <=> j$. We describe such situations by saying that a *symmetry* exists between i and j.

2.03. When the choice is not mutual, that is $i => j$ or $j => i$ but not both, we say an *antimetry* exists between i and j.

2.04.* The data to be analyzed are presented in a matrix X as follows: the i,j entry (x_{ij}) has the value of 1 if $i => j$ and the value 0 if $i \neq > j$. For convenience we place the main diagonal terms equal to zero, i.e., $x_{ii} = 0$ for all i. This convention, $i \neq > i$, does not restrict the applicability of the method, since there is little significance in such statements as "Jones chooses himself as a friend."

Suppose, for example, that we had a group of four members with the following relationships: $a => b$, $b => a$, $b => d$, $d => b$, $c => a$, $c => b$, $d => a$, and $d => c$. All other possible combinations of $a,b,c,$ and d are related by the symbol $\neq >$. The X matrix associated with this group is:

$$
\begin{array}{c}
\quad\ \begin{array}{cccc} a & b & c & d \end{array} \\
\begin{array}{c} a \\ b \\ c \\ d \end{array}
\left[
\begin{array}{cccc}
0 & 1 & 0 & 0 \\
1 & 0 & 0 & 1 \\
1 & 1 & 0 & 0 \\
1 & 1 & 1 & 0
\end{array}
\right]
\end{array}
$$

2.05. From the X matrix we extract a symmetric matrix S having entries s_{ij} determined by $s_{ij} = s_{ji} = 1$ if $x_{ij} = x_{ji} = 1$, and otherwise $s_{ij} = s_{ji} = 0$. All the symmetries in the group are indicated in the matrix S. The S matrix associated with the above X matrix is:

$$
\left[
\begin{array}{cccc}
0 & 1 & 0 & 0 \\
1 & 0 & 0 & 1 \\
0 & 0 & 0 & 0 \\
0 & 1 & 0 & 0
\end{array}
\right]
$$

*In the course of the present work it was brought to our attention that in "A matrix approach to the analysis of sociometric data," *Sociometry*, 1946, **9**, 340-347, Elaine Forsyth and Leo Katz have used matrices to represent sociometric relations. They considered a three-valued logic rather than the present two-valued one, and the operations on the matrices are different from the ones discussed in this paper.

To indicate the *i,j* entry of the matrix X^n, which is the nth power of X, we shall employ the symbol $x_{ij}^{(n)}$. Similarly, the *i,j* entry of S^n is $s_{ij}^{(n)}$.

2.06. In the group considered above, we had $a => b$, $b => d$, and $d => c$ as three of the relations. If the symbol $=>$ indicates the relationship "sends messages to," it appears that a can send a message to c in three steps, via b and d. We call this three-step path a 3-chain from a to c. Rather than write out the above sequence of relations, we may omit the symbol $=>$ and simply write the 3-chain as *a,b,d,c*.

In a group involving more elements one might have the 5-chains *a,e,c,b,d,f* and *a,d,b,c,d,e*. We notice that the first sequence involves five steps between six elements of the group. The second sequence also involves five steps but only five elements of the group, since the element d appears as both the second and fifth member of the sequence. Thus, although these two five-step sequences contain different numbers of elements of the group, they both have six members. Using this concept of membership in a sequence, an *n*-step sequence has $n+1$ members.

These examples of 3-chains and 5-chains suggest a general definition for a property within the group: an ordered sequence with $n+1$ members, $i, a, b, \cdots, p, q, j$, is an n-*chain* from i to j if and only if

$$i => a, a => b, \cdots, p => q, q => j.$$

2.07. When two *n*-chains have the same elements in the same order, that is, the same members, then they are said to be *equal*, and otherwise they are *distinct*. It is important in this definition of equality that it be recognized that both the elements of the group and their order in the sequence are considered. The two chains *i,j,k,l,p* and *i,p,k,j,l* are distinct though they contain the same five elements.

2.08. When the same element occurs more than once in an *n*-chain, the *n*-chain is said to be *redundant*. (Thus, in a group of *m* elements any *n*-chain with *n* greater than *m* is redundant.) The chains *a,b,e,d,b,c* and *a,c,a,b,d,c,e*, for example, are both redundant, for the element *b* occurs twice in the former and the elements *a* and *c* both occur twice in the latter. An example of a nonredundant 5-chain is *a,d,p,b,q,j*.

2.09. A subset of the group forms a *clique* provided that it consists of three or more members each in the symmetric relation to each other member of the subset, and provided further that there can be found no element outside the subset that is in the symmetric relation to each of the elements of the subset. The application of this definition to the concept of friendship is immediate: it states that a set of more than two people form a clique if they are all mutual friends of one another. In addition, the definition specifies that subsets of cliques are not cliques, so that in a clique of five friends we shall not say that any three form a clique. Although the word *clique* immediately suggests friendship, the definition is useful in the study of other relationships.

2.10. This definition of *clique* has two possible weaknesses: first, if each element of the group is related by $=>$ to no more than c other elements of the group, then we can detect only cliques with at most $c+1$ members; and second, there may exist within the group certain tightly knit subgroups which by the omission of a few symmetries fail to satisfy the definition of a clique but which nonetheless would be termed, nontechnically, cliques. It may be possible to alleviate these difficulties by the introduction of so-called *n*-cliques, which comprise the set of n elements that form two distinct *n*-chains from each element of the set to itself. This requires that the *n*-chains be redundant, with the only recurring element being the endpoint and also that all the relations in the *n*-chains be symmetric.

This definition means that the four elements $a,b,c,$ and d form a 4-clique if the 4-chains (for example) a,b,c,d,a and a,d,c,b,a both exist. These, by the definition of *n*-chain, require that the relations

$$a <=> b, b <=> c, c <=> d, d <=> a$$

exist, but nothing is said about the relations between a and c and between b and d. The original definition requires, in addition, that

$$a <=> c \quad \text{and} \quad b <=> d$$

for $a,b,c,$ and d to form a clique of four members. Thus we see that the definition of *n*-clique considers "circles" of symmetries, but it fails to consider the symmetric "cross" terms that exist between the members of the *n*-clique. These cross terms will be investigated, however, by determining whether any m of these *n*-elements form an *m*-clique.

The usefulness of the definition of n-*clique* can be judged only after experience has been gained in its application. This is not conveniently possible at present, unfortunately, because the problem of the general determination of redundant *n*-chains has not been solved (see §5.09).

The most general definition of a cliquelike structure including antimetries will not be discussed, for it is believed that this will not be amenable to a concise mathematical formulation.

3. Statement of Results

3.01. In X^n the entry $x_{ij}^{(n)} = c$ if and only if there are c distinct *n*-chains from i to j (for proof, see §5.04). Thus, if in the fifth power of a matrix of data X we find that the number 9 occurs in the third row of the seventh column, we may conclude that there are 9 distinct 5-chains from element 3 to element 7.

3.02. In X^2 the ith main diagonal entry has the value m if and only if i is in the symmetric relation with m elements of the group (§5.05). Since by the definition of a clique each element i in a clique of t members must be in the symmetric relation to each of the $t-1$ other elements, it is necessary that $x_{ii}^{(2)} \geq t-1$ for i to be in a clique of t members. We may not, however, conclude from the fact that $x_{ii}^{(2)} \geq t-1$ that i is necessarily contained in a clique of t members.

3.03. An element i is contained in a clique if and only if the ith entry of the main diagonal of S^3 is positive (§5.06). The main diagonal terms of S^3 will be either 0 or even positive numbers in all cases, and when the value of the entry is 0 the associated element is not in a clique.

3.04. If, in S^3, t entries of the main diagonal have the value $(t-2)(t-1)$ and all other entries of the main diagonal are zero, then these t elements form a clique of t members (§3.08). It also follows from the next statement (§3.05) that if there is only one clique of t members, then these t elements will have a main diagonal value in S^3 of $(t-2)(t-1)$. The former statement is, however, the more significant in analysis, for it is the aim to go from the matrix representation to the group structure. There is no difficulty in going from the structure to the matrices.

3.05. Since by statement 3.03 the main diagonal values of S^3 are dependent only on the clique structure of the group, it is to be expected that a formula relating these values and the clique structure is possible. If an element i is contained in m different cliques each having t_ν members, and if there are d_k elements common to the kth clique and all the preceding ones, then

$$s_{ii}^{(3)} = \sum_{\nu=1}^{m} \{ (t_\nu - 2)(t_\nu - 1) - (d_\nu - 2)(d_\nu - 1) \} + 2$$

(§5.07). Thus, if we have three cliques (5,7,9,10), (1,4,9), and (1,2,5,9,11), then $d_1 = 0$, for there are no preceding cliques; $d_2 = 1$, for only element 9 is common to the second and first cliques; and $d_3 = 3$, for clique three has the elements 1, 5, and 9 common with the first two cliques. Substituting $t_1 = 4$, $t_2 = 3$, $t_3 = 5$, $d_1 = 0$, $d_2 = 1$, and $d_3 = 3$ and evaluating the formula for element 9, which is the only one common to all three cliques, we obtain:

$$
\begin{aligned}
s_{99}^{(3)} = \, & [(4-2)(4-1) - (0-2)(0-1)] \\
& + [(3-2)(3-1) - (1-2)(1-1)] \\
& + [(5-2)(5-1) - (3-2)(3-1)] + 2 \\
= \, & 18
\end{aligned}
$$

In the evaluation of this formula it is immaterial how the cliques are numbered initially; however, it is essential, once the numbering is chosen, that we be consistent.*

3.06. The redundant 2-chains of a matrix X are the main diagonal entries of X^2 (§5.09). Thus for a matrix

$$X = \begin{bmatrix} 0 & 1 & 0 & 1 & 0 \\ 0 & 0 & 1 & 1 & 0 \\ 1 & 0 & 0 & 0 & 1 \\ 1 & 0 & 0 & 0 & 1 \\ 1 & 1 & 0 & 0 & 0 \end{bmatrix}$$

with the square

$$X^2 = \begin{bmatrix} 1 & 0 & 1 & 1 & 1 \\ 2 & 0 & 0 & 0 & 2 \\ 1 & 2 & 0 & 1 & 0 \\ 1 & 2 & 0 & 1 & 0 \\ 0 & 1 & 1 & 2 & 0 \end{bmatrix}$$

the matrix of redundant 2-chains is

$$\begin{bmatrix} 1 & 0 & 0 & 0 & 0 \\ 0 & 0 & 0 & 0 & 0 \\ 0 & 0 & 0 & 0 & 0 \\ 0 & 0 & 0 & 1 & 0 \\ 0 & 0 & 0 & 0 & 0 \end{bmatrix}$$

To obtain the matrix of redundant 3-chains we compute the following matrix, in which the symbol $R^{(2)}$ stands for the matrix of redundant 2-chains:

$$XR^{(2)} + R^{(2)}X - S.$$

Deleting in this sum the main diagonal and replacing it with the main diagonal of X^3 gives the matrix of redundant 3-chains (§5.09). If the main diagonal of $XR^{(2)} + R^{(2)}X - S$ is denoted by $Y^{(3)}$ and the main diagonal of $X^{(3)}$ by $Z^{(3)}$, then let $E^{(3)} = Z^{(3)} - Y^{(3)}$ and thus the matrix of redundant 3-chains, $R^{(3)}$, is given by

$$R^{(3)} = XR^{(2)} + R^{(2)}X + E^{(3)} - S.$$

It has not yet been possible to develop formulas which will give the

---

*[EDITORS' NOTE: The above formula for $s_{ii}^{(3)}$ is not correct. See the editors' note in sec. 5.07.]

matrix of redundant n-chains for n larger than 3. What work has been done in this direction is presented in §5.09.

3.07. The several theorems on cliques give a method that to some extent determines the clique structure independent of the rest of the group structure. It would be desirable to find a simple scheme that determines the clique structure directly. Since a certain amount of knowledge in this direction can be obtained from S^3, it is conjectured that possibly there is a simple formula relating clique structure to the numbers in S^3. As yet no such formula has been developed.

In a consideration of this problem, it was questioned whether certain aspects of the structure would be lost in the multiplication, which, if true, might make the discovery of the desired formula impossible. The following theorem shows that neither the clique structure nor any of the properties of S are lost in the matrix S^3: Any real symmetric matrix has one and only one real symmetric n^{th} root if n is a positive odd integer (§5.12). This theorem is somewhat more general than was required, since it does not restrict the entries in the nth root to 0 and 1, and since it is true for any odd root rather than just the cube root. (In general the real symmetric even roots are not unique.)

This theorem suggests a further problem to be solved: to find a symmetric group structure which will ensure the presence of certain prescribed minimum n-chain conditions for odd n. To carry this out it will probably prove necessary to discover a theorem that uses not only the realness and symmetry of the S matrix and its powers, but in addition the fact that only the numbers 1 and 0 may be entries in S.

4. Examples

4.01. As the first example, let us compare and analyze the friendship structure in the following two hypothetical groups. The matrices are (where a blank entry indicates a zero):

I

	1	2	3	4	5	6	7	8	9	10
1		1		1		1	1			1
2	1			1	1		1	1		1
3	1						1			
4	1	1						1		1
5						1				
6					1					
7	1	1		1				1		
8	1	1		1			1			1
9										
10	1	1			1	1				

II

	1	2	3	4	5	6	7	8	9	10
1			1	1	1					1
2						1			1	
3	1			1						
4	1	1				1			1	1
5	1									
6		1					1			
7		1				1				
8				1				1		
9				1	1			1		
10	1		1				1			

The associated S matrices are:

	1	2	3	4	5	6	7	8	9	10
1		1		1			1	1		1
2	1			1			1	1		1
3										
4	1	1					1			1
5						1				
6					1					
7	1	1		1				1		
8	1	1					1			
9										
10	1	1		1						

	1	2	3	4	5	6	7	8	9	10
1			1	1	1					1
2						1				
3	1			1						
4	1		1						1	
5	1									
6		1					1			
7						1				
8									1	
9				1				1		
10	1									

The S^2 matrices are:

I

	1	2	3	4	5	6	7	8	9	10
1	5	4		3			3	2		2
2	4	5		3			3	2		2
3										
4	3	3		4			2	3		2
5					1					
6						1				
7	3	3		2			4	2		3
8	2	2		3			2	3		2
9										
10	2	2		2			3	2		3

II

	1	2	3	4	5	6	7	8	9	10
1	4		1	1					1	
2		1					1			
3	1		2	1	1				1	1
4	1		1	3	1			1		1
5			1	1	1					1
6						2				
7		1					1			
8				1				1		
9	1		1						2	
10			1	1	1					1

Here the differences between the groups are becoming evident. In Group I, men 3 and 9 have no mutual friends, since $s_{33}^{(2)} = s_{99}^{(2)} = 0$ (§3.02). Thus, as far as symmetric relationships are concerned, these men are isolated from the group. In the same way we determine that 5 and 6 each have just one symmetric friendship relation ($s_{55}^{(2)} = s_{66}^{(2)} = 1$, §3.02), which we determine to be $5 <=> 6$ from the S matrix. The remaining elements in S^2 form a rather dense set of quite large numbers, which means, roughly, a tightly knit group.

In the second group, on the other hand, every man has a nonzero main diagonal in S^2. The men 2, 5, 7, 8, and 10 each have a single mutual friend, which we determine to be $2 <=> 6$, $5 <=> 1$, $7 <=> 6$, $8 <=> 9$, and $10 <=> 1$. Then, since $s_{66}^{(2)} = 2$ and since we have just cited 6's two mutual friends, 6 need not be considered further. We note that the off-diagonal areas of this S^2 matrix are not so completely filled as Group I, indicating that the group is not so tightly bound.

The S^3 matrices indicate the differences in compactness of the structures quite clearly:

I

	1	2	3	4	5	6	7	8	9	10
1	14	15		14			14	12		12
2	15	14		14			14	12		12
3										
4	14	14		10			13	8		10
5						1				
6					1					
7	14	14		13			10	10		8
8	12	12		8			10	6		7
9										
10	12	12		10			8	7		6

II

	1	2	3	4	5	6	7	8	9	10
1	2		5	6	4			1	1	4
2						2				
3	5		2	4	1			1	1	1
4	6		4	2	1				4	1
5	4		1	1					1	
6		2					2			
7						2				
8	1		1						2	
9	1		1	4	1			2		1
10	4		1	1					1	

Since the corresponding main diagonal terms are nonzero, men 1, 2, 4, 7, 8, and 10 of Group I are in cliques (§3.03). These, with 3 and 9 which have no symmetries in the group and 5 and 6 which are mutual friends, account for all members of the group. The terms $s_{88}^{(3)} = s_{1010}^{(3)} = 6$ suggest a clique of four members; however, the existence of other main diagonal terms makes it impossible to apply the formula $(t-2)(t-1)$ (§3.04). Investigating in S first the elements 1, 2, and 4 because their columns have the largest values in the tenth row, we find that elements 1, 2, 4, and 10 form a clique of four members. In the eighth row the largest entries are in columns 1, 2, and 7, and an investigation reveals that 1, 2, 7, and 8 form a clique of four men, which then overlaps the first clique by the men 1 and 2. In row four the largest entries are found in columns 1, 2, and 7. We then find that 1, 2, 4, and 7 form a clique of four elements which overlaps the preceding two. All the men contained in cliques have been accounted for at least once, and a check either with the formula for main diagonal entries (§3.05) or directly in the S matrix indicates that all the cliques have been discovered. This, coupled with what we discovered in S^2, completely determines the symmetric structure of the first group.

For purposes of qualitative judgment and a guide to carrying out analysis, we note that the first two rows of S^3 present an interesting summary of the clique structure. The entries $s_{12}^{(3)}$ and $s_{21}^{(3)}$ have the largest values; next largest are in columns four and seven, and then finally in columns eight and ten. Men 1 and 2 are contained in all three cliques, 4 and 7 are each contained in two cliques, and finally men 8 and 10 are each in only one clique. This indicates that the magnitude of the off-diagonal terms determines to some extent the amount and structural position of the overlap of cliques.

In Group II there are only three elements with nonzero main-diagonal entries, all with the value 2. This fits the formula $(t-2)(t-1)$ with $t = 3$

(§3.04). Thus the men 1, 3, and 4 form a clique of three members. Returning to S^2, we see that there remains one unaccounted symmetry each for men 4 and 9, hence $4 < = > 9$.

In Group I, the off-diagonal terms are large in magnitude and are quite dense in the array, with some rows completely empty or with single entries in the S^3 matrix. This indicates a closely knit group with certain men definitely excluded. The S^3 matrix for the second group has fewer entries of a smaller value, indicating a less tightly knit structure, but it has no empty rows and only one row with a single entry; that is, it has fewer people than Group I who are not accepted by the group or who do not accept it.

A consideration of the matrix $X - S$ will give all the antimetries in the groups and complete the analysis of the structures.

It is clear that this procedure gains strength as the complexity of the problem increases, for the analysis of a twenty-element group is little more difficult than that of a ten-element group.

4.02. The second example is a communications system comprising two-way links between seven stations such as might occur in a telephone or telegraph circuit. The number of channels of a given number of steps (i.e., n-chains in the general theory) between any two points and the minimum number of steps required to complete contact between two stations will be determined. Suppose the matrix of one-step contacts is:

	1	2	3	4	5	6	7
1		1	1				1
2	1		1				
3	1	1		1	1		
4			1		1	1	1
5		1	1			1	1
6				1	1		1
7	1			1	1	1	

which in this case is also the S matrix. Then two-step connections are given by X^2:

	1	2	3	4	5	6	7
1	3	1	1	2	2	1	0
2	1	2	1	1	1	0	1
3	1	1	4	1	1	2	3
4	2	1	1	4	3	2	2
5	2	1	1	3	4	2	2
6	1	0	2	2	2	3	2
7	0	1	3	2	2	2	4

and the three-step ones by X^3:

	1	2	3	4	5	6	7
1	2	4	8	4	4	4	8
2	4	2	5	3	3	3	3
3	8	5	4	10	10	5	5
4	4	3	10	8	9	9	11
5	4	3	10	9	8	9	11
6	4	3	5	9	9	6	8
7	8	3	5	11	11	8	6

From the former, the two connections $1 < \overset{(2)}{=} > 7$ and $2 < \overset{(2)}{=} > 6$ cannot be realized, because $x_{17}^{(2)} = x_{71}^{(2)} = 0$ and $x_{26}^{(2)} = x_{62}^{(2)} = 0$ (§3.01). The contacts are possible in three steps, however, since X^3 is completely filled. Thus two steps are sufficient for most contacts and three steps for all.

In determining the number of paths between two points it is desirable to eliminate redundant paths. For two-step communication this is done by deleting the main diagonal of X^2. The remaining terms represent the number of two-step paths between the stations indicated. The matrix of redundancies for three-step communication is given by $R^{(3)} = XR^{(2)} + R^{(2)}X + E^{(3)} - S$ (§3.06), which works out to be:

	1	2	3	4	5	6	7
1	2	4	6				6
2	4	2	5				
3	6	5	4	7	7		
4			7	8	7	6	7
5			7	7	8	6	7
6				6	6	5	6
7	6			7	7	6	6

The matrix of nonredundant three-step communication paths is $X^3 - R^{(3)}$:

	1	2	3	4	5	6	7
1			2	4	4	4	2
2				3	3	3	3
3	2			3	3	5	5
4	4	3	3		2	3	4
5	4	3	3	2		3	4
6	4	3	5	3	3		2
7	2	3	5	4	4	2	

We notice that the three-step paths between 1 and 2 and 2 and 3 are all redundant but that there are two-step paths for these combinations. All other combinations have at least two three-step paths joining them.

5. Mathematical Theory

5.01. To carry out the following mathematical formulation and the proofs of theorems, it is convenient to use some of the symbolism and nomenclature of point set theory. As there is some diversity in the literature, the symbols used are as follows:

Sets are defined either by enumeration or by properties of the elements of the set in the form: symbol for the set [symbols used for elements of the set | defining properties of these elements]. When a single element i is treated as a set it will be denoted by (i); otherwise sets will be denoted by uppercase Greek letters.

The intersection of (elements common to) two sets Γ and Φ is denoted by $\Gamma \cdot \Phi$.

The union of two sets Γ and Φ (elements contained in either or both) is denoted by $\Gamma + \Phi$. The context will make it clear whether the symbol $+$ refers to addition, matrix addition, or union.

The inclusion of a set Γ in another set Φ (all elements of Γ are elements of Φ) is denoted by $\Gamma < \Phi$. The negation is $\Gamma <^* \Phi$.

If $\Phi < \Xi$, then the complement of Φ with respect to Ξ, Φ', is defined by $\Phi + \Phi' = \Xi$ and $\Phi \cdot \Phi' = 0$, where 0 is the null set.

The inclusion of a single element i in a set Φ is denoted by $i \in \Phi$.

For any two elements i and j of a set Ξ and a subset Ω of Ξ:

$(i) + (j) < \Omega$ if and only if $i \in \Omega$ and $j \in \Omega$.

$(i) + (j) <^* \Omega$ implies $i \in \Omega'$ and/or $j \in \Omega'$.

The symbol $\delta_{ij} \begin{array}{l} = 1 \quad \text{if } i = j. \\ = 0 \quad \text{if } i \neq j. \end{array}$

5.02. Consider a finite set Ξ of x elements denoted by $1, 2, \cdots, i, \cdots, j, \cdots, x$ for which there is defined a relation $=>$ between elements and its negation $\neq>$ having these properties:

1. Either $i => j$ or $i \neq > j$ for all i and $j \in \Xi$.
2. $i \neq > i$.

Let a number x_{ij} be associated with i and j such that

$x_{ij} \begin{array}{l} = 1 \quad \text{if } i => j. \\ = 0 \quad \text{if } i \neq > j. \end{array}$

A matrix $X = [x_{ij}]$ is formed from the numbers x_{ij}. It will be found useful to denote the i,j entry of the nth power of X, X^n, by $x_{ij}^{(n)}$.

A *symmetry* is said to exist between i and j if and only if $i => j$ and $j => i$, in which case we can write $i <=> j$. For the matrix X this requires that $x_{ij} = x_{ji} = 1$. If, however, either $i => j$ and $j \neq > i$ or $i \neq > j$ and $j => i$, then an *antimetry* is said to exist between i and j.

The *symmetric matrix* S associated with the matrix X is defined by $S = [s_{ij}]$, where

$$s_{ij} = s_{ji} \begin{matrix} = 1 & \text{if} & x_{ij} = x_{ji} = 1, & \text{i.e.,} & i <=> j. \\ = 0 & \text{otherwise.} \end{matrix}$$

The i,j entry of the nth power of S is $s_{ij}^{(n)}$.

5.03. Definitions:

1. An ordered sequence with $n+1$ members, $i \equiv \gamma_1, \gamma_2, \cdots, \gamma_n, \gamma_{n+1} \equiv j$, is an n-*chain* Γ from i to j if and only if

$$i \equiv \gamma_1 => \gamma_2, \gamma_2 => \gamma_3, \cdots, \gamma_n => \gamma_{n+1} \equiv j.$$

In brief, $i \overset{(n)}{=} > j$ indicates that there exists an n-chain from i to j, which can also be enumerated as $i \equiv \gamma_1, \gamma_2, \cdots, \gamma_n, \gamma_{n+1} \equiv j$ or, when no ambiguity will arise, as $i, k, l, \cdots, p, q, j$, with the ordering being indicated by the written order of the sequence.

2. Two n-*chains* Γ and Φ *are equal* if and only if the rth member of Γ equals the rth member of Φ, i.e., $\gamma_r = \Phi_r$, for $1 \leq r \leq n + 1$.

If this is not true, then Γ and Φ are *distinct*.

3. Each pair of elements γ_k and γ_m of an n-chain with $1 \leq k < m \leq n + 1$ and $\gamma_k = \gamma_m$ is said to be the *redundant pair* (k,m). An n-chain is *redundant* if and only if it contains at least one redundant pair.

4. The elements $1, 2, \cdots, t$ $(t \geq 3)$ form a *clique* Θ of t members if and only if each element of Θ is symmetric with each other element of Θ, and there is no element not in Θ symmetric with all elements of Θ.

This is equivalent to $x_{ij} = 1 - \delta_{ij}$ for $i, j = 1, 2, \cdots, t$ but not for $i, j = 1, 2, \cdots, t, t + 1$, whatever the $(t + 1)^{st}$ element.

5.04. Theorem 1: $x_{ij}^{(n)} = c$ if and only if there exist c distinct n-chains from i to j.

Proof: By definition of matrix multiplication

$$x_{ij}^{(n)} = \sum_{k \in \Xi} \cdots \sum_{q \in \Xi} x_{ik} x_{kl} \cdots x_{pq} x_{qj}$$

with the summations over $n - 1$ indices. Suppose that the indices have been selected such that $i, k, l, \cdots, p, q, j$ is an n-chain from i to j.

Then by definition 1 (§5.03)

$$x_{ik} = x_{kl} = \cdots = x_{pq} = x_{qj} = 1$$

and if the indices were not so selected, then at least one $x_{rs} = 0$. Thus n-chains contribute 1 to the sum and other ordered sequences contribute 0. Since the indices take on each possible combination of values just once, every distinct n-chain is represented just once. If there are c such n-chains, then there is a total of c ones in the summation.

5.05. Theorem 2: An element of Ξ has a main diagonal value of c in X^2 if and only if it is symmetric with c elements of Ξ.

Proof: Let Φ be the set of j's for which $i < = > j$. By definition

$$x_{ii}^{(2)} = \sum_{j \, \epsilon \, \Phi} x_{ij} x_{ji} + \sum_{j \, \epsilon \, \Phi'} x_{ij} x_{ji} = \sum_1 + \sum_2.$$

$\sum_1 = c$ by theorem 1 (§5.04) and $\sum_2 = 0$ because i and j are not symmetric for $j \, \epsilon \, \Phi'$, so either $x_{ij} = 0$ or $x_{ji} = 0$ or both. Thus if i is symmetric with c elements of Ξ, $x_{ii}^{(2)} = c$.

If $x_{ii}^{(2)} = c$, then by theorem 1 there exist c distinct j's such that $x_{ij} = x_{ji} = 1$, i.e., $i < = > j$ for c j's.

5.06. Theorem 3: An element i is contained in a clique if and only if the ith entry of the main diagonal of S^3 is positive.

Proof: Suppose that i is contained in a clique Θ.

By definition

$$s_{ii}^{(3)} = \sum_{(j) + (k) < \Xi} \sum s_{ij} s_{jk} s_{ki}.$$

Select j and k such that $(j) + (k) < \Theta$ and such that $i \neq j \neq k \neq i$. Such elements exist by the definition of a clique (definition 4, §5.03). It is true by the definition of a clique and of the matrix S that $s_{ij} = s_{ji} = s_{jk} = s_{kj} = s_{ik} = s_{ki} = 1$ for such j and k. Thus this choice of j and k contributes 2 to the summation; and because $s_{ij} \geq 0$ for all i and j, there are no negative contributions to the sum. Therefore $s_{ii}^{(3)} \geq 2 > 0$.

Suppose that $s_{ii}^{(3)} > 0$. Then there exists at least one pair of elements of j and k such that $s_{ij} = s_{jk} = s_{ki} = 1$ and this implies $i < = > j$, $j < = > k$, and $k < = > i$. If there are no other elements symmetric with i, j, and k, then these three form a clique. If there is another element symmetric with these three, then consider the set of four formed by adding it to the previous three. If there is no other element symmetric with these four, they form a clique. If there is, add it to the set and continue the process. Since the set Ξ contains only a finite number of elements, the process must terminate giving a clique containing i.

[EDITORS' NOTE: We have omitted section 5.07, which contained theorem 4. Professor Luce pointed out that this theorem, which gave a formula for the diagonal terms of S^3, was in error. The following expression is the only correct statement we have been able to make concerning this quantity.

Let $\theta_1, \theta_2, \theta_3, \ldots, \theta_m$ be the cliques which contain the element i. Let t_σ be the number of elements in clique θ_σ; let $t_{\sigma\nu}$ be the number of elements that are common to cliques θ_σ and θ_ν; let $t_{\sigma\nu\tau}$ be the number of elements that are common to cliques θ_σ, θ_ν and θ_τ; and so on. Then $s_{ii}^{(3)}$ the ith diagonal entry of S^3, is equal to:

$$\sum_{\sigma=1}^{m} (t_\sigma - 2)(t_\sigma - 1) - \sum\sum_{\sigma \neq \nu} (t_{\sigma\nu} - 2)(t_{\sigma\nu} - 1) + \sum\sum\sum_{\sigma,\nu,\tau} (t_{\sigma\nu\tau} - 2)(t_{\sigma\nu\tau} - 1)$$
$$- \ldots \pm t_{12 \ldots m}$$

where the $+$ and $-$ signs alternate throughout the sequence of summations.]

5.08. Theorem 5: If (1) Θ is a set of t members with $t \geq 3$, (2) $s_{ii}^{(3)} = (t-2)(t-1)$ for i contained in Θ, and (3) $s_{jj}^{(3)} = 0$ for j contained in Θ', then Θ is a clique of t members.

Proof: There are two cases:

1. $i < = > j$ for all $i, j \in \Theta$, then Θ is a clique by definition 4 (§5.03) and theorem 3 (§5.06), and it has t members by part 1 of the hypothesis.

2. There exist p and $q \in \Theta$ such that p and q are not symmetric. Then by definition

$$S_{ii}^{(3)} = \sum\sum_{(j)+(k)<\Theta} s_{ij}s_{jk}s_{ki}$$
$$+ \sum\sum_{(j)+(k)<{}^*\Theta} s_{ij}s_{jk}s_{ki}.$$

If $s_{ij}s_{jk}s_{ki} = 1$, the elements i, j, and k are a clique or a subset of a clique and thus by hypothesis 3 and theorem 3 (§5.06) they are all contained in Θ; therefore the second sum $= 0$. Introduce in Ξ sufficient relationships $p => q$ to make Θ a clique Φ of t members. Since $s_{ij} \geq 0$ for all i and j, the introduction of these $s_{pq} = 1$ must increase the sum by 2 or more, for at least two additional 3-chains are introduced (i,p,q,i and i,q,p,i); hence by theorem 4 (§5.07)

$$S_{ii}^{(3)} = \sum\sum_{(j)+(k)<\Phi} s_{ij}s_{jk}s_{ki} - 2 = (t-2)(t-1) - 2$$
$$< (t-2)(t-1),$$

which is contrary to hypothesis 2. Therefore Θ is a clique of t members.

5.09. Redundancies:

By definition 3 (§5.03), an n-chain is redundant if and only if it contains at least one redundant pair (k,m), where a redundant pair defines two members of the n-chain γ_k and γ_m, with $\gamma_k = \gamma_m$ and $k < m$. If these ordered subscript pairs (k,m) and the endpoint pair (i,j) (the latter not necessarily a redundant pair) are considered as sets, then five classes of mutually exclusive redundant n-chains can be defined which include all redundant n-chains:

1. The A_n class: There exists at least one redundant pair (k,m) and it has the property

$$(k,m) \cdot (i,j) = 0.$$

2. The B_n class: There exists one and only one redundant pair (k,m) and it has the property

$$(k,m) \cdot (i,j) = i.$$

3. The C_n class: There exists one and only one redundant pair (k,m) and it has the property

$$(k,m) \cdot (i,j) = j.$$

4. The D_n class: There exist two and only two redundant pairs (k,m) and (p,q) and they have the properties

$$(k,m) \cdot (i,j) = i$$
$$(p,q) \cdot (i,j) = j.$$

5. The E_n class: There exists one and only one redundant pair (k,m) and it has the property

$$(k,m) \cdot (i,j) = (i,j).$$

If there are t n-chains $i \overset{(n)}{=} > j$ of the class A_n from i to j, then define $a_{ij}^{(n)} = t$. From these numbers the matrix $A^{(n)} = [a_{ij}^{(n)}]$ is formed. This is the matrix of redundant n-chains of the class A_n. If $R^{(n)}$ is the matrix of redundant n-chains it follows, if analogous definitions are made for matrices of the other four classes, that

$$R^{(n)} = A^{(n)} + B^{(n)} + C^{(n)} + D^{(n)} + E^{(n)}.$$

It follows directly from the definitions and the limitations on n that

$$R^{(1)} = 0$$
$$R^{(2)} = [\delta_{ij} x_{ij}^{(2)}] = E^{(2)}$$
$$A^{(3)} = 0.$$

It will now be proved that $D^{(3)} = S$. By the definition of the class D_3, there exist two and only two redundant pairs (k,m) and (p,q), and they have the properties

$$(k,m) \cdot (i,j) = i$$
$$(p,q) \cdot (i,j) = j.$$

These pairs may define in total either three or four members of the 3-chain — three members when $m = p$, but no fewer, for if $k = p$ and $m = q$, then $(k,m) \cdot (i,j) = (i,j)$, which is contrary to the definition of D_3. Suppose $m = p$. Then either $i = \gamma_2 = j$ or $i = \gamma_3 = j$, which is impossible, for $i \neq > i$ by assumption. Thus $m \neq p$. With four members there are two possibilities for a redundant 3-chain: either $i = \gamma_2$, $\gamma_3 = j$ or $i = \gamma_3$, $\gamma_2 = j$. The former is impossible by the previous argument; thus the only 3-chains of the class D_3 are of the form

$$i, \gamma_2, \gamma_3, j \equiv i, j, i, j;$$

that is,

$$d_{ij}{}^{(3)} \begin{aligned} &= 1 \quad \text{if} \quad i <=> j \\ &= 0 \quad \text{otherwise.} \end{aligned}$$

Therefore, by the definition of S, we have $D^{(3)} = S$.

If the matrices of redundancies up to and including $R^{(n-2)}$ are known, then we can find $A^{(n)}$ by $A^{(n)} = X R^{(n-2)} X$.

Proof: By the definition of the class A_n, a redundant n-chain of this class has the form

$$i \equiv \gamma_1, \gamma_2, \overset{(a)}{\rule{1cm}{0.4pt}}, \gamma_k, \overset{(b)}{\rule{1cm}{0.4pt}}, \gamma_m, \overset{(c)}{\rule{1cm}{0.4pt}}, \gamma_n, \gamma_{n+1} \equiv j,$$

where $a + b + c + 5 = n$, $k < m$, and $\gamma_k = \gamma_m$.

It follows from the definition that $p \equiv \gamma_2 \overset{(n-2)}{=\!=\!=} > \gamma_n \equiv q$ is a redundant $n - 2$ chain, and each such distinct $n - 2$ chain determines no more than one distinct redundant n-chain from i to j. Thus the number of redundant n-chains of type A_n from i to j is the sum over all combinations $p \equiv \gamma_2$ and $q \equiv \gamma_n$ for the number of redundant $n - 2$ chains from p to q, that is,

$$a_{ij}{}^{(n)} = \sum_{(p)+(q)<\equiv} \sum x_{ip} r_{pq}{}^{(n-2)} x_{qj}$$

or

$$A^{(n)} = X R^{(n-2)} X.$$

If the matrix $[e_{ij}^{(n)}]$ is defined as

$$[e_{ij}^{(n)}] = XR^{(n-2)}X + D^{(n)}$$

then the relations

$$A^{(n)} + B^{(n)} + D^{(n)} = R^{(n-1)}X$$
$$A^{(n)} + C^{(n)} + D^{(n)} = XR^{(n-1)}$$
$$E^{(n)} = [\delta_{ij}(x_{ij}^{(n)} - e_{ij}^{(n)})]$$

follow through an enumeration of cases and by using patterns of proof similar to that just given.

These various relations permit the specific conclusions

$$R^{(2)} = [\delta_{ij}x_{ij}^{(2)}] = E^{(2)}$$
$$R^{(3)} = XR^{(2)} + R^{(2)}X + E^{(3)} - S$$

and the general result

$$R^{(n)} = XR^{(n-1)} + R^{(n-1)}X - XR^{(n-2)}X$$
$$+ E^{(n)} - D^{(n)}.$$

This latter expression is not useful in its present form, because $D^{(n)}$ has not been expressed in terms of the matrices of redundancies up to and including $R^{(n-1)}$. This problem of the determination of the matrix of redundant n-chains is left as an unsolved problem of both theoretical and practical interest.

5.10. Uniqueness:

In certain applications it is desirable to know whether a power of a matrix uniquely determines the matrix. This is not true in general, for Sylvester's theorem gives a multiplicity of nth roots of a matrix. The matrices being considered are rather specialized, however, and it is possible that some degree of uniqueness may exist.

The following two theorems indicate certain sufficient conditions for uniqueness. Since these theorems do not utilize completely the special characteristics of the matrices in this study, it is probable that more appropriate theorems can be proved.

5.11. Theorem 6: If p and q are positive integers, if two integers a and b can be found such that $ap - bq = 1$, and if X is a nonsingular matrix, then the powers X^p and X^q uniquely determine X.

Proof: Suppose that there exist two nonsingular matrices X and Y such that $X^p = Y^p$ and $X^q = Y^q$. Then $X^{ap} = Y^{ap}$ and $X^{bq} = Y^{bq}$. Now, form $X^{bq}Y = Y^{bq}Y = Y^{bq+1} = Y^{ap}$, since $ap - bq = 1$. Similarly $X^{bq}X = X^{bq+1} = X^{ap}$. But since $X^{ap} = Y^{ap}$, it follows that $X^{bq}X = X^{bq}Y$.

Since X is nonsingular, $|X^{bq}| \neq 0$, and thus there exists a unique inverse of X^{bq}, X^{-bq}, such that $X^{-bq}X^{bq} = I$; therefore $X = Y$.

5.12. Theorem 7: If n is a positive odd integer and S a real symmetric matrix, then there is one and only one real symmetric n^{th} root of S.
Proof: 1. There is one such n^{th} root.

Since S is real and symmetric, there exists a real orthogonal matrix P such that $P'SP = D$ (P' is the transpose of P) is diagonal with real entries d_{ii} which are the characteristic roots of S.* Assume P is so chosen that $d_{11} \leqslant d_{22} \leqslant \cdots \leqslant d_{mm}$. Let B be the diagonal matrix of the real n^{th} roots of the elements of D, that is, $b_{ii} =$ real $(d_{ii})^{1/n}$, so

$$B^n = D. \tag{1}$$

Define $R = PBP'$. Then $R^n = S$, for

$$R^n = (PBP')^n = PB^nP' = PDP' = S.$$

Since B is real and diagonal and P is real and orthogonal, R is real and symmetric.

2. There is only one such n^{th} root.

Suppose there exists a real symmetric matrix R_1 not equal to R such that $R_1{}^n = S$. Then there exists an orthogonal matrix Q such that $Q'R_1Q = T$ is diagonal in the characteristic roots of R_1, and ordered as before. Consider the nth power of T:

$$\begin{aligned} T^n &= (Q'R_1Q)^n = Q'R_1{}^nQ = Q'SQ \\ &= Q'PDP'Q = (P'Q)'D(P'Q) \\ T^n &= U'DU, \end{aligned} \tag{2}$$

where U is the orthogonal matrix $P'Q$. Since $U' = U^{-1}$, T^n and D are similar, and hence have the same characteristic roots.† Because they are diagonal in the characteristic roots, ordered in the same way, they are equal:

$$D = T^n. \tag{3}$$

Substituting (3) in (2),

$$D = U'DU$$

or

$$UD = DU.$$

By definition of matrix multiplication, this means

---

*C. C. MacDuffee, *Vectors and Matrices* (Ithaca, N.Y.: Mathematical Assn. of America, 1943), pp. 166–70.
†*Ibid.*, p. 113.

$$\sum_j u_{ij}d_{jk} = \sum_j d_{ij}u_{jk}.$$

Since D is diagonal, this reduces to

$$u_{ik}d_{kk} = d_{ii}u_{ik}$$

or

$$u_{ik}(d_{kk} - d_{ii}) = 0. \tag{4}$$

Since the d_{kk} are real and n is odd, equation (4) implies

$$u_{ik}[(d_{kk})^{1/n} - (d_{ii})^{1/n}] = 0,$$

where the $(d_{kk})^{1/n}$ are real. Thus by the definition of B,

$$UB = BU$$

or

$$B = U'BU. \tag{5}$$

By (1) and (3)

$$T^n = D = B^n,$$

but by construction T and B are both real diagonal matrices and n is odd, so this implies

$$T = B.$$

This substituted in (5) gives

$$T = U'BU = Q'PBP'Q$$

or

$$QTQ' = PBP'.$$

But $QTQ' = R_1$ and $PBP' = R$ by definition; therefore

$$R_1 = R.$$

6. Acknowledgment

We wish to acknowledge our indebtedness to Dr. Leon Festinger, assistant professor of psychology, Massachusetts Institute of Technology, for his kindness in directing this research to useful ends, encouraging the application of this method to practical problems, and providing many constructive criticisms of the work.

Mechanisms Involved in Pressures Toward Uniformity in Groups

Herbert A. Simon   *Carnegie Institute of Technology*
Harold Guetzkow   *Northwestern University*

Leon Festinger and his associates (2) have stated and tested a number of propositions about communication processes in small groups. This paper carries forward the synthesis of these propositions into an inter-related system, differentiating short-run mechanisms from those involved in the long run. First, we shall formalize some of Festinger's propositions and organize them into a model. Then, we shall examine two of the empirical studies in their relation to the mechanisms involved in pressures toward uniformity in groups.

1. THE POSTULATED AGGREGATIVE MODEL

Some of Festinger's hypotheses deal with aggregative relations—that is, they are concerned with the members of a group taken as a whole. Others focus on the behaviors of particular individuals in the group.[2] Let us confine our work for the present to his aggregative propositions.

The Aggregative Variables. Five of Festinger's hypotheses—those numbered 1a, 1b, 1c, 3a, and 3b—are stated in terms of six aggregative variables, in addition to time.

$D(t)$: The perceived *discrepancy* of opinion on an issue among members of a group at time t;

$P(t)$: *Pressure* upon members of the group to communicate with each other at time t;

$L(t)$: Receptivity (*listening*) of members of the group to influence by communications from other members at time t;

$C(t)$: Strength of the attraction of individuals to the group (*cohesiveness*) at time t;

$U(t)$: Pressure felt by the group to achieve *uniformity* of opinion, i.e., to reduce perceived discrepancy of opinion at time t;

R: *Relevance* of the issue to the group. This variable appears as a parameter, and hence is constant in time.

---

[1]This chapter was written jointly with my colleague, Harold Guetzkow. An earlier version of this paper was presented to the Summer Seminar on Design of Experiments on Decision Processes at Santa Monica in July, 1952. In revising the paper we have had the benefit of valuable comments from Leon Festinger, James Coleman, and Chris Argyris.

[2]A model handling the deviate member is described in the next Chapter, Chapter 8.

In constructing the model we shall assume that each variable is some kind of average or aggregate for members of the group. For example, D might be measured by locating the opinions of group members on a scale, attaching numbers to scale positions and calculating the standard deviation of the members' opinions in terms of these numbers. Even the intervening variables, although not directly measured, can be thought of as averages of the values for individual members. We will assume that the magnitude of each variable at time t for a given group can be represented by a real variable, using the latter term in its mathematical sense.

Representation of the Hypotheses by Equations. Festinger's aggregative propositions (2, pp. 273–277) state relationships between variables, as follows:

Number of the Proposition	Variables Interrelated
1a	D and P
1b	R and P
1c	C and P
3a	Change(s) in D and U
3b	Change(s) in D and C

We could now translate each of these five propositions into a corresponding mathematical relationship. This would not do justice, however, to their meaning, and might fail to represent adequately the dynamic mechanisms that Festinger implicitly postulates. Instead, we shall set forth a model of five equations which, we believe, constitutes a reasonable interpretation of the mechanisms. Then we shall show the relation of Festinger's explicit propositions to the system we have constructed. The five equations comprising the model are as follows:

$$(1.1) \qquad \frac{dD}{dt} = f[P(t), L(t), D(t)],^{3}$$

$$(1.2) \qquad P(t) = P[D(t), U(t)],$$

$$(1.3) \qquad L(t) = L[U(t)],$$

$$(1.4) \qquad \frac{dC}{dt} = g[D(t), U(t), C(t)],$$

$$(1.5) \qquad U(t) = U[C(t), R].$$

Note that two of the equations, 1.1 and 1.4, postulate a process of adjustment, of D and C, respectively, that takes place gradually over time.

---

[3] Read: The time rate of change in the discrepancy of opinion is a function of the pressure to communicate, the receptivity to influence, and the existing discrepancy. The remaining four equations may be read in an analogous fashion. The change in the "is a function of" designation from f to P to L to g to U is simply to indicate that the functions involved in the five equations are not necessarily identical in form.

The remaining equations, 1.2, 1.3, and 1.5, make P, L, and U, respectively, change instantaneously with the variables on which they depend. The term "instantaneously" need not, of course, be interpreted literally, but may be taken to mean that the mechanisms represented by these three equations bring about more rapid adjustment in the dependent variable than the mechanisms in the other two. This part of the system enables us to make clear distinctions between the short-run and long-run mechanisms involved in pressures toward uniformity. While the equations permit the values of the variable to change through time, the forms of the equations themselves are assumed to be independent of the length of time the group is in existence.

The propositions are stated so as to involve only *ordinal* and not *cardinal* properties of the variables. This is important, since in the present stage of development of operational definition of the variables the scale units are arbitrary. We can observe that group A is more cohesive than group B, but not that A is twice as cohesive as B, or that the cohesiveness of A exceeds the cohesiveness of B by a greater amount than the cohesiveness of C exceeds the cohesiveness of D. It should be stressed that our treatment does not impose any requirements of measurability not already present, implicitly or explicitly, in Festinger's verbal theory. The equations make statements about certain variables as being "greater" or "less," but precisely the same kinds of statements are required in the verbal theory.

Now let us compare Festinger's propositions with our model.

Hypothesis 1a: *The pressure on members to communicate to others in the group concerning "item x" increases monotonically with increase in the perceived discrepancy in opinion concerning "item x" among members of the group.*

This proposition states that there is a relation between P and D, and that a change in the latter brings about a change in the former in the same direction. We have expressed this in equation 1.2 by making P dependent on D. To encompass Festinger's proposition we need to add the additional hypothesis that $P_D > 0$; where P_D symbolizes the partial derivative of P with respect to D, and designates the change in P for a unit change in D when U is held constant. If the sign of the derivative is positive (greater than zero), the relation between the variables is of the form, "if x_1 increases, x_2 increases." When the derivative is negative, the relation is the inverse.

Hypothesis 1b: *The pressure on a member to communicate to others in the group concerning "item x" increases monotonically with increase in the degree of relevance of "item x" to the functioning of the group.*

This proposition states that there is a relation between P and R and that the two vary in the same direction. Festinger also postulates (2, p. 274) that an increase in R brings about an increase in P *via* an increase in U. These hypotheses are represented by our equations 1.2 and 1.5. To translate the whole of Festinger's hypothesis we need to postulate further that $P_U > 0$ and $U_R > 0$. Note that in this instance Festinger's more formal hypothesis was supplemented by an explanatory discussion linking the more simply stated proposition to other parts of the system.

Hypothesis 1c: *The pressure on members to communicate to others in the group concerning "item x" increases monotonically with increase in the cohesiveness of the group.*

This proposition is precisely parallel to 1b, with C replacing R. Hence, it is translated by equations 1.2 and 1.5 with the conditions that $U_C > 0$ and $P_U > 0$.

Hypothesis 3a: *The amount of change in opinion resulting from receiving a communication will increase as the pressure toward uniformity in the group increases.*

The amount of change in opinion—in the direction of greater or less uniformity—between times t_0 and t_1, is expressed by the integral of dD/dt from t_0 to t_1, dD/dt being defined by equation 1.1. Let us assume, now, that $f_P < 0$ and $f_L < 0$; that is, the greater the pressure to communicate and the greater the receptivity to influence, the more rapid will be the change (decrease) in the discrepancy of opinion. We assume further, with Festinger, that $L_U > 0$ in equation 1.3. We have already assumed that $P_U > 0$. It follows that $\dfrac{\partial f}{\partial U} = f_L L_U + f_P P_U < 0$, and hence that the rate of change of opinion toward uniformity will be the greater, the larger is U. The total change of opinion in the interval t_0 to t_1 will be the greater, the larger is dD/dt during this interval. Represent this total change in D by ΔD, i.e.,

$$(1.6) \qquad \Delta D = \int_{t_0}^{t_1} \frac{dD(t)}{dt}\, dt.$$

Then Festinger's hypothesis 3a is equivalent to the foregoing statement that ΔD is the greater, the larger is U during the interval t_0 to t_1.

Hypothesis 3b: *The amount of change in opinion resulting from receiving a communication will increase as the strength of the resultant force to remain in the group increases for the recipient.*

This hypothesis states that ΔD is the greater, the larger is C. But C is related to U, via equation 1.5, with the requirement that $U_C > 0$. And U, in turn, is related to L via equation 1.3, with $L_U > 0$. Then, since dD/dt is related in equation 1.1 to L, with $\partial f/\partial L < 0$, it follows that the integral of dD/dt for the interval t_0 to t_1 (or ΔD) will be greater, the larger is C. This indicates that Festinger's hypothesis 3b is not independent but follows from the earlier assumptions, namely those made in 1c and 3a.

We have now established an interpretation of Festinger's five hypotheses in terms of (*a*) four equations involving six variables (we have not
yet made use of equation 1.4); and (*b*) a number of statements about the
signs of the partial derivatives of the dependent variables with respect
to the independent variables in these equations.[4] For convenient reference, let us restate the assumptions implied by the hypotheses about the
signs of partial derivatives:

(1.1a) $f_P < 0$,   (1.1b) $f_L < 0$,

(1.2a) $P_D > 0$,   (1.2b) $P_U > 0$,

(1.3a) $L_U > 0$,

(1.5a) $U_C > 0$,   (1.5b) $U_R > 0$.

Thus far we have said nothing about equation 1.4. This equation is
not embodied in any of Festinger's more formal hypotheses, but is a translation of his statement that "People tend to locomote *into* [groups which
share their opinions and attitudes] and *out of* groups which do not agree
with them" (2, p. 273). Equation 1.4 states that the rate of change in
cohesiveness of a group depends upon the discrepancy of opinion and the
pressure toward uniformity. We postulate further that:

(1.4a) $g_D < 0$,   (1.4b) $g_U < 0$.

That is, a large discrepancy of opinion, for a given pressure toward uniformity, or a large pressure toward uniformity, for a given discrepancy in
opinion, both bring about a rapid decrease in group cohesiveness. Note
that we have also postulated that the change in cohesion is dependent
upon the level of cohesion itself. Equation 1.4, or some alternative, is
needed to make the dynamic system complete. We shall see that in some
of the empirical studies, the mechanism of equation 1.4 is in fact involved; in others of the studies we need to assume instead that C is
constant for the time interval of the experiment, that is, $dC/dt = 0$.

Interpretations have now been provided for all five equations, but
nothing has been said about the signs of two of the partial derivatives,
f_D in equation 1.1, and g_C in equation 1.4. Let us suppose a system
governed by these five equations to be in equilibrium, so that $dD/dt = 0$,
and $dC/dt = 0$. Then the values of the five dependent variables, D, P,
L, C, and U will depend only on the value of the single remaining inde-

---

[4]Since the appearance or nonappearance of particular variables in particular
equations and the signs of the partial derivatives in these equations do not depend upon the scales on which the variables are measured, our hypotheses satisfy the condition, earlier stated, that they should require only ordinal, and not
cardinal, measurement of the variables.

pendent variable R. Each value of R will determine a corresponding equilibrium position of the system. Now if P and L vary, as the system moves from one position of equilibrium to another, a determinate change in D must take place in order to satisfy equation 1.1. The direction of change in D, for increases in P and L, will depend on the signs of the two partial derivatives already assumed to be negative: f_P and f_L; and upon the sign of f_D. In this situation, using the chain rule for differentiation,[5] we get:

$$(1.7) \qquad f_P \delta P + f_L \delta L + f_D \delta D = 0,$$

where δP, δL, and δD represent the changes in these variables in moving

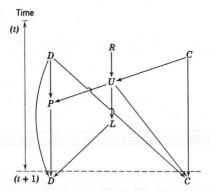

Fig. 1. Psychological mechanisms postulated in the model.

from one equilibrium position to a neighboring one. Applying the chain rule to equation 1.4 we find that:

$$(1.8) \qquad g_D \delta D + g_U \delta U + g_C \delta C = 0.$$

On the basis of the interpretations we have given to the mechanisms, it is plausible to assume that if pressure to communicate (P) and receptivity (L) are large, then the discrepancy of opinion (D) will be pushed down to a lower equilibrium level through the mechanism of equation 1.1 than if P and L are small. This is equivalent to saying that $\delta D/\delta P = -(f_P/f_D) < 0$, and $\delta D/\delta L = -(f_L/f_D) < 0$; whence,

$$(1.1c) \qquad\qquad f_D < 0.$$

Similarly, high levels of discrepancy of opinion (D) and of pressure toward uniformity (U), if maintained, may be assumed to drive cohesiveness (C) to lower levels, through the mechanism of equation 1.4, than will low

[5] See the chapter on partial differentiation in any standard calculus, e.g., Granville, *Elements of the Differential and Integral Calculus*, (rev. ed.), 1929, p. 419; or Osgood, *Advanced Calculus*, 1935, pp. 112–119.

levels of D and U. It then follows by an argument similar to that just given that

(1.4c) $g_C < 0$.

This completes the comparison of Festinger's propositions with our model. Note that in addition to the five equations, it was necessary to make explicit assumptions about the signs of eleven partial derivatives. By way of summary, we diagram in Fig. 1 the causal relations among the variables that are implied by the equations. For simplicity we assume changes in the variables to take place at discrete intervals in time rather than continuously. Thus $D(t + 1)$ is the value of D one time interval after t. By equation 1.1, $D(t + 1)$ is determined by $D(t)$, $P(t)$, and $L(t)$. By equation 1.2, $P(t)$ is determined by $D(t)$ and $U(t)$; by equation 1.3, $L(t)$ is determined by $U(t)$; by equation 1.4, $C(t + 1)$ is determined by $C(t)$, $D(t)$, and $U(t)$; and by equation 1.5, $U(t)$ is determined by R and $C(t)$.

2. EXAMINATION OF THE EMPIRICAL STUDIES

Festinger draws upon evidence obtained in a number of experiments and a field study for confirmation of the hypotheses. In this section we shall re-examine the evidence from three of the studies in terms of the aggregative model that has been formulated. Our purposes are twofold: (a) We want to check the extent to which the empirical data support or contradict our reformulation of Festinger's system; and (b) we want to know whether all of the eleven "derivative" hypotheses have been tested —and if not, just which ones remain to be tested in future experimental work.

Back's Influence Experiment. Back (1) performed an experiment with teams of two subjects each. Each team member was instructed to write an interpretation of pictures he had seen alone before discussion with his teammate, and again after discussion. Each subject believed his pictures were identical with those seen by his teammate, but they were in fact somewhat different.

Opinion change in a team was measured by a content analysis of the similarities and differences in the interpretations of teammates. In this way, a measure could have been obtained of D_O, the discrepancy at the beginning of the trial, and D_T, the discrepancy at the end of the trial. Back did not, in fact, measure D_O and D_T. Instead, he noticed the number of changes that took place between the initial and final interpretations in the direction of the partner's interpretation (1, Tables 4 and 5). The number of such changes may be taken as a measure of the *decrease* in difference in opinion, i.e., $D_O - D_T$. Since the times of all trials were short and equal, $D_O - D_T$ will be approximately proportional to dD/dt at time t_O. We shall accordingly represent it by the symbol ΔD_O.

No measurement was made that can be regarded unequivocally as a direct measure of pressure to communicate (P), receptivity (L), or pressure toward uniformity (U). This is hardly surprising, since all these variables refer to "states" of the subject, lie entirely inside his skin, and hence can be observed only indirectly through behaviors they produce. Back made three sets of observations intended to serve as indices of these latent variables. The first measure was a rating of the team discussion by observers as *active* or *withdrawing*. An active pattern will be interpreted as evidence of high P, a withdrawing pattern as evidence of low P. The second measure was the report of subjects as to whether they felt, in the discussion situation, some or no pressure from their partners to change their interpretations. Reported pressure will be interpreted as high U, lack of pressure as low U. Third, subjects were also asked to report whether they had been receptive to influence by the partner. These reports will be regarded as measures of L.

No direct measurement was made of cohesiveness or relevance. The instructions given to team members at the beginning of the trials were intended to produce high cohesiveness in half the teams and low cohesiveness in the others. The instructions, as interpreted by Back, are given as indirect measures of C_O. That certain instructions to the subjects will produce high or low cohesiveness is based only on "common sense" and introspective interpretation of the psychological impact of the instructions. Hence, it would have been better if C also had been measured directly.

It is not clear whether the intergroup differences produced by the instructions should be regarded only as differences in C_O, or whether they should be regarded as differences in R_O as well. In three different sets of experimental groups, Back attempted to employ three different bases for inducing high or low cohesiveness: personal attraction to the team partner, reward for group performance, and the prestige of the group. Back argues that pressure toward uniformity arises from two sources: the function of the group as a reference group in determining social reality (which depends on *cohesiveness*), and the function of the group as a means toward reaching a personal goal (which operates through the *relevance* of uniformity of opinion to goal achievement). It is reasonable, therefore, to interpret the first and third of the motivations in Back's experiment as cohesiveness-producing motivations; but to interpret the second—reward for performance—as a relevance-producing motivation. Hence, we shall assume that the experimental instructions produce differences both in C_O and in R_O for all three sets of groups. In the present interpretations of the model this distinction is not vital, for U_C and U_R are both positive, and hence act upon U in equation 1.5 in the same direction. A clarification of the distinction would appear important, however, to further development and testing of the theoretical scheme, if any operational significance is to be attached to the asserted difference between these two variables.

It is implicitly assumed in the experimental design involving team discussions of about ten minutes that the effect of the instructions upon cohesiveness and relevance persisted for the duration of the experiment. If this is correct we can eliminate equation 1.4 from the system, and assume that C, like R, in equation 1.5 is a parameter, constant for the duration of the experiment with any one group. This amounts to an interpretation of this experiment in terms of a "short-run" model in which the mechanisms represented by the remaining four equations were operating, but in which the system did not have time to settle to a final equilibrium. We simply ignore the "feedback" effect of dD/dt on D. Then we may regard the equations as four relations that determine the values of the dependent variables ΔD_O, P_O, L_O, and U_O as functions of the independent variables (or "parameters") D_O, C_O, and R_O. Finally, since D_O is assumed to be the same for all groups (the same sets of pictures were shown to all groups), this variable may be ignored in analyzing the intergroup differences.

What predictions can we make from the model of the Back experiment so interpreted? If we employ symbols like δP, again, to designate intergroup differences in the initial values of the dependent variables as functions of intergroup differences in the independent variables, we can deduce the following from our previous equations by differentiating them, using the chain rule:

(2.1) $\delta U_O = U_C \delta C + U_R \delta R$,   (from equation 1.5),

(2.2) $\delta L_O = L_U \delta U$,   (from equation 1.3),

(2.3) $\delta P_O = P_U \delta U$,   (from equation 1.2),

(2.4) $\delta \Delta D_O = f_P \delta P + f_L \delta L$,   (from equation 1.1).

From these relations, together with the previous assumptions as to the signs of partial derivatives, the following hypotheses can be derived by algebraic means, taking C and R as independent variables:

(2.1a) $\delta U / \delta C = U_C > 0$,

(2.1b) $\delta U / \delta R = U_R > 0$,

(2.2a) $\delta L / \delta C = L_U U_C > 0$,

(2.2b) $\delta L / \delta R = L_U U_R > 0$,

(2.3a) $\delta P / \delta C = P_U U_C > 0$,

(2.3b) $\delta P / \delta R = P_U U_R > 0$,

(2.4a) $\delta \Delta D / \delta C = (f_P P_U + f_L L_U) U_C < 0$,

(2.4b) $\delta \Delta D / \delta R = (f_P P_U + f_L L_U) U_R < 0$.

Let us now check the extent to which Back's empirical findings confirm these predictions. The fact that persons in the high cohesive groups tried to influence (P) their partners more actively (chi square significant at .02 level) than did individuals in the low cohesive groups, who tended to withdraw (1, p. 15), may be taken as confirmation of equations 2.3a and 2.3b. His finding that "less than half of the members of the low cohesive group reported that they felt some pressure (U), while more than two thirds of the members of the high cohesive group did so" (1, p. 16) (again significant at the .02 level), does not contradict equations 2.1a and 2.1b. Although Back says "Self-ratings on resistance [the inverse of L] ··· show a slight decrease" (1, p. 16) in level in the high cohesive groups, he reports the difference is not statistically significant. Thus, there is only weak confirmation of equations 2.2a or 2.2b.

Table 4 in Back's report (1) provides confirmation for equation 2.4a, $\delta\Delta D/\delta C < 0$; and equation 2.4b, $\delta\Delta D/\delta R < 0$. These significant findings are *consistent* with the assumptions of the original model but *do not*, it should be noted, *verify* all the individual assumptions about the signs of partial derivatives. The lack of confirmation, at a significant level, of equations 2.2a and 2.2b is disturbing, since $L_U U_C$ or $L_U U_R$, or both, appear in all the other hypotheses, too. Since $\partial L/\partial C$ and $\partial L/\partial R$ are found empirically not to be significantly different from zero, either L_U or both U_C and U_R must be close to zero. But inasmuch as confirmation of equations 2.1a and 2.1b indicates that $U_C \neq 0$, L_U must be close to zero; such a conclusion is not contradicted by our confirmation of equations 2.4a and 2.4b, for the $f_L L_U$ terms might be zero without changing the signs of $\delta\Delta D/\delta C$ or $\delta\Delta D/\delta R$.

In summary, we may say that Back's experiment constitutes a test of some short-run properties of the present mathematical model. The findings of the experiment verified some, but not all, of the assumptions regarding the signs of partial derivatives, and strongly contradicted none of the assumptions. If the experiment were to be repeated, its power to test the model could be increased by introducing additional procedures for measuring certain of the variables, such as R, C_O, and C_T.

The Festinger-Thibaut Experiment on Interpersonal Communication. This experiment (4) involved variables referring to individual members of a group, as well as variables defined as group averages. The present discussion is limited to those findings of the experiment that can be stated in terms of aggregates.

A problem was given to members of a discussion group, and they were asked to record their solutions before and after discussion. The standard deviations of the opinions in each group at the beginning of the twenty-minute discussion and at the end are taken as measurements of the variable D—specifically, D_O and D_T. The several experimental groups were initially given different sets of instructions. The instructions that aimed at inducing "homogeneity" stressed the similarity of group members, and can be interpreted as cohesiveness-producing vari--ables. The instructions aimed at producing "pressure toward uniformity" stated that the group should arrive at agreement on opinion or at the "correct" opinion. In Festinger's scheme, this variable may be translated as *relevance*. We shall treat the homogeneity-heterogeneity instructions as determining C_O, and the other instructions as determining R_O.

The appropriate model for this experiment would appear to be the same as for the Back experiment. The experimental findings can be expressed (4, p. 99, Fig. 2) as $\delta\Delta D/\delta C < 0$ and $\delta\Delta D/\delta R < 0$. Thus we see that the findings in this experiment exactly parallel one of the findings in the Back experiment.

The need for further clarification of the variables C and R is evidenced by the fact that Festinger cites Back's experiment as evidence for his hypothesis 3b, and the Festinger-Thibaut study as evidence for his hypothesis 3a, while we have concluded that there is no difference in the findings regarding ΔD in the two experiments. The reason for this difference is that Festinger treats the instructions in the Back experiment as determining C and instructions in the Festinger-Thibaut experiment as determining U, while we have interpreted these instructions as determining C and R in both experiments.

The Housing Study. Unlike the two experiments already discussed, the housing study (3) was a field study and not an experiment. This has two consequences. First, the field situation reflects the working of *all* the mechanisms actually present. Individual variables cannot be made "independent" through experimental control and randomization, as they can in the laboratory. Second, the relevant time span during which the mechanisms operate is much longer in the field situation than in the laboratory. In a relatively stable field situation of this sort we can expect to observe the variables only in the neighborhood of the equilibrium position or positions of the system.

In the field study, a correlation of .74 was found between (*a*) the cohesiveness of groups in a housing project, and (*b*) the effectiveness with which a group standard relevant to the functioning of the groups was maintained (3, p. 12, Table 16). Festinger treats these findings as parallel to the findings in Back's work in confirmation of hypothesis 3b.

In interpreting the earlier experiments, because of the short time period involved, the feedback described by equations 1.1 and 1.4 could be ignored. Moreover, the variable D_O was assumed to be the same for all groups at the outset of the experiment. In the field study, there is no reason to suppose that we can ignore the change of D and C through time, as determined by equations 1.1 and 1.4. Furthermore, the variables that are correlated are D_T with C_T, and not D_O with C_O and R_O, for the measurements were made after the residents of the housing project had been residing there and interacting for a considerable period (up to 15 months).

These considerations suggest that the appropriate model for representing the field study is the complete model of equations 1.1 through 1.5, together with the corresponding inequalities. If this is so, then the short-run assumptions that permitted us to apply the method of comparative statics in the two experiments are no longer applicable. Given the initial conditions, the time path of the behavior of the group will be determined by equations 1.1 through 1.5, and two groups with the same initial positions will have the same paths. If we assume that the initial values of at least some variables were different for the various groups, we can derive a plausible interpretation of the field study, and can show also that the field results prove something quite different from (but not inconsistent with) Back's experiment—contrary to Festinger's interpretation of the two sets of data as supporting the same proposition.

Using equations 1.2, 1.3, and 1.5 to solve for P, L, and U, respectively, the system can be rewritten in terms of two different equations in C and D:

$$(2.6) \qquad \frac{dD}{dt} = f\{P[D, U(C)], L[U(C)], D\},$$

$$(2.7) \qquad \frac{dC}{dt} = g\{D, U(C), C\}.$$

Now for a system obeying these equations and starting off from some initial position $[D_O, C_O]$ we can represent its path by a curve in the D-C plane. Each point on the curve $[D(t), C(t)]$ will represent the position of the system at some time, t. What can we say in general about the various paths corresponding to different initial conditions?[6]

Consider the points for which $dD/dt = f = 0$. These lie on a curve on the D-C plane. Moving along this curve, the requirement that $f = 0$ gives us the following equation for the ratio between the rate of change of C, i.e., δC, and the rate of change of D, δD:

$$(2.8) \qquad f_P\{P_D\delta D + P_U U_C \delta C\} + f_L L_U U_C \delta C + f_D \delta D = 0.$$

This expression is obtained by differentiating equation 2.7, using the chain rule. Then we have for the slope of this curve:

$$(2.9) \qquad \rho = \left[\frac{\delta C}{\delta D}\right]_{dD/dt=0} = -\frac{(f_P P_D + f_D)}{U_C(f_P P_U + f_L L_U)} < 0.$$

[6] For the methods applied here, see Lester R. Ford, *Differential Equations*, pp. 9–12; and A. A. Andronow and C. E. Chaikin, *Theory of Oscillations*, 1949, pp. 8–12, 182–193, 203–8.

Similarly, for the curve on which $dC/dt = g = 0$, we obtain:

$$(2.10) \qquad \sigma = \left[\frac{\delta C}{\delta D}\right]_{dC/dt=0} = -\frac{g_D}{g_U U_C + g_C} < 0.$$

By using our assumptions about the signs of these partial derivatives already made above, it can be shown that the slopes of both these curves are negative in the *D-C* plane.

Now there are grounds of plausibility for making assumptions which enable us to say that these curves have a particular shape—specifically, that σ approaches zero for very large and very small values of *C*, and that $1/\rho$ approaches zero for very large and very small values of *D*. The argument is as follows: Equation 2.7 describes a mechanism whereby cohesiveness adjusts to discrepancy of opinion. It is plausible to suppose that this mechanism is subject to saturation—that when *C* reaches very

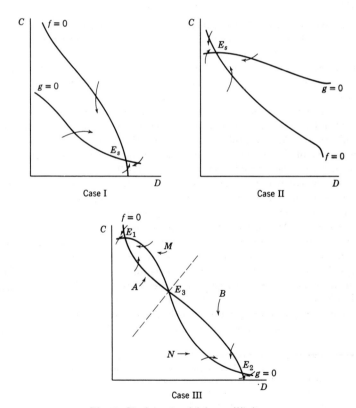

Fig. 2. Single and multiple equilibriums.

high levels it will not be driven much higher by further decreases in D; and that when C reaches very low levels it will not be driven much lower by further increases in D. A similar saturation assumption is plausible for the mechanism of equation 2.6 which determines the equilibrium level of D as a function of C.[7]

If the two saturation hypotheses hold, then the curves $f = 0$ and $g = 0$ must have one of three possible configurations (Fig. 2). In cases I and II we have a single point of equilibrium—a point for which simultaneously $f = dD/dt = 0$, and $g = dC/dt = 0$. In case III we have three such points of equilibrium. An analysis by standard methods (omitted here) shows that certain conditions must be satisfied if the equilibrium position is to be dynamically stable (so that if the system is disturbed slightly from equilibrium, it will tend to move back toward the equilibrium position). The stability condition is:

$$(2.11) \qquad\qquad \sigma/\rho < 1.$$

We observe from Fig. 2 that equation 2.11 is satisfied for the equilibrium points (E_s) in case I and case II, and for the two extreme equilibrium points $(E_1$ and $E_2)$ in case III. [See editors' note on page 147.]

In the housing study tenants were assigned to particular courts in the housing project, virtually at random. The initial cohesiveness ("tendency to associate") of residents of a court might depend largely on the opportunities people found to meet others inside and outside the project. The initial discrepancy of opinion in a court with regard to a tenants' organization might be regarded as a chance variable depending on the past experiences of the tenants with such neighborhood activities. Quite by chance, some courts would have a higher initial D or C than others.

Now suppose that two groups (A and B) initially had the same cohesiveness within their courts, but that there was much less initial divergence of opinions with regard to the desirability of a tenants' organization in one (A) than in the other (B), as is illustrated in case III of Fig. 3. If the D_O of a particular court is low, as in A, the cohesiveness of the tenants will increase, which in turn will cause them to accommodate their opinions to each others', further decreasing D. If the D_O of a court is high, as in B, the cohesiveness of the tenants will decrease, which will promote further divergence of opinion. All these consequences follow from the postulates of the mathematical model. Hence, when the system reaches equilibrium we should expect to find some courts with

---

[7]These two saturation hypotheses each imply cardinal measurement of C and D. The conclusions we shall draw from the two of them together, with respect to the existence and location of stable and unstable equilibrium points, depend, however, on only ordinal measurement. It would be desirable to restate the saturation hypotheses—or that part of them we need—so as to remove the cardinality assumptions. This must be possible, but we have not yet been able to do it.

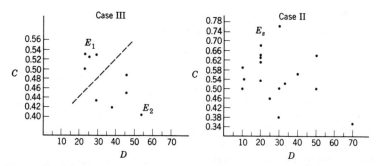

Fig. 3. Empirical tests of the equilibrium cases. In Case III, data are from reference 3, p. 92, Table 16; in Case II, data are from reference 3, p. 93, Table 17.

high C and low D, and some with low C and high D, giving a negative correlation between C and D. Further, as the process approaches equilibrium, one would expect a clustering of points (representing the courts) around the two stable equilibria, E_1 and E_2. A plot of the data from the Festinger, Schachter, and Back study, as presented in Fig. 3, case III, reveals just such a clustering, giving empirical confirmation of our postulation that the feedback process has been in operation.

This interpretation of the field work permits a prediction of the observed correlation from the postulates of the mathematical model. The predicted correlation depends, however, on a larger set of hypotheses than those used in the interpretation of the Back and the Festinger-Thibaut experiments. To account for the findings, both feedbacks provided in equations 1.1 and 1.4 were needed, and the two saturation assumptions were added. Festinger's original interpretation of the laboratory and field results as supporting hypothesis 3b was hardly accurate. Our formalization of the hypothesis shows its complexity, and indicates that the Back experiment supports the short-run static model, while the Festinger, Schachter, and Back data support the enlarged dynamic model.

Note that only case III of Fig. 2 predicts a negative correlation; cases I and II predict that the points in the C-D plane should cluster around E_s thus yielding a zero correlation. Yet data supporting any one of the three cases would be consonant with the hypotheses used in developing the model. Which of the three cases will hold depends upon the equilibrium equations (the relative positions of the two equilibrium curves on the D-C plane). If we plot the data obtained in the second housing project (3, p. 93, Table 17), we find that these data seem to correspond to case II, presented in the "Case II" graph in Fig. 3. According to our arguments, Festinger, Schachter, and Back incorrectly interpret their zero correlation as indicating no feedback had yet occurred in the few months Westgate West had been in operation. The clustering of points at E_s indicates that the dynamic model is applicable, and that some groups in this cluster of points are close to equilibrium. The zero correlation between C_T and D_T actually confirms the existence of feedback.

SUMMARY

In this paper we have undertaken to carry further the development of a set of hypotheses about pressures toward uniformity in groups into a more integrated, less redundant system. We have constructed explicit postulates about the intervening mechanisms to provide linkages among variables, such as "Relevance" and "Pressure to Communicate." Although the model covers static situations in which there is no feedback, it also postulates dynamic mechanisms by which, for example, cohesion at one time influences the cohesion of the same group at a later time. In the present paper, all the variables considered were averages of the behaviors of all members of a group.

A number of deductions were obtained from the system. Some of these were verified by bringing field and experimental data to bear. The model led us to examine correlational data for bimodality characteristics, indicating the existence of two stable equilibrium points when groups experience uniformity.

REFERENCES

1. Back, K. W., "Influence Through Social Communication," *Journal of Abnormal and Social Psychology*, 1951, 46, pp. 9–23.
2. Festinger, L., "Informal Social Communication," *Psychological Review*, 1950, 57, pp. 271–282.
3. Festinger, L., Schachter, S., and Back, K., *Social Pressures in Informal Groups*, New York: Harper, 1950.
4. Festinger, L., and Thibaut, J., "Interpersonal Communication in Small Groups," *Journal of Abnormal and Social Psychology*, 1951, 46, pp. 92–99.

[EDITORS' NOTE: We give the following brief sketch of how the equilibrium conditions, equation 2.11, are derived.

The functions $f = dD/dt$ and $g = dC/dt$ are each functions of D and C. We want to know how these functions behave in the vicinity of an equilibrium point. The linear approximations to f and g near such a point are

$$f = \delta D \left(f_P P_D + f_D \right) + \delta C \left(U_C (f_P P_U + f_L L_U) \right)$$
$$g = \delta D \left(g_D \right) + \delta C \left(g_U U_C + g_C \right)$$

where δD and δC are the deviations from the equilibrium point. As long as they are small, the linear equations above will give a good approximation of the actual behavior of f and g. The terms in parentheses are the appropriate partial derivatives of f and g, with respect to D and C. Simon showed in the text that all four of these quantities were negative.

If we are to move back toward the equilibrium point, then f must have the opposite sign of δD and g must have the opposite sign of δC, since these derivatives of D and C, respectively, determine whether D and C will tend to increase or decrease. Since all four terms in parentheses are negative, there will always be a tendency to move toward the equilibrium point if δD and δC have the same sign.

If δD and δC are of opposite sign, however, there will be movement back to the equilibrium only if $\sigma/\rho < 1$. This can be illustrated (but not proved) by letting $\delta D = 1$ and $\delta C = -1$. Convergence occurs if

$$f = f_P P_D + f_D - U_C (f_P P_U + f_L L_U) < 0$$

and

$$g = g_D - (g_U U_C + g_C) > 0.$$

The first inequality implies that

$$\rho < -1$$

while the second implies that

$$\sigma > -1.$$

In working out these implications, remember that ρ and σ, as defined by Simon, are always negative. Thus $\sigma > \rho$ implies that $\sigma/\rho < 1$, the condition for the stability of the equilibrium. If this were not satisfied, δD would become more and more positive, and δC would become more and more negative.]

A Markov Chain Model in Sociology

John G. Kemeny and **J. Laurie Snell**   *Dartmouth College*

1. Statement of the problem. In this chapter we develop a mathematical model to describe a specific type of experiment. The experiment is quite easy to perform and is repeated many times, with the result that certain regularities are observed.

The experiment that we consider was first performed by Asch: A naive subject is seated at the end of a row of seven pretrained confederates of the experimenter. Instructions are read aloud which lead the subject to believe that he is participating in the following experiment on visual perception: On each of a sequence of trials, the eight individuals present are required to choose aloud (and from a distance) that particular one from among three comparison lines which has the same length as a standard line.

For each set of lines, the naive subject's turn to choose çomes only after he has heard the unanimous, though incorrect, responses of the seven confederates. Thus, he is motivated, on the one hand, to answer according to his perceptions and, on the other, to conform to the unanimous choice of the group.

The data for the experiment consist of a sequence of responses for each subject, each response being either a conforming or a nonconforming response.

It is clear that in an experiment like this there is no hope of constructing a mathematical model which predicts exactly what the subject will do on each trial. However, it is possible to construct a probabilistic model which predicts certain average properties of the data and some relations between observable quantities. We shall consider the problem of developing such a model.

The data for testing our model come from a series of experiments carried out by B. Cohen. Each of 33 subjects was exposed to 35 trials. Choices were recorded as *a* if the subject gave the correct answer, or *b* if he conformed to the opinion expressed by the stooges. For example, one subject reacted as follows:

$$\underbrace{aaabbaaabbbaaaab}_{\text{initial segment}}\underbrace{aaaaaaaaaaaaaaaaaaa}_{\text{final segment}}$$

Fig. 1

We define as the *terminal response* the response (*a* or *b*) on the 35th trial, and as the *final segment* the sequence of those consecutive responses — ending at the 35th — which are the same as the terminal response. The earlier responses form the *initial segment*. It was not unusual to find fairly long final segments in the data, and occasionally the entire sequence was the final segment.

What quantities can we observe conveniently in such a series of trials? We will start by counting transitions: Let n_{aa} be the number of transitions from *a* to *a* in the initial segment, n_{ab} the number of transitions from *a* to *b*, and let n_{ba} and n_{bb} be defined similarly. These quantities are well defined except for the first response, which, for example, could be classified either as an $a-a$ or as a $b-a$ transition in Fig. 1. For reasons that will become clear later, we will count it as an $a-a$ transition. Hence in the sequence in Fig. 1, $n_{aa} = 8$, $n_{ab} = 3$, $n_{ba} = 3$, $n_{bb} = 3$.

We choose the first response to be $a-a$ in conformity with our eventual model, which assumes that initially the subject has an *a* attitude — that he is inclined to give the right answer. Thus we modify the initial segment by adding a "0-th response" which is an *a*. Our modified initial segment is shown in Fig. 2.

$$aaaabbaaabbbaaaab$$

Fig. 2

A number of other easily observable quantities can be deduced from knowledge of the four given *n*'s. For example, if n_a is the total number of times that an *a* response is given in the (modified) initial segment, and n_b is the total number of *b* responses, then we have the following relations:

$$n_a = n_{aa} + n_{ab}, \quad n_b = n_{ba} + n_{bb},$$

(1)
$$\text{length of initial segment} = n_a + n_b,$$

$$\text{length of final segment} = 36 - (n_a + n_b).$$

To know the total number of *a* responses we need only one additional piece of information, the terminal response. But that, too, is deducible. If $n_{ab} = n_{ba}$, then the terminal response must be *a*, whereas if $n_{ab} = n_{ba} + 1$, then the terminal response is *b*. All of these relations can be established by elementary logical arguments.

Actually, we will not be interested in numbers dealing with a single subject; rather, our concern will be with the data of all 33 subjects. Thus we will, from now on, let n_{aa} be the total number of $a-a$ transitions in the (modified) initial segments of all subjects. The remaining quantities will be defined similarly. The first two relations in (1) still hold, but n_a is now the total of all a responses in all initial segments, n_b the total of b responses, and their sum is the total length of all initial segments. For these totals there are three more interesting quantities: n is the number of subjects ($n = 33$ in our data), t_a is the number of a terminal responses, and t_b is the number of b terminal responses. From previous remarks we see that

$$(2) \qquad t_b = n_{ab} - n_{ba}, \quad t_a = n - t_b.$$

It will be the task of our model to describe and predict such observational quantities. In one of Cohen's experiments, it was found that

$$(3) \quad \begin{aligned} n_{aa} &= 196, \quad n_{ab} = 117, \quad n_{ba} = 106, \quad n_{bb} = 102, \\ n_a &= 313, \quad n_b = 208, \quad t_a = 22, \quad t_b = 11, \quad n = 33. \end{aligned}$$

We shall discuss a model that is designed to make predictions concerning the possible outcomes of such experiments. What kind of predictions should we expect? Since the choice of n, that is, of the number of subjects, is completely arbitrary, and since outcomes vary greatly from subject to subject, our goal will be the prediction of average values, such as t_b/n and n_{aa}/n. Our model will allow the calculation of the mean values of these averages, and the calculations should be as good as any mean value for the prediction of actual outcomes. In other words, we expect the predictions to differ from actual observations only within precisely calculable bounds, and we expect better agreement as n is increased.

Our procedure will be one common in science. We shall formulate a certain model, without attempting to state how it was originally found. From the model we shall derive a variety of consequences, which are testable by means of the given data. The model will then be judged solely on whether the predictions are in good agreement with observations. It is important to keep this in mind. For example, in describing the model certain intuitively suggestive names will be applied, such as "mental state," or "temporary conforming"; however, the value of the model will in no way be affected by the reasonableness of these names.

2. Mathematical formulation. Let us now describe the model proposed by Cohen for the type of experiment described in Section 1. He assumes that a subject on any one trial may be in one of four mental states:

> State 1: Nonconforming
> State 2: Temporary Nonconforming
> State 3: Temporary Conforming
> State 4: Conforming

The model assumes that the subject starts in State 2. On successive trials it is assumed that the changes in state can be described by a four-state Markov chain with transition matrix of the form

$$P = \begin{array}{c} \\ 1 \\ 2 \\ 3 \\ 4 \end{array} \begin{array}{c} \begin{array}{cccc} 1 & 2 & 3 & 4 \end{array} \\ \left(\begin{array}{cccc} 1 & 0 & 0 & 0 \\ p_{21} & p_{22} & p_{23} & 0 \\ 0 & p_{32} & p_{33} & p_{34} \\ 0 & 0 & 0 & 1 \end{array} \right) \end{array}.$$

Note that transitions from 2 to 4 and from 3 to 1 are excluded. States 1 and 4 cannot be left, and hence are absorbing states. Since it is possible to reach these states from States 2 and 3, we have a four-state absorbing Markov chain.

It is assumed that when the subject is in State 1 or 2 he gives a nonconforming response *a,* and when he is in State 3 or 4 he gives a conforming response *b.* When an experiment is performed, the experimenter is not able to observe the states of this chain, but only whether the subject conforms or does not conform.

Thus we know that, for the observed sequence of responses in Fig. 2, the mental states were as in Fig. 3, but we do not know just where in the final segment the subject reached State 1.

$$22223322233322223(2 \ldots 1)$$

Fig. 3

Since the chain is an absorbing chain, we know that (given enough time) the subject must reach State 1 or State 4, that is, be absorbed. It is implicit in our treatment of the final segment that we assume that 35 trials is enough time for each of our subjects to be absorbed.

3. Mathematical treatment. We can now employ Markov chain theory to deduce from our model the mean values of various observed quantities. First of all, we shall put our transition matrix in canonical form by listing the absorbing states first:

$$P = \left(\begin{array}{c|c} I & O \\ \hline R & Q \end{array} \right) = \begin{array}{c} \\ 1 \\ 4 \\ 2 \\ 3 \end{array} \begin{array}{c} \begin{array}{cccc} 1 & 4 & 2 & 3 \end{array} \\ \left(\begin{array}{cc|cc} 1 & 0 & 0 & 0 \\ 0 & 1 & 0 & 0 \\ \hline p_{21} & 0 & p_{22} & p_{23} \\ 0 & p_{34} & p_{32} & p_{33} \end{array} \right) \end{array}.$$

Here I is the identity matrix (has 1's on the main diagonal and 0's elsewhere), and O is a matrix of zeros. These correspond to the fact that once an absorbing state is entered the chain stays there, and to the fact that from an absorbing chain one cannot enter a nonabsorbing state, respectively. Q and R are nonnegative matrices representing transition probabilities from nonabsorbing states. Since P has row sums equal to 1, and R cannot be identically O, Q has row sums ≤ 1, and at least one row has a sum less than 1. It is this feature that distinguishes a set which can be left from an ergodic set of states.

The basic result about finite absorbing chains is that the process is sure to reach an absorbing state. Hence Q^n tends to O. Even more important is the fact that the infinite series $N = I + Q + Q^2 + \cdots$ always converges (in each entry), and that the limit is the inverse of the matrix $I - Q$, that is, $N = (I - Q)^{-1}$. The matrix N is called the *fundamental matrix* of the chain. We shall also use the following quantities:

1 is a column vector all of whose components are 1.

τ is the vector giving the row sums of N. This equals $N1$.

n_{ij} is the mean number of times in state s_j when the chain is started in state s_i. (s_i and s_j are nonabsorbing states.) This is the ijth entry of N.

t_i is the mean number of steps before absorption, if the chain is started in state s_j. This is the ith entry of τ.

b_{ik} is the probability starting in the nonabsorbing state s_i that the process is absorbed in the absorbing state s_k. This is the ikth entry of the matrix $B = NR$.

The fundamental matrix is

$$N = (I - Q)^{-1} = \begin{pmatrix} 1 - p_{22} & -p_{23} \\ -p_{32} & 1 - p_{33} \end{pmatrix}^{-1}.$$

Hence

$$N = \begin{matrix} 2 \\ 3 \end{matrix} \begin{pmatrix} \dfrac{1 - p_{33}}{\Delta} & \dfrac{p_{23}}{\Delta} \\ \dfrac{p_{32}}{\Delta} & \dfrac{1 - p_{22}}{\Delta} \end{pmatrix} = \left(\dfrac{1}{\Delta}\right) \begin{pmatrix} 1 - p_{33} & p_{23} \\ p_{32} & 1 - p_{22} \end{pmatrix},$$

where

$$\Delta = (1 - p_{22})(1 - p_{33}) - p_{23}p_{32}.$$

The matrix of absorption probabilities is $B = NR$. Hence

$$B = NR = \begin{array}{c} \\ 2 \\ 3 \end{array}\begin{array}{c} \overset{1}{} \qquad \overset{4}{} \\ \left(\begin{array}{cc} \dfrac{p_{21}(1 - p_{33})}{\Delta} & \dfrac{p_{23}p_{34}}{\Delta} \\[2ex] \dfrac{p_{32}p_{21}}{\Delta} & \dfrac{p_{34}(1 - p_{22})}{\Delta} \end{array} \right) \end{array}$$

$$= \left(\frac{1}{\Delta} \right) \left(\begin{array}{cc} p_{21}(1 - p_{33}) & p_{23}p_{34} \\ p_{32}p_{21} & p_{34}(1 - p_{22}) \end{array} \right).$$

Thus, for example, if we start in State 2 the probability of absorption in State 4, that is, the probability of the subject eventually giving conforming responses, is

$$b_{24} = \frac{p_{23}p_{34}}{\Delta},$$

and $b_{21} = 1 - b_{24}$.

Since the process starts in State 2, according to our model, the entry n_{23} of N gives the mean of the total number of times that the subject is in Mental State 3 during a sequence of trials. Let f_{23} be the mean of the number of times in State 3 in the final segment; then

(4) $$\mathbf{M}[n_b/n] = n_{23} - f_{23},$$

where $\mathbf{M}[f]$ is the mean of function f, and n_b/n is the average number of b responses per subject in the initial segments. Let q_m be the probability that there are exactly m occurrences of State 3 in the final segment. There will be no such occurrence if the terminal state is 1; hence

$$q_0 = b_{21}.$$

A simple probabilistic computation will show that

$$q_{m+1} = p_{33}q_m \quad \text{if } m > 0.$$

Hence

$$q_{m+1} = p_{33}^m q_1.$$

Since

$$1 = \sum_{m=0}^{\infty} q_m = b_{21} + \frac{q_1}{1 - p_{33}},$$

we have

$$q_1 = (1 - p_{33})b_{24}$$

and

$$q_m = p_{33}^{m-1}(1 - p_{33}) b_{24}.$$

Hence

$$f_{23} = \sum_{m=1}^{\infty} m p_{33}^{m-1}(1 - p_{33}) b_{24}$$

$$= \frac{b_{24}}{1 - p_{33}} = \frac{p_{23} p_{34}}{\Delta(1 - p_{33})}.$$

And thus, from (4),

$$(5) \qquad \mathbf{M}[n_b/n] = \frac{p_{23}}{\Delta} - \frac{p_{23} p_{34}}{\Delta(1 - p_{33})} = \frac{p_{23} p_{32}}{\Delta(1 - p_{33})}.$$

In an analogous manner, we can write $\mathbf{M}[n_a/n] = n_{22} - f_{22}$. Then, carrying out step by step the exact analogue of the above computation, we see that

$$(6) \qquad \mathbf{M}[n_a/n] = \frac{1 - p_{33}}{\Delta} - \frac{p_{21}(1 - p_{33})}{\Delta(1 - p_{22})} = \frac{p_{23}(1 - p_{33})}{\Delta(1 - p_{22})}.$$

From the matrix B we obtain

$$(7) \qquad \mathbf{M}[t_b/n] = b_{24} = \frac{p_{23} p_{34}}{\Delta}$$

and also $\mathbf{M}[t_a/n] = b_{21}$. However, the latter follows from (7) and (2), since $b_{21} + b_{24} = 1$. (Starting in State 2, the chain must be absorbed in State 1 or 4.)

So far we have obtained three independent estimates for our observational quantities (5), (6), and (7). To obtain a final one, we introduce a modification in our Markov chain. Suppose that the chain is observed only when a change of state takes place. That is, we keep our four states, but we count as a transition only a step from one state to a different state. We again obtain an absorbing Markov chain, and its transition matrix is

$$P = \begin{array}{c} \\ 1 \\ 2 \\ 3 \\ 4 \end{array} \begin{array}{cccc} 1 & 2 & 3 & 4 \\ \left(\begin{array}{cccc} 1 & 0 & 0 & 0 \\ \dfrac{p_{21}}{1 - p_{22}} & 0 & \dfrac{p_{23}}{1 - p_{22}} & 0 \\ 0 & \dfrac{p_{32}}{1 - p_{33}} & 0 & \dfrac{p_{34}}{1 - p_{33}} \\ 0 & 0 & 0 & 1 \end{array}\right). \end{array}$$

The fundamental matrix of this process is

$$\hat{N} = \frac{1}{\Delta} \begin{pmatrix} (1-p_{22})(1-p_{33}) & p_{23}(1-p_{33}) \\ p_{32}(1-p_{22}) & (1-p_{22})(1-p_{33}) \end{pmatrix}.$$

The entry $\hat{n}_{23}$ is the mean of the number of changes from Mental State 2 to Mental State 3. This is the same as the number of changes from response a to response b, since a change from State 2 directly to State 4 is impossible. As a matter of fact, it is also the same as the number of such changes in the initial segment, since an $a-b$ change is necessarily in the initial segment. Hence

$$(8) \qquad \mathbf{M}_{ab} = \mathbf{M}[n_{ab}/n] = \hat{n}_{23} = \frac{p_{23}(1-p_{33})}{\Delta}.$$

We can now obtain the mean of n_{aa}/n from (1), (6), and (8),

$$(9) \qquad \mathbf{M}_{aa} = \mathbf{M}[n_{aa}/n] = \frac{p_{22}p_{23}(1-p_{33})}{\Delta(1-p_{22})}.$$

From (2), (7), and (8),

$$(10) \qquad \mathbf{M}_{ba} = \mathbf{M}[n_{ba}/n] = \frac{p_{23}p_{32}}{\Delta}.$$

And finally, from (1), (5), and (10),

$$(11) \qquad \mathbf{M}_{bb} = \mathbf{M}[n_{bb}/n] = \frac{p_{23}p_{32}p_{33}}{\Delta(1-p_{33})}.$$

We can show that, conversely, the four means in (8)–(11) determine our transition probabilities. Recalling that the sum of the entries of any row of P is 1, we easily verify that

$$(12) \qquad \begin{aligned} p_{21} &= \mathbf{M}_{ab}(1 - \mathbf{M}_{ab} + \mathbf{M}_{ba})/(\mathbf{M}_{aa} + \mathbf{M}_{ab})(1 + \mathbf{M}_{ba}) \\ p_{22} &= \mathbf{M}_{aa}/(\mathbf{M}_{aa} + \mathbf{M}_{ab}) \\ p_{23} &= \mathbf{M}_{ab}^2/(\mathbf{M}_{aa} + \mathbf{M}_{ab})(1 + \mathbf{M}_{ba}) \\ p_{32} &= \mathbf{M}_{ba}^2/\mathbf{M}_{ab}(\mathbf{M}_{ba} + \mathbf{M}_{bb}) \\ p_{33} &= \mathbf{M}_{bb}/(\mathbf{M}_{ba} + \mathbf{M}_{bb}) \\ p_{34} &= \mathbf{M}_{ba}(\mathbf{M}_{ab} - \mathbf{M}_{ba})/\mathbf{M}_{ab}(\mathbf{M}_{ba} + \mathbf{M}_{bb}). \end{aligned}$$

4. Interpretation of results. The key to the interpretation of a probabilistic model is the Law of Large Numbers. It tells us that if an experiment is repeated a large number of times, and if we compute the average of a certain observable quantity, this average will be very likely to be near its predicted mean. Therefore, if the sequence of trials is repeated for a large number of subjects (i.e., n is large), then the value of n_{ab}/n computed from the data should lie near its mean value $\mathbf{M}_{ab}$ given in (8), and similarly for $\mathbf{M}_{aa}$, $\mathbf{M}_{ba}$, and $\mathbf{M}_{bb}$. We make a connection between theory and data by assuming that the averages are exactly equal to the predicted means. This enables us to compute the theoretical transition matrix P.

From the data in (3) and the definitions of the $\mathbf{M}$'s, the "observed values" are

$$(13) \qquad \mathbf{M}_{aa} = {}^{196}\!/_{33}, \quad \mathbf{M}_{ab} = {}^{117}\!/_{33}, \quad \mathbf{M}_{ba} = {}^{106}\!/_{33}, \quad \mathbf{M}_{bb} = {}^{102}\!/_{33}.$$

Hence, from (12),

$$(14) \qquad P = \begin{pmatrix} 1 & 0 & 0 & 0 \\ .06 & .63 & .31 & 0 \\ 0 & .46 & .49 & .05 \\ 0 & 0 & 0 & 1 \end{pmatrix}$$

Therefore the observed data allow us to estimate the transition probabilities of our model; we have completed our model on the basis of observations. We must now test the model by making predictions concerning the outcome of experiments and seeing how well these predictions agree with our data.

We could, of course, use Formulas (5) through (11) to predict the means of various observable quantities. Indeed, this could be used to predict outcomes of an additional set of experiments. But it would yield nothing new for the given data, since our P was designed so as to yield the correct values of n_{aa}, n_{ab}, n_{ba}, and n_{bb}, and the other quantities are determined by these. We must therefore predict some additional quantities.

Let us make some predictions concerning the number of times that the subject switches responses (from correct to incorrect, or vice versa). The mean number of such switches is $\mathbf{M}_{ab} + \mathbf{M}_{ba}$; hence it is not new. However, we can also compute the probability of exactly k switches. We show in Table 1 the comparison of observation and prediction.

Since the numbers for larger k are rather small, we have combined cases. However, we have kept even and odd k separate, since an even k represents a terminal a response, whereas an odd k represents a terminal b response. We see from Table 1 that the predictions are not completely unreasonable, but they tend to underestimate the number of $k = 0$ cases and the number of high k-values. Indeed, if we apply a standard statistical test known as the

χ^2-test, we find that in more than 99 percent of such cases the predictions could be expected to be in better agreement than in Table 1. We are therefore led to reject this model as not being in sufficiently good agreement with the observed data.

Table 1

k	NUMBER OF SUBJECTS WHO SWITCHED k TIMES	PREDICTED NUMBER
0	10	5.22
1	1	2.61
2 or 4	5	7.01
3 or 5	4	3.51
6, 8, or 10	2	5.41
7, 9, or 11	1	2.71
Larger even no.	5	4.30
Larger odd no.	5	2.15

5. An improved model. The usefulness of a precise mathematical model is shown by our ability to demonstrate its shortcomings numerically. And the same reasoning that led us to reject the Cohen model in its original form will lead us to a fairly obvious modification. The major discrepancy in Table 1 is that the model underestimates badly the number of subjects who never switch their response from an *a* (or correct) response.

This suggests that there may be a significant minority of subjects to whom the model does not apply in that they refuse to be intimidated by the unanimous action of stooges. Let us modify the Cohen model by adding the assumption that some 20 percent of subjects are of this type, and that the original model is applicable only to the remaining ones. Specifically, we will assume that in his sample 7 men fell into this category and we shall apply our computations of Section 3 only to the remaining 26.

If a subject never switches his response, his entire sequence of responses consists of a final segment. Thus his answers do not contribute to the n's computed from initial segments, and hence n_{aa}, n_{ab}, n_{ba}, and n_{bb} are as in (3), but n is reduced to 26. This changes only the denominators in (13), and we obtain as our modified transition matrix

$$(14') \qquad P' = \begin{pmatrix} 1 & 0 & 0 & 0 \\ .04 & .63 & .33 & 0 \\ 0 & .46 & .49 & .05 \\ 0 & 0 & 0 & 1 \end{pmatrix}.$$

We can use this P' to recompute the figures for the expected number of switches. Recalling that seven subjects have been removed, we obtain Table 2.

We immediately see that these predictions are in much better agreement with our observed data. If we apply a χ^2-test again, we find that our deviations are well within the margin of error expected for the worst in 95 percent of such cases. Hence we decide that our present model is in reasonable agreement with the observations recorded in the Cohen experiments. Of course, further experimentation is very likely to refute this modified model as well, and to lead in turn to a more sophisticated approach.

Table 2

k	NUMBER OF SUBJECTS WHO SWITCHED k TIMES	PREDICTED NUMBER
0	3	2.95
1	1	2.16
2 or 4	5	4.27
3 or 5	4	3.13
6, 8, or 10	2	3.74
7, 9, or 11	1	2.75
Larger even no.	5	4.01
Larger odd no.	5	2.94

References

ASCH, S. E. *Social Psychology.* New York: Prentice-Hall, 1952.
COHEN, B. P. *Conflict and Conformity.* Cambridge, Mass.: MIT Press, 1963.
———. "A Probability Model for Conformity," *Sociometry,* **21,** 1, 1958, 69–81.
KEMENY, J. G., and others. *Finite Mathematical Structures.* New York: Prentice-Hall, 1958.

Reward Structures and the Allocation of Effort

James S. Coleman   *The Johns Hopkins University*

In society just as in the laboratory, men work to gain rewards and escape punishments. In society, however, there is no experimenter to establish the reward schedule. Instead, social systems, whether they be large or small, establish their own structures of reward and punishment to motivate their members. Of course, these structures of reward are ordinarily not imposed by an omnipotent "society," nor do they occur purely capriciously.

It is, in fact, the peculiar character of social systems that the various members are, for one another, the purveyors of rewards and punishments. One person's reward or punishment occurs through the actions of another member of the system. For example, in a team activity, one member's accomplishments bring rewards for the other team members. Or in a race, the winner's accomplishments constitute a punishment for the others, who automatically become losers. Or whenever a group establishes a set of norms, the norms act to punish those members who violate them, or reward those who live up to them. In a delinquent gang, the members reward one another for one set of activities; in a women's bridge club, the members reward one another for a totally different set of activities.

It is my purpose in this paper to begin to examine how the structure of rewards in a group affects the effort expended in the rewarded (or punished) activity. The motivation to do this came from a number of observations, some casual, some systematic, about the distribution of activities in groups. Some examples will indicate what I mean.

(a) In gangs, boys will carry out delinquent acts together that they would never initiate alone. Systematic observation of this behavior indicates that it depends for its sustenance upon the rewards provided by other gang members.

(b) In a high school, there are usually norms holding down scholastic effort; on the other hand, norms about athletics encourage unlimited effort. Research has indicated that this is because scholastic achievements on the part of one student in effect reduce the rewards accruing to others, while athletic achievements in interscholastic games benefit all students of the school.

(c) Best track times are generally recorded in competitive races, rather than in races against time. Concurrently, however, casual observation suggests that the poorest runners in a race run more slowly, even to the point of dropping out, than they do in races against time.

(d) In team activity, where the efforts of each aid the team, there is ordinarily more expenditure of effort than in individual activity. And in small group experiments testing ability to withstand electric shock, persons will subject themselves to a stronger shock in a social situation than when alone.

Thus my intent is wholly substantive here: to establish some ways of characterizing reward structures that can first explain, then make more precise and explicit, their effects on allocation of effort.

In particular, there are two kinds of reward structures that I want to focus on:

(1) Situations where one person's achievement contributes to another's goals, and where, in turn, the other person encourages the efforts leading to such achievement. An example is an athletic contest between two high schools: The achievements of one school's athletes contribute to the goals of all members of that school, who in turn cheer their team on, accord the athletes high status, and give them numerous other rewards.

(2) Situations in which one person's achievement takes away from another's success, and in turn the other person discourages efforts leading to such achievement. For example, in scholastic activity in a high school, one person's extra efforts force others to work harder simply to maintain the same relative position, and as a consequence the others discourage such unlimited efforts.

There is a special case of these two structures, of particular interest because of its frequent occurrence: the case where the activities are *alike* among performers and rewarders, so that each performer is a rewarder (or punisher), and each rewarder is a performer.

The problem, then, is to examine the allocation of group members' efforts between two or more activities under these two different reward structures: when one member's efforts help bring success to others who are engaging in that activity, and when his efforts subtract from their success. Depending on the particular situation found in nature or experiment, different mathematical models are appropriate. One very general situation, however, might be modelled this way: Each individual, alone, vacillates between two activities, allocating his effort to one or the other. Diagrammatically, we can characterize him as being in one of two states, A or B, with the possibility of movement from each to the other (figure 1). If the probability of his movement from A to B in a very small period of time is independent of the length of time he has been in A (and similarly for the reverse movement), then the system

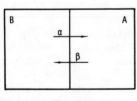

Fig. 1.

is a continuous-time Markov process governed by the following equation:

$$(1) \qquad \frac{dP_A}{dt} = -\beta P_A + \alpha P_B \,,$$

where P_A is the probability of being in state A, α is the transition rate from B to A, independent of time $(0 \leqq \beta < \infty)$, β is the transition rate from A to B, independent of time $(0 \leqq \beta < \infty)$, and $P_B = 1 - P_A$. (Since P_A is a function of t, the correct notation is $P_A(t)$; however, the notation is shortened for convenience.)

That is, as an individual, each member of the group has "tendencies" α and β toward states A and B, respectively. If there were no encouragement or discouragement from others, then his probability of being in each state at any time τ after initially being observed in one of the two states could be calculated. Similarly, the relative amounts of time he would spend in each state at stochastic equilibrium could easily be found by setting equation (1) equal to zero. This gives

$$(2) \qquad \frac{P_A}{P_B} = \frac{\alpha}{\beta} \,,$$

or

$$(3) \qquad P_A = \frac{\alpha}{\alpha + \beta} \,.$$

If a group of N members consisted merely of N persons governed independently by this process, then what distribution of activities would we expect to find in the group? Obviously, we would expect to find a proportion P_A engaging in activity A, and P_B engaging in activity B. And since each person acts independently of each of the others, we have, in effect, a binomial process, so that if we observed this group a number of times, we would expect to find a binomial distribution,

$$(4) \qquad p_i = \binom{N}{i} P_A^i P_B^{N-i} \,,$$

where p_i is the probability that i persons will be carrying out activity A, given N persons in the group, and P_A is the probability that each will carry out A (will be in state A).

1. Structures with Mutual Reward

Suppose, however, that the activities are interrelated so that a member's efforts can help others when they are engaged in the same activity, and he is consequently encouraged to join in this activity by those engaging in it. One way this effect may occur is through an added transition rate γ toward an activity from every person engaging in the activity.[1] If there are i per-

---

[1] This is not the only way that such effects may occur. Part of the difficulty in deciding between alternative forms of effect resides in the very concept of reward. This problem is discussed briefly toward the end of the paper.

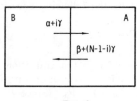

sons in activity A, and he is in B, then his transition rate to A will be $\alpha + i\gamma$; the remainder of the $N-1$ persons, $N-1-i$, are in activity B, so that if he finds himself in A, the transition rate to B will be $\beta + (N-1-i)\gamma$ (see figure 2).

If all other members of the group were fixed in their choice of A or B (as in the Asch experiments, where all members of the group but one were accomplices of the experimenter), then the variable individual, governed by the process pictured in figure 2, would be found in A and B with probabilities as follows:[2]

$$
(5) \qquad P_A = \frac{\alpha + i\gamma}{\alpha + \beta + (N-1)\gamma} ,
$$

$$
(6) \qquad P_B = \frac{\beta + (N-1-i)\gamma}{\alpha + \beta + (N-1)\gamma} .
$$

However, the interesting systemic problem arises when we let all N-group members be variable. What division of activities would we then expect to find among the N members, and what distribution would we expect to find around this number if we observed the group a number of times? The answer to this will tell something different from the answers given by equations (5) and (6), which show how the individual's behavior is influenced by others in his group under a particular assumption about individuals' effects on one another. These latter questions ask how the *group's* behavior is affected by this reward structure.

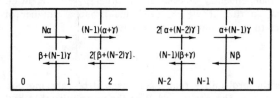

FIG. 3

It is useful, in answering these questions, to diagram, as in figure 3, the states of the group in the stochastic process that characterizes the group's behavior. The transition rates for this stochastic process consist simply of the sum of the transition rates for every member who could, by his change, move the group across the given boundary. For example, when the group is in state 2, this means that two persons are carrying out activity A, each of them characterized by a transition rate to B of $\beta + (N-2)\gamma$. Thus

[2] It is evident from Asch's data that the subjects in his experiments did not behave in accordance with equations (5) and (6). However, there are a number of factors that make Asch's experiments differ from those necessary to test the above model.

the group transition rate to state 1 is simply the sum of these two (for if either transition occurred, the group would move into state 1), i.e., $2[\beta + (N-2)\gamma]$. The expected distribution of groups at stochastic equilibrium in the case of independence was simply a binomial distribution. In this case, the distribution may be found from the fact that at equilibrium, the "flow" across each boundary must be equal in the two directions.

By setting up a set of N simultaneous equations (one for each boundary), then expressing each p_i in terms of p_0, we obtain equations of the following sort:

(7)
$$\frac{p_0}{p_0} = 1 ,$$

(8)
$$\frac{p_1}{p_0} = \frac{N\alpha}{\beta + (N-1)\gamma} ,$$

(9)
$$\frac{p_2}{p_0} = \frac{N(N-1)\alpha(\alpha+\gamma)}{2[\beta + (N-1)\gamma][\beta + (N-2)\gamma]} .$$

By using the fact that the sum of p_i is 1, it is possible to solve for p_0 and then get a general expression for p_i (first letting $\alpha/(\alpha + \beta) = a$, and letting $\gamma/(\alpha + \beta) = c$):[3]

(10)
$$p_i = \frac{\binom{N}{i} \prod_{j=0}^{i-1}(a + jc) \prod_{j=0}^{N-i-1}(1 - a + jc)}{\prod_{j=0}^{N-1}(1 + jc)} .$$

This distribution is analogous to the binomial distribution, but under the condition that there is a particular kind of interdependence, i.e., that a reward structure of the sort shown in figures 2 and 3 exists. The distribution may be thought of as a kind of "contagious binomial," for the rewards act so as to induce more and more of the group into the activity that most people are doing. The parameters a and c may be estimated by using the mean and variance of i, which are estimated as follows:

(11)
$$\mu = \sum i p_i ,$$

and

(12)
$$\sigma^2 = \sum i^2 p_i - \mu^2 .$$

Then

(13)
$$a = \frac{\mu}{N} ,$$

and

(14)
$$c = \frac{\sigma^2 N - \mu(N - \mu)}{N\mu(N - \mu) - \sigma^2 N} .$$

Curiously (or so it seemed to me when I first discovered it), the equilibrium distribution obtained from this process is the same as a Pólya distribution derived from a somewhat different physical model: N balls are drawn from

---

[3] The terms under the first product sign of the numerator vanish for p_0, and those under the second product term vanish for p_N. The same convention holds for equation (17).

an urn containing α "A" balls and β "B" balls. Every time an A ball is drawn, c other A's are added to the urn when it is replaced; every time a B ball is drawn, c other B's are added when the B is replaced. Such an experiment produces as an expected distribution equation (10) above (see [2, p. 109]). This identity with the Pólya distribution is of merely incidental interest, however, for the process we are concerned with is one mirrored by the group stochastic process illustrated in figure 3.

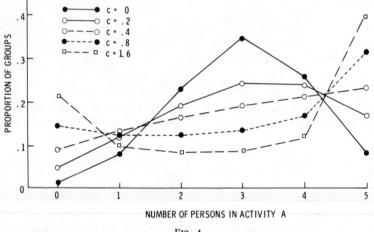

NUMBER OF PERSONS IN ACTIVITY A

FIG. 4

An indication of the way in which this distribution relates to the binomial distribution is shown in figure 4, by giving a set of distributions with varying c's for $N = 5$ and $a = .6$. Note where the difference between this distribution and the unrewarded, independent activities of the binomial distribution lies. The difference is not at all in the *average* allocation of effort in the group: it remains divided proportionally to the individual tendencies α and β. The difference lies in the group's *stability* around this average. If the reward coefficient γ is large relative to α and β, the group is highly unstable near its mean and finds stability only at one or the other extreme, when *all* are engaging in A or all in B. Thus the behavior of this social system as a system differs sharply from that of the aggregate of independent persons.

After a discussion of the other model, examination of empirical data will be carried out.

2. Structures with Mutual Punishments

In structures of activity where each member's achievements reduce the success of others in that activity, the interdependence is of a very different sort (e.g., if several boys are competing for the attention of two girls, each boy will attempt to discourage the others from trying for the same girl he is trying for). If $N-1$ of the group members are fixed, and i are in A, while $N-1-i$ are in B, then the one variable member might be characterized by the process shown in figure 5, where θ is the transition rate brought about by each member's punishment.[4] In this model, the i other persons carrying out activity A act to force this variable member *out*

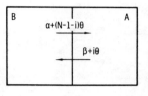

FIG. 5

of A if he is there, while previously they acted to induce him *into* A, if he was in B. In this case, the equilibrium probabilities of an individual's being found in A and B are

$$(15) \qquad P_A = \frac{\alpha + (N-1-i)\theta}{\alpha + \beta + (N-1)\theta},$$

and

$$(16) \qquad P_B = \frac{\beta + i\theta}{\alpha + \beta + (N-1)\theta}.$$

But as in the previous case, our interest is not in the behavior of the individual but rather in the behavior of the *group*, under this structure of punishments. A diagram for the group stochastic process is given in figure 6. By a procedure similar to that carried out for the reward model, it is possible to find the expected distribution of groups that would be found at equilibrium:

$$(17) \qquad p_i = \frac{\binom{N}{i} \prod\limits_{j=N-i}^{N-1} (a+js) \prod\limits_{j=i}^{N-1} (1-a+js)}{\prod\limits_{j=N-1}^{2N-2} (1+js)},$$

where $s = \theta/(\alpha + \beta)$. The mean and variance of i are related to the parameters a and s as follows:

$$(18) \qquad \mu = \frac{N[a + (N-1)s]}{1 + 2(N-1)s},$$

$$(19) \qquad \sigma^2 = \mu\left[1 + \frac{(N-1)[a+(N-2)s]}{1+(2N-3)s}\right] - \mu^2.$$

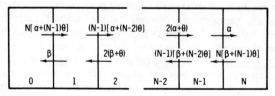

FIG. 6

---

[4] Again, this is not the only form for a punishment mechanism, as later discussion will indicate.

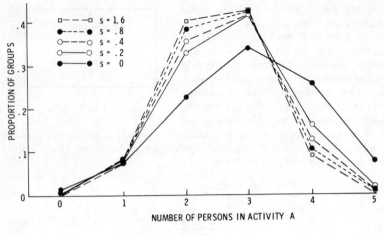

FIG. 7

The two parameters of the distribution, *a* and *s*, may be estimated by first estimating the mean and variance from equations (11) and (12). Then

$$(20) \qquad s = \frac{\mu(N - \mu) - \sigma^2 N}{\sigma^2 N(2N - 3) - \mu(N - 2)(N - \mu)},$$

$$(21) \qquad a = \frac{\mu}{N} + \left(\frac{2\mu - N}{N}\right)(N-1)s .$$

It is interesting to compare the parameters of this "punishment" distribution with those of the "reward" distribution as given in equations (13) and (14). In that case, the individualistic tendency *a* toward activity *A* was directly reflected by the mean number of people carrying out activity *A*, as is true also for the binomial. In this case, the individualistic tendencies described by *a* are not directly reflected by the mean. The punishment distorts the mean in the direction of *N*/2, as equation (18) and figure 7 indicate. The mean mirrors *a* only under special circumstances: if the mean of *i* is equal to *N*/2 [so that $2\mu - N = 0$ in equation (21)], or if the variance equals the binomial variance [so that $\mu(N - \mu) - \sigma^2 N = 0$ in equation (21)]. In the latter case, of course, the punishment parameter *s* is zero, and the process reduces to a binomial. The reward parameter *c* and the punishment parameter *s* are completely dependent on the amount that the estimated variance from equation (12) departs from the binomial variance, being larger for the reward process [see equation (14)] and smaller for the punishment process. The denominators in equations (14) and (20) are positive so long as the estimated variance does not exceed, for the reward process, or fall below, for the punishment process, the maximum or minimum variances consistent with the model, i.e., when $\gamma \to \infty$ or $\theta \to \infty$.

The relation of this punishment distribution to the independent binomial distribution is shown in figure 7 by the set of distributions having $N = 5$ and $a = .6$ as before, with varying values of s. The effect of this punishment structure is to hold the group far closer to an equal number of persons engaging in each activity than would be found if people were behaving independently.

3. Empirical Examination

Suppose I am now confronted with a sceptic who says: "So what? These are nice intellectual exercises, but what relation do they have to the real world? And, in fact, just how do you mean them to be used in relation to experiments or observations in groups?" The sceptic's intuitions would be precisely right, because serious problems do arise in the application of models such as these. I will state several possible ways the models might be used in relation to data, and let the sceptic indicate the objections he might find in each.

(1) In controlled experiments, the model can test the mathematical form taken by the effect of rewards and punishments in a group. That is, the effects shown by figures 4 and 7 are only single possibilities out of a wide range. Since different forms of effect will give different equilibrium distributions of effort in groups, the empirical distributions could be used to test the form of the effect.

"But," says the sceptic, "such testing is obviously inefficient, for it is possible in most cases to test the form of the effect by holding constant all the group except one member. This allows testing at the individual level, a far stronger test than the group-level test. Obviously, if we're interested in the form of psychological mechanisms, it is best to test them without letting the group vary without control."

(2) Suppose, however, that the rewards provided by group members for one another are so fragile and difficult to control that we cannot easily "hold the group constant" as implied in paragraph (1) above. In this case, it seems to be clearly necessary to turn to the systemic consequences rather than to the consequences for a single "dependent" individual.

"This is a valid use of these models," says the sceptic. "Nevertheless, it should be remembered that the equilibrium distribution is merely one deduction that can be tested. Even if the group is not 'held constant,' separate individuals can be observed over time, thus providing stronger tests than that of the single distribution."

(3) But suppose now we *know* that the individual mechanisms are as implied in these models. Then clearly the models provide a useful calculating device to predict the allocation of effort in groups when we know the parameters a and c or a and s.

"To be sure," says the sceptic. "But we are a long way from such knowledge. At best, we know when a process fulfills the assumption of independent Bernoulli trials, and thus gives rise to the binomial distribution, a degenerate case of both of these models."

(4) The models may be used in connection with observed data from nat-

urally occurring groups, to "explain" these data. (An example of such a use will be given below.)

"Clearly, this is one frequent use of models of this sort," says the sceptic. "Nevertheless, one must remain fully aware that the data might be equally well explained by a number of other models, proceeding from different assumptions. Such a use of the model can hardly be considered a 'test.' Rather, it seems that this use of the model is to reduce a distribution to a pair of parameters, whose interpretation is open to argument."

(5) Even without our knowing the precise form of the effect of reward and punishment, these models, and elaborations of them, can be used to deduce the systemic consequences of a particular structure of activities. Because the form of the effect would differ only in detail from that postulated, it is likely that the systemic deductions would be wrong only in detail, if at all. This is important to a sociologist, who is interested in the behavior of the system. If the psychologists are not going to give him the form of individual-level processes, he must assume some form in order to get on to the things that concern him.

"Ah, now," says the sceptic, "I begin to understand what you are doing. You're really interested in developing a theory to relate two variables at the level of the group itself—in this case, reward structures as the independent variable, and distribution of effort in various activities as the dependent one. Your only concern with the form of the individual-level process is as a necessary evil, which must be used in order to link these two variables together. In that case, the data you need to test your theory consist of group data in which *both* variables are explicitly measured: the reward structure along with the distribution of effort."

But now I must reply to the sceptic that he is still not absolutely clear about my intentions. If the psychologists had done their job well, so that I could have confidence in the form of effect that reward and punishment take, there would be no question of "testing" the group-level deductions, any more than there is a question of testing the binomial distribution when we have N independent trials, each with the same probability of success. In such a case, the model in effect tells you the systemic or aggregate consequences of this individual-level process. Thus the sociologist's interest in such model-building lies not so much in testing separate processes as in synthesizing so as to examine systemic consequences.

But it is here that I must point to an extreme weakness of these models in synthesis. They constitute a far lesser accomplishment than is desirable, and fall far short of the goal I have in mind. I hope, for example, to consider a model with a number of activities, each with its own reward structure, and then to generate the equilibrium distribution of activities in the various activities. Such a model would be far more appropriate to any naturally occurring system than those above, for in social systems, different activities have different reward structures. In schools, for example, where my interest is greatest, athletic and scholastic activity have quite different reward structures, as I indicated earlier. One of my major aims is to derive the expected distribution of effort in these activities, given these reward structures.

Furthermore, since reward and punishment structures have consequences other than channeling of effort, I hope to examine some of these other consequences. For example, rewards received from an experimenter or a fellow group member cause the performer to associate pleasure with the rewarder, and to be attracted toward him; punishments cause the performer to associate discomfort with the punisher, and to be repelled from him. Such effects are as evident in rats in the laboratory as they are in human subjects. But suppose that the rewarder or punisher is not merely an experimenter but is himself a performer, and suppose that the reward or punishment schedule is established by the structure of activities in the group. Then it becomes possible to conceive of a model in which the dependent variable is not the distribution of effort but rather the consequent attraction or repulsion that members feel for one another.

These are some of the directions in which I hope models of this sort may be carried in the future. Because of the discrepancy between these ambitious goals and the modest results so far produced, I must present these results somewhat hesitantly. I do so partly to indicate the direction in which I hope to proceed and partly to point out a way that I hope some others may follow.

3.1 A Use of the Reward Model to Explain Naturally Occurring Data. In making a choice between two activities that are mutually supportive, or in lending one's allegiance to one of two candidates in an election, the conditions exist in which one would expect the reward structure to operate. For the election situation, voting data is sometimes recorded for groups. The largest collection of such data of which I am aware consists of voting data in union elections among typographers in small printshops. Voting records by size of shop for shops from 2 to 8 men in size are shown in table 1. Men's votes are obviously not distributed randomly relative to these groups, for there are far too many groups whose votes are near the extremes. For

TABLE 1

NUMBER OF SHOPS OF SIZE N IN NEW YORK TYPOGRAPHICAL UNION IN WHICH
i MEN VOTED FOR THE WINNING CANDIDATE (CANDIDATE A)

N \ i	0	1	2	3	4	5	6	7	8
2	3	2	11						
3	32	15	30	52					
4	22	13	20	26	62				
5	16	7	15	13	20	24			
6	9	8	19	14	17	18	21		
7	4	7	13	14	12	12	13	20	
8	5	4	2	6	8	9	6	9	16

TABLE 2

VALUES OF a AND c FROM EQUATIONS (13) AND (14) APPLIED TO
DATA OF TABLE 1

N	a	c
2	.75	2.00
3	.60	1.08
4	.66	0.95
5	.65	0.86
6	.58	0.42
7	.60	0.40
8	.63	0.56

each size of shop, values of a (the individual tendency toward candidate A) and c (the reward parameter) have been calculated separately, and from these values the theoretical distributions have been regenerated, as shown in figures 8 and 9. In table 2, the values of a and c are listed for each size of group. Of some interest is the value of c for different-sized groups, since (according to the model) c measures the reward provided by each member for each other member. Obviously, from table 2, c decreases as group size increases. But to answer the question of how c decreases with increase in group size, and what accounts for this decrease, requires further data for larger groups, which cannot be presented here. (A more complete examination of data is given in [1].)

This empirical application of the reward model is an example of paragraph (4) above in the discussion of uses. The full value of such a use occurs

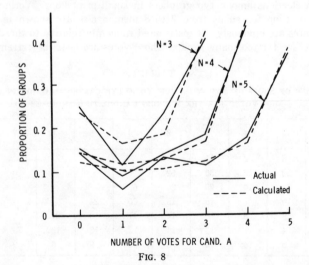

FIG. 8

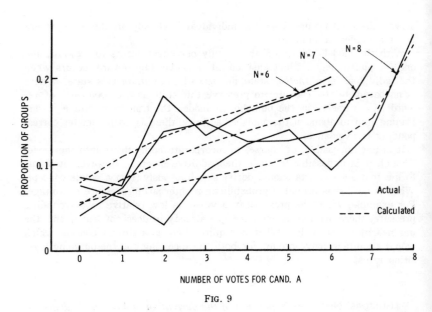

FIG. 9

when the variation of a parameter with some group attribute (such as the variation of c with group size) is studied. But it should be reiterated that the last-described use of these models [see paragraph (5)] is probably the most valuable from the sociologist's viewpoint.

I would like to have a similarly illustrative set of data for the punishment model, either from naturally occurring situations or from experiments. It would be simple to set up experiments in which each member, by carrying out an activity, provided punishment for all others who were in the same activity. Unfortunately, however, I know of no systematic data that can illustrate the application of this model.

4. A Note About the Effect of Rewards and Punishments

In Thorndike's early discussion of the "law of effect," he defined a satisfying state of affairs (that resulting from reward) and an annoying state of affairs (that resulting from punishment) as follows: "By a satisfying state of affairs is meant one which the animal does nothing to avoid, often doing such things as attain and preserve it. By a discomforting or annoying state of affairs is meant one which the animal commonly avoids and abandons." [3, p. 241.]

This statement of the effect of rewards and punishments implies that each has *two* effects. Reward induces the subject to both *attain* and *preserve* the state which brings reward. Punishment leads him to *avoid* and *abandon* the state which brings punishment. The first pair of these effects (attain, avoid) occurs when the individual is in another state; the second pair (preserve, abandon) occurs when the individual is already in the state where he is rewarded or punished.

With the models presented above, only one effect occurs for reward, and one for punishment. The transition rate γ, induced by reward, occurs when the individual is in *another* state, and leads him to *attain* this state. There is no parameter to lead him to preserve this state as a consequence of reward. Conversely, in the punishment model, the transition rate θ is one leading him to abandon the punished activity; there is no parameter corresponding to avoidance.

It is not impossible, of course, to incorporate both effects into the model (though it is impossible to make them additive effects). However, it seems to me that such effects should derive simultaneously from a single concept. What is needed is a kind of probabilistic counterpart of pressure or voltage. For example, when the pressure in a vessel is low relative to surrounding pressure, there are two effects: the gas already in does not leave; and the gas nearby is drawn in. What is required here is a similar concept which would simultaneously account for both the incoming and the outgoing transition rates.

[EDITORS' NOTE: *An expansion of the derivation of Coleman's distribution (10):* Coleman has, in his equations (7), (8), and (9), indicated the derivation of the relation:

$$(1) \qquad p_j/p_0 = \binom{N}{j} \prod_{k=0}^{j-1} (\alpha + k\gamma) / \prod_{N-j}^{N-1} (\beta + k\gamma)$$

which can be written in the following form, if we let $a = \alpha/(\alpha + \beta)$, $b = \beta/(\alpha + \beta)$, and $c = \gamma/(\alpha + \beta)$:

$$(2) \qquad p_j/p_0 = \binom{N}{j} \prod_{k=0}^{j-1} (a + kc) \prod_{k=0}^{N-j-1} (b + kc) / \prod_{k=0}^{N-1} (b + kc).$$

Since the sum of all the p_j must be 1, an explicit expression for p_j can be obtained. Coleman presents, as a solution, his equation (10):

$$(3) \qquad p_i = \binom{N}{i} \prod_{k=0}^{i-1} (a + kc) \prod_{k=0}^{N-i-1} (b + kc) / \prod_{k=0}^{N-1} (1 + kc).$$

Since $p_0 = \prod_{k=0}^{N-1} (b + kc) / \prod_{k=0}^{N-1} (1 + kc)$, it is clear that the ratios p_j/p_0 will take on the desired values (2). It is only necessary to show that $\sum_{j=0}^{N} p_j = 1$

or, from (3), that:

$$(4) \qquad \prod_{k=0}^{N-1} (1+kc) = \sum_{i=0}^{N} \binom{N}{i} \prod_{k=0}^{i-1} (a+kc) \prod_{k=0}^{N-i-1} (b+kc).$$

We proceed by induction, proving that if (4) is true for a certain value of N, then it must also hold for $N+1$.

To carry out this proof, we first multiply both sides of (4) by $(1+Nc)$. The left side then has the desired form, i.e.,

$$\prod_{k=0}^{N} (1+kc)$$

On the right, we use the fact that $1 + Nc = a + b + Nc = a + ic + b + (N-i)c$ for any value of i. Multiplying term by term within the summation, we have

$$\prod_{k=0}^{N} (b+kc) + \sum_{i=1}^{N} \binom{N}{i} \prod_{k=0}^{i-1} (a+kc) \prod_{k=0}^{N-i} (b+kc)$$

$$+ \sum_{i=0}^{N-1} \binom{N}{i} \prod_{k=0}^{i} (a+kc) \prod_{k=0}^{N-i-1} (b+kc) + \prod_{k=0}^{N} (a+kc).$$

Replacing i with $i-1$ in the second summation, and changing the limits of summation accordingly, we find that it reduces to:

$$\prod_{k=0}^{N} (b+kc) + \sum_{i=1}^{N} \left(\binom{N}{i} + \binom{N}{i-1} \right) \left(\prod_{k=0}^{i-1} (a+kc) \prod_{k=0}^{N-i} (b+kc) \right) + \prod_{k=0}^{N} (a+kc)$$

which, since $\binom{N}{i} + \binom{N}{i-1} = \binom{N+1}{i}$, is in the form necessary to complete the derivation,

$$\prod_{k=0}^{N} (1+kc) = \sum_{i=0}^{N+1} \binom{N+1}{i} \prod_{k=0}^{i-1} (a+kc) \prod_{k=0}^{N-i} (b+kc).]$$

References

[1] COLEMAN, JAMES S. *Introduction to Mathematical Sociology*. Glencoe, Ill.. Free Press, 1964.
[2] FELLER, WILLIAM. *An Introduction to Probability Theory and Its Applications*. 2d ed., Vol. I New York: Wiley, 1957.
[3] THORNDIKE, E. L. *Animal Intelligence*. New York: Macmillan, 1911.

A Model for Opinion Change During Repeated Balloting

Germain Kreweras   *University of Paris*

This article consists of an application of Markov chains to the study of the evolution of the opinion expressed by a collectivity on some given topic.

Sections 1 and 2 show the formal conditions under which the individual opinions are to be expressed. They deal primarily with simple choices between possible opinions and not with orders of preference, but with a possibility of expressing opinions in succession (for example, an election with several runoffs). The concept "state of opinion" is introduced.

Section 3 defines a distinction between decided and undecided voters and states more precisely in terms of probability how the latter are supposed to be influenced on each vote by the announced result of the preceding vote.

Section 4 shows with a general transition probability matrix the random succession law of the different possible states of opinion.

Section 5 recalls elementary ideas of spectral analysis, useful for establishing qualitative and quantitative characteristics of the process.

Section 6 shows the results of spectral analysis when applied to the given matrices and gives an outline of the proof.

Section 7 explains the results in the case of ergodic processes, that is, when there actually are decided voters. We examine in turn the case where every option has its determined followers, the case where some options do not have any such followers, and the case where only one option has determined followers. In the last case there is a tendency toward unanimity.

Section 8 refers to a case where all the voters are undecided. We prove that there is still a tendency (although very slow) toward unanimity, but the type of unanimity depends this time on the initial state.

Section 9 presents a method of calculating the *mean duration* of the process under different conditions.

Section 10 gives a few numerical examples of the results shown above.

Section 11 concludes with a few comments about the significance of the model and some of its possible uses.

Bibliographical references, to which figures in brackets refer, are at the end.

1. Formal Hypotheses

Let us suppose that the members of a collectivity V made up of v voters are asked to express their individual choices among a set Ω of ω options that are presented to them.

By hypothesis, each of the v voters must make a single choice: he may not choose several options simultaneously. (But he may be allowed to "abstain"; we only need to agree that Ω contains the particular option of abstention.)

It is quite clear that there exist ω^v distinct possible sets of responses of group V to the set Ω of options. Each of these sets of responses characterizes a *nominative state of public opinion,* and this nominative state would be evident when counting the votes if each voter stated his opinion opposite his name on a list of nominees or if he wrote it on a paper bearing a personal identification mark.

In many procedures actually used — probably in most of them — we are not interested in the nominative state, but only in the numerical state of public opinion — that is, in the number of votes in favor of each option. Often drastic measures are taken so that the counting of ballots cannot (except in the exceptional case of unanimity) identify the nominative state: this is the basic principle of the secret ballot.

If we agree to designate the various options by numbers running from 1 to ω, each numerical state of public opinion (from now on we shall just say "state") can be characterized by:

the number v_1 of voters having chosen Option 1

$$v_2 \qquad '' \qquad\qquad '' \qquad\qquad 2$$
$$v_3 \qquad '' \qquad\qquad '' \qquad\qquad 3$$
$$v_\omega \qquad '' \qquad\qquad '' \qquad\qquad \omega, \text{ etc.}$$

— that is, by a list of ω nonnegative integers whose sum is equal to v. It is important to be able to compute how many distinct conceivable — that is, a priori possible — states exist. It is easy to show that there are

$$\frac{(\omega - 1 + v)!}{(\omega - 1)!\, v!} = \binom{\omega - 1 + v}{\omega - 1}$$

such states.

For example, if there are $v = 7$ votes and $\omega = 3$ options, there are $\binom{9}{2} = 36$ possible states (numerical states, of course; naturally the number of possible nominative states would be $3^7 = 2187$). In what follows, we will consider the special case where $\omega = 2$; there are then exactly $v + 1$ conceivable states.

2. Technical Hypotheses

The aim of an inquiry such as the one being described is, in principle, to "find a majority" in favor of a particular option, which we will then say has been chosen by the group.

The word *majority* has different meanings according to the various electoral agreements adopted, a complete list of which will not be put down here. In certain cases option n can be considered adopted (or "elected") if it has received more votes than any other option. This is called the relative majority rule. In other cases option n will be considered adopted if it has received more votes than all the other options put together; this is called the absolute majority rule. It is also possible to strengthen the absolute majority rule by demanding that in order to adopt an option, it must be chosen by at least a certain "critical" fraction (above one-half) of the voters, often two-thirds, sometimes even 100 percent. This is called a qualified majority. Another rule weakens the absolute majority rule by requiring some critical fraction below one-half and at the same time combining this condition with that of the relative majority rule.

Two kinds of formal reasons might prevent the inquiry from reaching its goal. The first one, especially if there are few voters (v small), sometimes prevents even a relative majority from being reached, because there arise states of opinion in which two or more options lead with the same number of votes. Sometimes this is dealt with by lot or by a preferential ranking according to a subsidiary criterion (such as age if the choice is between candidates for a certain office). Other reasons, arising from more serious difficulties, occur especially if there are many options, and are due to the possibility that no option gets enough votes to go beyond the critical level assigned by the rule agreed on. For example, in the simple case of the absolute majority rule, this kind of risk arises as soon as the number of options is greater than 2; and it even exists for $\omega = 2$ if, for example, the critical fraction is two-thirds (except, of course, in the exceptional case of only three voters).

One of the most common ways of dealing with the absence of a sufficient majority consists in repeating the election in an identical manner. (There are other ways: for example, we could allow, or even make compulsory, changes in the set Ω of options offered to the voters, but we shall speak here only of those that leave Ω unchanged, as well as V.) This is the procedure of "repeated balloting."

The number of successive ballots is sometimes strictly limited by the electoral rule itself, which may state that the maximum number will be N and that in case the required majority is not reached by the Nth ballot, such and such should be done (reduce the majority required or start again later, or some other trick). But sometimes the rule does not limit the number of ballots and requires as many as are necessary for an option to be chosen.

Ballots may then, theoretically, follow each other indefinitely. This is the hypothesis we shall follow from now on, except where the contrary is stated.

3. Psychological Hypotheses

The use of several ballots is clearly based on the belief that individual choices will change from one run to the next, a fact that has been repeatedly substantiated by experience.

The actual causes of such changes can be very diverse, and it is not our aim to make a list of them. The most important ones seem to be linked with the numerical results reported after each ballot, and especially with the influence that this knowledge of the "public opinion" shown by the preceding ballot exerts on each voter when he is making up his mind.

We must form some hypotheses about how this influence is exerted. These hypotheses may seem too simple, and indeed they are. But more attractive hypotheses would have given us serious trouble with our mathematical model, and, furthermore, the consequences we shall derive do not seem to conflict with a good many of the facts we can observe.

So here are our hypotheses: The collectivity of v voters consists of two categories of voters that we shall call "decided" and "undecided": the latter number s people and the former $v - s$. We suppose that the decided voters never change their minds and vote the same way on every ballot.

If $\omega = 2$, it will be convenient to let 0 and 1 denote the two options, and r and r' denote the number of decided partisans in favor of Option 0 and Option 1, respectively, so that

$$r + r' = v - s.$$

As for the undecided, we shall suppose that their votes are to a certain extent due to chance, that is, have a certain probability. In order to specify these probabilities exactly, we shall suppose that they are proportional to the total number of votes the two options received on the preceding ballot.

For example, let us assume there are 13 voters altogether ($v = 13$) and that Options 0 and 1 have 9 and 4 votes respectively (state (9,4) if we adopt a natural notation). Then *each of the undecided* is assumed to vote in favor of 0 with a probability of $\frac{9}{13}$ and in favor of 1 with a probability $\frac{4}{13}$. In this example there are 14 conceivable states, but all cannot occur if we suppose that there are decided voters. If, for example, there are three decided participants in favor of 0 and two in favor of 1 ($r = 3$; $r' = 2$), there are ($s =$)8 undecided and therefore only ($s + 1 =$)9 possible states, ranging from the situation (11,2) where all the undecided would have voted in favor of 0 to the situation (3,10) where all the undecided would have voted in favor of 1.

It will be convenient in what follows to adopt for the different possible states a simpler notation: one indicating only the number of undecided votes in favor of Option 0. Thus, with the numerical data above ($v = 13$, $r = 3$, $r' = 2$), instead of speaking of the state (9,4) we shall speak of the state (6), it being understood that this is just an easier mathematical notation. On a given ballot, the number j never occurs, nor does the number $j' = s - j$, nor even the sum s; only $j + r$ and $j' + r'$ (here 9 and 4), whose sum is v (here 13), are known.

4. The Definition of the Process

The conditions stated above define the sequence of ballots to be a Markov chain process on the set of $s + 1$ possible states. This process is essentially defined by the square matrix M of transition probabilities (p_i^j) from the state (j) to the state (i). We shall adopt i as the row index and j as the column index, so that the column sums are equal to 1.*

$$(1) \qquad \sum_{i=0}^{s} p_i^j = 1 \ (j = 0, 1, \ldots, s)$$

If state (j) has just occurred, each of the s undecided voters will vote for Option 0 with the probability $\dfrac{j + r}{v}$ and for Option 1 with the complementary probability $\dfrac{j' + r'}{v}$; under such conditions the probability that Option 0 gets i votes from the undecided voters is precisely p_i^j, which is given by the binomial law (let $i' = s - 1$)

$$(2) \qquad p_i^j = \frac{s!}{i! \, i'!} \left(\frac{j + r}{v}\right)^i \left(\frac{j' + r'}{v}\right)^{i'}$$

or

$$(2) \qquad p_i^j = \frac{s!}{v^s} \frac{(j + r)^i}{i!} \frac{(j' + r')^{i'}}{i'!}.$$

---

*[EDITORS' NOTE: Notice that Kreweras defines the matrix of transition probabilities so that the *columns* add up to 1, in contrast to the usual American notation in which the row sums are 1. (See, for example, the paper by Kemeny and Snell in this volume.)]

Thus matrix M is completely defined. If we let P_N be a column vector whose components are the probabilities for the various states after N ballots, we get (by elementary probability and matrix multiplication rules)

$$P_{N+1} = MP_N.$$

In order to define completely the column vector P_N, we must give ourselves an "initial hypothesis" which will be a vector P_0, allowing us then to write

$$P_N = M^N P_0.$$

P_0 can be concretely interpreted in the following manner:

1) If we become interested in the process as soon as it has begun, we let the numbers $1, 2, \ldots, N, \ldots$ be the future ballots and number 0 be the one just completed. The result of the latter is a certain state (j_0). Vector P_0 has one component equal to 1, that corresponding to state (j_0), and all its other components equal to 0 (a pure initial vector).

2) There may not be a "zeroth" ballot, but a newspaper or a poll may have created before the beginning of the process the same psychological conditions as if such a runoff had taken place, for example by "proclaiming" (j_0). P_0 is then still a vector whose components are all 0 except for the one corresponding to state (j_0), which is equal to 1.

3) In addition, we can imagine that there are several newspapers, each of them creating a "pure initial vector" of the preceding type. If we suppose that the undecided people are influenced randomly before the first ballot by these various newspapers, the probability of being confronted with a newspaper proclaiming (j_0) gives an interpretation for the (j_0) component of the vector P_0 (mixed initial vector).

5. Concepts of Spectral Analysis

1) M being a matrix with $(s+1)$ rows and $(s+1)$ columns, M^N can be found by computing the powers Δ^N of a matrix Δ which is *similar* to M. Δ is said to be similar to M if an invertible matrix A can be found such that

$$(3) \qquad M = A^{-1}\Delta A.$$

Then, whatever the positive integer N may be,

$$(4) \qquad M^N = A^{-1}\Delta^N A.$$

This similarity transformation is especially useful if among the matrices similar to M there is one, Δ, that is diagonal; its diagonal entries being

λ_0, λ_1, λ_2, ..., λ_s, and all the other entries 0. Then Δ^N is diagonal, and its diagonal entries are λ_0^N, ..., λ_s^N. Let us call the rows of $A(L_0, L_1, ..., L_s)$ and the columns of $A^{-1}(C_0, C_1, ..., C_s)$. Then it is easy to deduce from 4 that

(5) $$M^N = \lambda_0^N C_0 L_0 + \lambda_1^N C_1 L_1 + ... + \lambda_s^N C_s L_s.$$

2) All the computing needed to put M in the form of Equation 3 is generally called *spectral analysis* (see [4] or [7] for example); if it leads to a diagonal matrix (which is often but not always the case), M is said to be a *diagonalizable*. The matrices M considered hereafter will always have this property. Equation 3 can be written as either

$$AM = \Delta A \quad \text{or} \quad MA^{-1} = A^{-1}\Delta.$$

These two forms sum up respectively, when M is diagonalizable, the $(s+1)$ equalities of row vectors:

(6) $$L_k M = \lambda_k L_k \ (k = 0, 1, ..., s)$$

and the $s + 1$ equalities of column vectors:

(7) $$M C_k = \lambda_k C_k \ (k = 0, 1, ..., s).$$

The L_k, which are $(s + 1)$ independent row vectors, are called the *characteristic row vectors* of M; likewise, the $(s + 1)$ independent column vectors C_k are called the *characteristic column vectors* of M. The characteristic vectors are vectors that give the same result whether multiplied by the matrix M or by the number λ_k. These numbers λ_k are called eigenvalues (spectral or characteristic values); together they make up the spectrum of M.

3) The most usual method of spectral analysis consists in finding first the eigenvalues as a solution of an equation in the unknown λ, called the characteristic equation, derived from the fact that the matrix $M - \lambda I$ (I being the identity matrix) is singular. This method would not be easy to use with the matrices M with which we are dealing. We shall see in Section 6 that the properties of the entries (p_i^j) of M allow us to compute the vectors L_k and their corresponding eigenvalues λ_k simultaneously.

The transition matrices of the Markov chain process (often called stochastic matrices) are characterized by the fact that all their entries are nonnegative and all the column sums are equal to 1. They all have, from the spectral point of view, a certain number of specific properties, of which the following will be especially useful (see [2]):

a) No eigenvalue may have a modulus greater than 1.

b) The integer 1 itself is always an eigenvalue — sometimes a simple one, sometimes a multiple one.

c) If $\lambda = 1$ is a simple eigenvalue (that is, occurs only once), and if, furthermore, all the other eigenvalues have moduli smaller than 1, Equation 5 proves that when N grows indefinitely, M^N converges to $C_0 L_0$. $P_N = M^N P_0$ then converges to $C_0 L_0 P_0$. But we can let L_0 be a row vector whose components are all equal to 1, for we have $L_0 M = L_0 (= 1 \times L_0)$ because of the properties of the column sums of M. Therefore $L_0 P_0 = 1$ no matter what P_0 is (for the entries of P_0 are probabilities the sum of which is 1), and P_N converges toward C_0 no matter what P_0 is. There is therefore a vector C_0 (hereafter it will be called E) that defines a limiting probability distribution toward which the probability vectors converge after N ballots, as N gets very large; this limit distribution *does not depend on the particular choice* of P_0.

When this happens, the vector limit E or C_0 (which is a characteristic column vector of the simple eigenvalue $\lambda_0 = 1$) is sometimes called the ergodic vector, and the process itself is called ergodic. An ergodic process enables us, given a sufficiently distant future, to make a probabilistic prognosis practically independent of what is known of the present.

6. Spectral Properties of the Process

Let us go back to the probability p_i^j relating state (j) to state (i) —

$$(7) \qquad p_i^j = \frac{s!}{v^s} \frac{(j+r)^i}{i!} \frac{(j'+r')^{i'}}{i'!}, \quad i + i' = j + j' = s$$

— and let us show that it satisfies the identities which enable spectral analysis of the matrix M. We shall use the short notation for "factorial polynomials" and shall agree that for every positive integer n

$$(8) \qquad (x)_n = x(x-1), \ldots, (x-n+1)$$

and that $(x)_0 = 1$ and $(x)_1 = x$.

1) Let us first prove that for every integer k such that $0 \leqslant k \leqslant s$, we have

$$(9) \qquad \sum_{i=0}^{s} (i)_k p_i^j = \frac{(s)_k}{v^k} (j+r)^k.$$

On the left side of Equation 9 we have only the terms $k \leqslant i \leqslant s$ because $(i)_k = 0$ for $i = 0, 1, \ldots, k-1$, because of Equation 8. Furthermore, note that for $i \geqslant k$ we have $\dfrac{(i)_k}{i!} = \dfrac{1}{(i-k)!}$ and $(j+r)^i = (j+r)^k (j+r)^{i-k}$, so that

$$\sum_{i=0}^{s} (i)_k p_i^j = \frac{s!}{v^s} (j+r)^k \sum_{i-k=0}^{s-k} \frac{(j+r)^{i-k}}{(i-k)!} \frac{(j'+r')^{i'}}{i'!}.$$

In this latter sum we let $i - k = \alpha$ and $i' = \alpha'$, with $\alpha + \alpha' = s - k$, in order to make things easier; then this sum can be written

$$\frac{1}{(s-k)!} \sum_{\alpha=0}^{s-k} \frac{(s-k)!}{\alpha!\,\alpha'!} (j+r)^\alpha (j'+r')^{\alpha'}$$

and the latter is equal to $\dfrac{v^{s-k}}{(s-k)!}$ because of the binomial theorem for $(j+r) + (j'+r') = v$. Finally we have

$$\sum_{i=0}^{s} (i)_k p_i^j = \frac{s!}{v^s} (j+r)^k \frac{v^{s-k}}{(s-k)!}$$

and because $\dfrac{s!}{(s-k)!} = (s)_k$, we have

$$\sum_{i=0}^{s} (i)_k p_i^j = \frac{(s)_k}{v^k} (j+r)^k.$$

Note that k is any integer satisfying the condition $0 \leq k \leq s$. Thus Equation 9 stands for $(s + 1)$ different identities. In particular, when $k = 0$, we arrive again at Equation 1.

2) Equation 9 enables us to find a set of polynomials in the unknown x,

$$L_0(x), L_1(x), \ldots, L_k(x), \ldots, L_s(x),$$

having the following properties: each has a degree equal to its index, the coefficient of the term of highest degree being equal to 1; and also

$$(10) \qquad \sum_{i=0}^{s} L_k(i)\, p_i^j = \frac{(s)_k}{v^k} L_k(j) \quad \text{for} \quad \begin{matrix} j = 0, 1, \ldots, s \\ k = 0, 1, \ldots, s. \end{matrix}$$

That is, $L_1(x) = x + B$, $L_2(x) = x^2 + Cx + D$, and so on, where the coefficients $B, C, D, \ldots$ must be chosen so that Equation 10 is satisfied. These polynomials can be determined recursively, beginning with $L_0(x) = 1$. For example, taking $L_1(x) = x + B$, and applying Equation 10, we have

$$\sum_{i=0}^{s} (i+B)\, p_i^j = \frac{s}{v} (j+B), \quad \text{whence}$$

$$\sum_{i=0}^{s} i\, p_i^j + B \sum_{i=0}^{s} p_i^j = \frac{sj}{v} + \frac{sB}{v}.$$

But Equation 9 tells us that

$$\sum_{i=0}^{s} i\, p_i^j = \frac{s}{v}(j+r) \quad \text{and} \quad \sum_{1=0}^{s} p_i^j = 1,$$

so that we have

$$\frac{rs}{v} = \frac{s}{v}B - B\,,\, B = \frac{-rs}{v-s}, \text{ and finally}$$

$$L_1(x) = x - \frac{rs}{v-s}.$$

Although it takes a long time to write this out, the calculation of the coefficients of any polynomial $L_k(x)$ is always possible, making use of Equation 9.*

Finally there are (in the general case where $s < v$) $s + 1$ eigenvalues, all different:

$$1, \frac{s}{v}, \frac{s(s-1)}{v^2}, \ldots, \frac{s!}{v^s}$$

and the entries of the corresponding characteristic row vectors can be computed by giving in turn the different values $0, 1, \ldots, s$ to the unknown x of $L_k(x)$.

Once the $(s + 1)$ characteristic row vectors have been computed, we can, if we need them, compute the characteristic column vectors C_k either by calculating the inverse of matrix A (itself computed from $L_0, L_1 \ldots, L_s$) or by solving Equation 7, in which we now know that $\lambda_k = \dfrac{(s)_k}{v^k}$.

7. The Case in Which There Are Decided Voters

This is the general case, characterized by the strict inequality $s < v$. 1 is a simple eigenvalue, and the rest of the spectrum is strictly included between 0 and 1; as we have seen above, this is sufficient for the process to be ergodic.

There is then an ergodic vector $E = (E_0, E_1, \ldots, E_i, \ldots, E_s)$ having non-

---

*[EDITORS' NOTE: Note that Equation 10 has the same form as Equation 6, the equation defining the characteristic roots and vectors of the transition matrix. The fact that polynomials $L_k(x)$ do exist satisfying 10 implies that the eigenvalues of the matrix are $(s)_k/(v)^k$ for all k.]

negative components defined uniquely by the system of equations:

$$(11) \qquad \sum_{j=0}^{s} p_i^j E_j = E_i (i = 0, 1, \ldots, s)$$

$$(12) \qquad \sum_{j=0}^{s} E_j = 1.$$

E_i is the limiting probability as N gets very large of candidate 0 collecting i votes in the Nth poll, whatever the initial conditions are.

1) Let us suppose first that both r and r' are nonzero (that is, each alternative has at least one determined supporter). It is clear from Equation 2 that in this case none of the p_i^j may be zero. Therefore none of the E_i can be zero, for if we had $E_i = 0$, it would follow from Equation 11 that *all* E_j must be zero and we could not have Equation 12.

This means that each of the realizable states has a nonzero ergodic probability, that is, will certainly occur eventually if the balloting is continued indefinitely. Suppose in particular that the electoral rule prescribes enough ballots for one of the alternatives 0 and 1 to collect, say, more than two-thirds of the votes: for this to be possible, it is *necessary* that the larger of the fractions $\dfrac{r+s}{v}$ and $\dfrac{r'+s}{v}$ reach or exceed two-thirds. We now know this is also *sufficient* for the process to be of finite length, the expectation of which can be calculated. (See below, Section 9.)

Finally, if the balloting were continued indefinitely (without any provision for stopping), the various possible states (i) would follow one another and recur in apparent confusion. However, if after the Nth ballot we calculated the mean of the undecided voters' responses for Option 0, that is, $(i_1 + i_2 + \ldots + i_N)/N$, we would find this random quantity tending to the fixed number

$$(13) \qquad e = \sum_{i=0}^{s} i E_i.$$

Though e is generally not an integer, nor is $e' = s - e$, one may consider that e defines a "mean state," or, in other words, that e and e' define a "mean distribution" of the voters hesitating between Options 0 and 1.

One interesting fact is the following: e and e' are proportional to r and r' — that is, the undecided voters are distributed "on the average" in proportion to the determined voters. Indeed, we have

$$e = \sum_{i=0}^{s} i E_i = \sum_{i=0}^{s} \left(i \sum_{j=0}^{s} p_i^j E_j \right) = \sum_{j=0}^{s} \left(\sum_{i=0}^{s} i p_i^j \right) E_j.$$

Now the quantity in parentheses, by Equation 10, is equal to $\frac{s}{v}\,(j+r)$; from which

$$e = \sum_{j=0}^{s} \frac{s}{v}\,(j+r)\,E_j = \frac{s}{v} \sum_{j=0}^{s} jE_j + \frac{sr}{v} \sum_{j=0}^{s} E_j,$$

and, by applying Equations 13 and 12,

$$e = \frac{se}{v} + \frac{sr}{v}$$

$$e = \frac{rs}{v-s}$$

and by subtraction from s,

$$e' = \frac{r's}{v-s},$$

just as we claimed.

2) Suppose now that one of the two alternatives 0 and 1, let us say 1, had determined supporters ($r = 0$, $r' \neq 0$), while the other alternative, 0, has none and thus can only appear as the temporary choice of undecided voters.

In column 0 of matrix M, therefore, we have

$$p_0^0 = 1 \text{ and } p_i^0 = 0 \text{ for } i \neq 0.$$

State (0), which is unanimity in favor of Option 1, is an "absorbing state": once it has occurred by chance, it must recur indefinitely by virtue of our hypotheses.

The process does not cease to be ergodic, but the component E_0 of the ergodic vector is equal to 1 and all the other components are zero.

Unanimity in favor of Option 1 is thus eventually certain, even when $r' = 1$, no matter how favorable to Option 0 the initial state may be. Thus obstinate minorities triumph in the end over hesitant majorities.

8. The Case in Which All the Voters Are Undecided

Here we consider the special case in which $r = r' = 0$, where $v = s$. The spectral analysis made in Section 6 is still valid, except that the eigenvalues 1 and $\frac{s}{v}$ cease to be distinct. 1 is a *double* eigenvalue, and there are $(s-1)$ other proper values, which are

$$\frac{s-1}{s}, \frac{(s-1)(s-2)}{s^2}, \ldots, \frac{(s-1)!}{s^{s-1}}.$$

But the diagonalization of M is still possible, for the two row vectors

$$L_0 = [1\ 1\ 1 \ldots 1]$$

and

$$L_1 = [0\ 1\ 2 \ldots s],$$

which are independent, are both characteristic vectors corresponding to the eigenvalue 1. This we see by applying Equation 10 for $k = 0$ and for $k = 1$, for $r = 0$ implies that $L_1(x) = x$.

Furthermore, $p_0^0 = p_s^s = 1$; column 0 of M is reduced to one unit followed by zeros, the last term of column s of M equals 1, and all its predecessors are zeros. But it is therefore possible to verify that every column vector with $(s + 1)$ components of which only the first and last are nonzero is a characteristic column vector corresponding to the eigenvalue 1. In particular, the first two columns C_0 and C_1 of A^{-1}, which can be determined by the four conditions

$$L_0 C_0 = L_1 C_1 = 1 \text{ and } L_0 C_1 = L_1 C_0 = 0$$

are then

$$C_0 = \begin{pmatrix} 1 \\ 0 \\ \cdot \\ \cdot \\ 0 \\ 0 \end{pmatrix} \text{ and } C_1 = \begin{pmatrix} -1/s \\ 0 \\ 0 \\ \cdot \\ \cdot \\ 1/s \end{pmatrix}.$$

When N increases indefinitely, M^N tends, by virtue of Equation 5, to $C_0 L_0 + C_1 L_1$, and $P_N = M^N P_0$ tends to

$$C_0 L_0 P_0 + C_1 L_1 P_0 = C_0 + C_1 (L_1 P_0).$$

But $L_1 P_0$ has a simple interpretation. For example, if P_0 is a "pure initial vector" (see Section 4) the one nonzero component of which is state (i_0), one has simply $L_1 P_0 = i_0$. P_N tends then toward $C_0 + i_0 C_1$, a column vector the first and last component of which (all the others being zero) are respectively

(14) $$1 - \frac{i_0}{s} \text{ and } \frac{i_0}{s}.$$

Finally, there will certainly be unanimity at length, and this unanimity will be absorbing. But the absence of ergodicity (since 1 is a double eigenvalue) makes the nature of the unanimity — the alternative which will be chosen — predictable only in terms of probability and dependent upon the "initial vector." Expressions 14 can be interpreted by saying that the expectations that Options 0 and 1 will achieve the final unanimity are always proportional to the number of votes that they have just collected.

9. Probable Duration of the Process

In any Markov chain process one can define an arbitrary partition of the set of possible states into two complementary classes, called "continuing states" and "stopping states," and can ask the following question: Given a continuing state, what number of steps is necessary to reach a stopping state? This number is actually a random variable; but what is the expectation of this variable?

The general solution of this problem is a very simple one; its conditions of validity may, for instance, be found in [5]. Let S_c be the set of continuing states and let (j) be such a state: $(j) \epsilon S_c$. Let us call s_j the expectation of the number of steps necessary to reach initially a stopping state. Then clearly

$$s_j = 1 + \sum_{(i) \epsilon S_c} p_i^j s_i.$$

This can be written in matrix language by introducing the submatrix M_c of M_s corresponding to the continuing states, the row vector S of the corresponding s_j, a row vector H all of whose components equal 1, and the unit matrix I.

$$S = H + S M_c;$$

whence

$$S (I - M_c) = H \text{ and } S = H(I - M_c)^{-1}.$$

This result permits the calculation, from any initial continuing state, of the expected duration of the process no matter what stopping rule is adopted, for example the first realization of a unanimity or of a "qualified majority."

10. Some Numerical Examples

Example A: $v = 7$, $\omega = 2$, $r = 2$, $r' = 1$ $(s = 4)$

The rows and columns of matrix M enumerate the five possible states (0), (1), (2), (3), (4) that correspond, respectively, to the proclaimed results (2,5) (3,4), (4,3), (5,2), (6,1).

$$M = \frac{1}{2401} \begin{array}{c} \\ \\ \end{array} \begin{matrix} 0 & 1 & 2 & 3 & 4 \\ \left(\begin{matrix} 625 & 256 & 81 & 16 & 1 \\ 1000 & 768 & 432 & 160 & 24 \\ 600 & 864 & 864 & 600 & 216 \\ 160 & 432 & 768 & 1000 & 864 \\ 16 & 81 & 256 & 625 & 1296 \end{matrix} \right) & \begin{matrix} 0 \\ 1 \\ 2 \\ 3 \\ 4 \end{matrix} \end{matrix}$$

The spectral values are all simple, since $\omega = 2$:

$$\lambda_0 = 1, \ \lambda_1 = \tfrac{4}{7}, \ \lambda_2 = \tfrac{12}{49}, \ \lambda_3 = \tfrac{24}{843}, \ \lambda_4 = \tfrac{24}{2401}$$

The ergodic vector is

$$E = \frac{1}{84,167,193} \begin{pmatrix} 2,713,569 \\ 10,320,040 \\ 21,002,136 \\ 28,404,256 \\ 21,727,192 \end{pmatrix} = \begin{pmatrix} 0.03 \\ 0.12 \\ 0.25 \\ 0.34 \\ 0.26 \end{pmatrix}$$

The divisor 84,167,193 is the product of the differences

$$(7 - 4) \ (49 - 12) \ (343 - 24) \ (2401 - 24),$$

which illustrates the occurrence of the factor $\left(1 - \dfrac{s}{v}\right) \ldots, \left(1 - \dfrac{s!}{v^s}\right)$ in the calculations.

Example B: The data are the same as in Example A, but the assumptions for starting and stopping are the following: At the start, each of the four undecided voters chooses randomly between Options 0 and 1; the option that first gets the "qualified majority" of two-thirds — at least 5 votes — is "elected."

Under these conditions the expected number of ballots necessary to reach a decision is 2.54 ..., and the a priori probabilities of the final choice are approximately

$$0.16 \text{ for Option 1 (by 5 votes to 2)}$$
$$0.84 \text{ for Option 0 (0.66 by 5 votes to 2)}$$
$$(0.18 \text{ by 6 votes to 1)}$$

Example C: $v = 5$, ω unrestricted. Option 1 has r_1 resolved partisans, and the remaining $s = 5 - r_1$ voters are undecided.

The expected number of ballots needed to reach unanimity, starting from an initial state in which none of the undecided voters has chosen Option 1, is, in the four possible cases:

$$r_1 = 4, s = 1: \quad \frac{5}{5-1} = 1.25 \ldots$$

$$r_1 = 3, s = 2: \quad \frac{145}{(5-2)(25-2)} = 2.10 \ldots$$

$$r_1 = 2, s = 3: \quad \frac{16915}{(5-3)(25-6)(125-6)} = 3.74 \ldots$$

$$r_1 = 1, s = 4: \quad \frac{6{,}085{,}625}{(5-4)(25-12)(125-24)(625-24)} = 7.71 \ldots$$

11. Conclusions

In its strictly mathematical aspect, the model shown in this paper is nothing but the study of a relatively wide class of matrices whose spectra have the pleasant peculiarity of always being rational, even though this property may not be immediately apparent.

A subclass of these matrices, corresponding in our notation to the case where $\omega = 2$, $r_1 = r_2 = 0$, and s is even, have been encountered on occasion in a problem of genetics, where only the largest of the eigenvalues other than 1 was mentioned (cf. [6]).

From the point of view of applications, the model can be interpreted in several ways.

On the one hand, it can be the probabilistic description of a formal voting procedure, whose "psychological hypothesis" may be exposed to serious objections, but whose "technical hypotheses" are reasonable and are rather frequently satisfied in practice.

On the other hand, the model could possibly be used in comparison with data drawn from recorded real situations, such as certain academic elections or even certain political elections that are carried out according to the technical hypotheses. The comparison would then have for a goal the precise testing of the psychological hypotheses.

If we do not apply ourselves to this work, it is because at this time the available documentation is widely scattered, and because we have the feeling that these tests would *prove* little: the general model, for a fixed total number of voters, depends, in fact, on as many parameters as there are options, these parameters being the r_n (number of resolved voters) for each option. It would seem, no doubt, that the possibilities for adjustment are too great; and as a consequence, in being led to reject a few numerically specified hypotheses, we would only rarely succeed in proving anything about the set of all possible numerical hypotheses.

In fact, if the model were so used, it would be rejected immediately each time there occurred a situation such as the following: A certain option received no votes on the Nth ballot but received one or more on the

$(N + 1)$th. We know very well that this sometimes happens. Nevertheless, if one were indulgent regarding the model, one could still defend it against such strictly applied tests by claiming that at least it usefully summarizes the psychology of the great majority of voters, if not that of all of them.

But it would be futile to try to save the model by refuting historical arguments that would be brought against it, because the evidence taken from common psychological observation appears to be enough to ruin it.

Recall that our decided voters are in some way unconditionally attached to one option, and that our undecided voters are actually indifferent, their "propensity" to choose one option being measured only by the degree of success that this same option has just achieved, and being manifested only by a probability. Or again, if one wishes, each of the undecided voters is content to adopt provisionally "the first option that comes up," this expression being understood in the following sense: The option favored by a person chosen at random has the same probability, whether the person is chosen from the decideds, from the undecideds, or from the set of all respondents taken together.

Let us add that absolute faithfulness to an option is an exceptional phenomenon, and that in reality attachment to a particular choice is most often combined with a series of positions of possible strategic withdrawal, which are adopted more or less reluctantly according to the circumstances.

Much better models would be those taking explicitly into account these more complex elements. The principal justification for the one developed here, however crude it is, is that it illustrates the possibility of formalizing for a group some hypotheses pertaining to the manner in which each member reacts to the influences that they exert on one another and thus of deriving dynamic properties of a suitably defined "collective will."

References

1. ARROW, K. J. *Social Choice and Individual Values.* (Cowles Commission Monograph 12.) New York: Wiley, 1951.
2. FELLER, W. *An Introduction to Probability Theory and Its Applications.* New York: Wiley, 1960.
3. GUILBAUD, G. T. "Les Théories de l'intérêt général et le problème logique de l'aggrégation," *Economie Appliquée,* No. 4. Paris: Publications de l'Université Français, 1952.*
4. HOHN, F. *Elementary Matrix Alegebra.* 2d ed. New York: Macmillan, 1964.
5. KEMENY, J. G., and SNELL, J. L. *Finite Markov Chains.* Princeton, N.J.: Van Nostrand, 1960.
6. MALECOT, G. "Sur un problème de probabilités en chaîne que pose la génétique," *C. R. de l'Académie des Sciences,* Vol. 219 (1944), p. 379.
7. VILLE, J. *Principes d'analyse matricielle.* Paris: Publications de l'Institut de Statistique de l'Université de Paris, 1955.

*[EDITORS' NOTE: An abridged translation of this article appears in this volume.]

Suggestions for Further Reading (Section Three)

BERGER, JOSEPH, and others. *Types of Formalization in Small Group Research.* Boston: Houghton Mifflin, 1963. Three different examples are presented to show how mathematical formalization can be of value to the development of social science theory. Although the examples are taken from the area of small groups, the discussion is pertinent to many areas. The monograph contains a bibliography of small-group research.

COLEMAN, JAMES S. "The Mathematical Study of Small Groups," in *Mathematical Thinking in the Measurement of Behavior,* ed. HERBERT SOLOMON. Chicago: Free Press, 1959. This paper surveys several applications of mathematics to small-group behavior. Coleman analyzes and comments on Simon's formalization of Homans' work in *The Human Group* (New York: Harcourt, Brace, 1950); some models that the experimental work of Bales has given rise to; the work of Rapoport on "random nets"; and models of group problem solving.

KATZ, LEO, and PROCTOR, C. H. "The Concept of Configuration of Interpersonal Relations in a Group as a Time Dependent Stochastic Process," *Psychometrika,* 1959, **24**, 317-27. The usual analysis of sociometric choices is extended to take into account changes in these choices over a period of time. A three-state Markov chain model is proposed that is based on each pair relation: that is, the three states corresponding to mutual choice, one-way choice, and no relation (for a pair). Data are examined that seem to support the model.

LORGE, IRVING, and SOLOMON, HERBERT. "Two Models of Group Behavior in the Solution of Eureka-type Problems," *Psychometrika,* 1955, **20**, 138-48. The authors, by setting up simple models of group behavior, try to test the hypothesis that groups are more successful than individuals at solving problems. Results of further research by the authors is reported in "Group and Individual Behavior in Free Recall Learning," in *Mathematical Methods in Small Group Processes* (eds. JOAN CRISWELL and others; Stanford, Calif.: Stanford Univ. Press, 1962).

RAPOPORT, A., and ORWANT, C. "Experimental Games: A Review," *Behavioral Science,* 1962, **7**, 1-37. A survey of the literature on experimental behavior in game or conflict situations.

Section Four **The Mathematical Study of More Complex Aggregates**

Models of Kinship Systems with Prescribed Marriage

Harrison C. White   *Harvard University*

1. Introduction

Background. In 1949 André Weil, in the appendix to Part I of *Elementary Structures of Kinship* by Lévi-Strauss, sketched out one way to analyze in algebraic terms the structures of certain kinship systems. A basic step in his conceptualization is the assignment of all members of the society to a set of a few mutually exclusive and exhaustive marriage types, each husband and wife having the same type. (Each type reflects prescribed marriage of men in one clan to women in another.) He confines himself to systems with bilateral and matrilateral first-cousin marriage which further can be described in termɔ of cyclic groups. After mentioning that the theory of groups of permutations is applicable, he solves concrete examples through an ingenious and rather specialized use of the addition of n-tuples modulo two.

R. R. Bush in an undated mimeo manuscript proposed permutation matrices as a more convenient tool for the analysis. Like Weil, Bush carries out the analysis in terms of marriage types, although the implications for clan membership are always drawn by both authors. Bush suggests that $(M!)^2$ societies with M marriage types are possible, and he works out a few concrete cases for small M.

Kemeny, Snell, and Thompson develop the work of Weil using the tool suggested by Bush. In Secs. 10 and 11 of Chapter 5 of *Introduction to Finite Mathematics* they develop the elementary properties of groups and subgroups of permutation matrices; then in Secs. 7 and 8 of Chapter 7 they present a reformulation of the Weil analysis. Although their book can be called an elementary text, these brief sections, with their extensive problem sets, are a major advance over the previous work. The properties of the societies to be investigated are formulated as an integrated set of axioms. The seventh and last axiom, which postulates a kind of homogeneity in the kinship structure, is not foreshadowed in the work of Weil and Bush. Using this plausible axiom, they show there are only a few allowed societies with a given number of marriage types.

Content. In this chapter we systematically derive and describe all distinct kinship structures that satisfy the Kemeny-Snell-Thompson axioms and exhibit one of several kinds of prescribed marriage of particular interest to anthropologists.

A considerable reformulation of the Kemeny-Snell-Thompson approach was desirable. Marriage type is not a concept to be found in the field notes of anthropologists or the thinking of members of the societies. It not only is possible but also proves to be simpler to define the permutation operators in terms of clans. Instead of having one matrix represent the transformation of parents' marriage type into son's type, and another similar matrix represent daughter's marriage type, we deal with one matrix for transforming husband's clan into wife's clan, and another for transforming father's clan into children's clan. Both the formulation and the results are easier to interpret concretely, and the derivations are somewhat simpler.

We show that any abstract group, or equivalently any group of permutations, which can be generated by two elements corresponds to at least one allowed society. Moreover, we find that the regular matrix representation of an abstract group, which is easily written down from the multiplication table, provides a convenient translation of the results of the abstract algebraic derivations into the explicit matrix operators in terms of which the societies can be visualized. However, the same abstract group can represent not only distinct societies but also different types of societies. It is much simpler to consider not groups but pairs of generators of groups in deriving all possible societies of a given kind. Even then it is necessary, after defining what is meant by distinct societies, to show that each allowed pair of generators found yields a distinct society.

Additional tools for analyzing these societies are developed in the remaining sections. In the three earlier works cited, the primary question asked for a given society or type of society was: Which of his female relations can male ego marry? A second question, which can be answered using the results of this chapter, is: What different kinds of relationship can exist between the same two persons in a given type of society? Since there are few clans relative to the number of people, and since everyone in the society is by hypothesis related to some degree, obviously a large number of distinct relationships must relate any pair of people. Two important special cases treated in some detail are the conditions under which (1) two persons can be bilateral cross cousins of the same degree and (2) second- and first-cousin relations of various kinds can coexist between the same two people.

2. Axioms

We wish to construct a typology of all prescribed marriage systems that have the following properties:

1. The entire population of the society is divided into mutually exclusive groups, which we call clans. The identification of a person with a clan is permanent. Hereafter n denotes the number of clans.

2. There is a permanent rule fixing the single clan among whose women the men of a given clan must find their wives.

3. By Rule 2, men from two different clans cannot marry women of the same clan.

4. All children of a couple are assigned to a single clan, uniquely determined by the clans of their mother and father.

5. Children whose fathers are in different clans must themselves be in different clans.

6. A man can never marry a woman of his own clan.

7. Every person in the society has some relative by marriage and descent in each other clan: that is, the society is not split into groups not related to each other.

8. Whether two people who are related by marriage and descent links are in the same clan depends only on the kind of relationship, not on the clan either one belongs to.

We also refer to these eight properties as axioms.

3. Marriage and Descent Rules as Permutation Matrices

The rule required by Axioms 2 and 3 can be presented in the form of a permutation matrix of side n: that is, a square matrix with exactly one entry of unity in each row and column and all other entries zero. Number the clans from 1 to n, and let the ith row and the ith column of the matrix correspond to the ith clan. Assume each row of the matrix corresponds to a husband's clan, the wife's clan being identified with the column in which the number 1 appears in that row. Call this matrix W. It shows the one clan from whom women of any given clan get their husbands and the one clan from whom the men of any given clan get their wives. Note that polygamy and polyandry are consistent with the axioms, though for simplicity we speak in terms of monogamy.

Since the wife's clan is uniquely determined by her husband's clan, the clan of a couple's children can by Axiom 4 be uniquely specified by the father's clan. Let C be the permutation matrix in which $C_{ij} = 1$ if fathers of clan i have children of clan j. C must be of the form of a permutation matrix since, by Axiom 5, children in any given clan have fathers in only one clan, as well as vice versa.

There are $n!$ possible permutation matrices, or all together there are $(n!)^2$ combinations of marriage and descent rules for societies with n clans which have the first five properties. Many of these combinations violate Axioms 6, 7, and 8, and only a small fraction of the valid combinations of rules are structurally distinct. It is necessary to define the latter term precisely in order to count and group distinct structures, but first we must study the implications of Axioms 6, 7, and 8.

W and C not only look like matrices but also can be meaningfully combined by the operation of matrix multiplication. For example, consider the element $(WC)_{ij}$ in the ith row and the jth column of the matrix WC formed by multiplying the matrices W and C in that order. By the standard definition of matrix multiplication,

$$(WC)_{ij} = \sum_{k=1}^{n} W_{ik} C_{kj}.$$

There is exactly one unity in the ith row of W: say it occurs in the p column. Similarly, in the jth column of C there is only one unity, say in the q row; so the sum on the right in the equation above is zero unless $p = q$, in which case the sum is just unity. In words this means the (i, j) element in (WC) is unity if and only if men in the ith clan marry women whose clan brothers are the fathers of children of clan j. But there must exist some j such that $C_{pj} = 1$, by Axioms 5 and 4. To put it affirmatively, the matrix (WC) specifies for a man of each clan the clan to which the children of his wife's brother belong. Any ordered series of any powers of W and C when multiplied together will, by the same logic, give a product matrix which is a permutation matrix specifying for each possible clan of a man the clan of a given relative of his.

One possible product matrix is the identity matrix, call it I, in which $I_{ij} = 1$ if and only if $i = j$, with all other elements zero. Whatever the clan of a man, any relative of his for whom the product matrix is I will have the same clan that he does. Axiom 6 requires that in the matrix W no diagonal element W_{ii} be unity; certainly W cannot be the identity matrix I. Approximately $n!/e$ (where $e = 2.71\ldots$) $n \times n$ permutation matrices satisfy this restriction. C on the other hand can be I when the children of men of any clan are in that clan. If any diagonal element of C is unity, all C_{ii} must be unity, for otherwise some men would be in the same clan as their children but not others, in contradiction of Axiom 8. A parallel argument leads to the conclusion that any product matrix formed from W and C must have no diagonal elements unity or else it must be I.

Axiom 8 has further implications. If any man is in the same clan as his own son's son, all men must be; so $C^2 = I$, and so on. If none of the powers $C, C^2, C^3, \ldots, C^{n-1}$ is the identity matrix, then C^n must be. For suppose $C^i \neq I$, $i = 1, \ldots, n$. Then each succeeding generation of sons of sons has a clan different not only from the clan of the man we started with but also from all clans of intermediate ancestors in the male line, given Axiom 8. Thus there must be $n + 1$ clans, in contradiction to our assumption in Axiom 1. So $C^p = I$ for some $1 \leq p \leq n$. Thus any power of C is equal to C to a power between 1 and p, inclusive. The same conclusion obviously can be drawn concerning the powers of W and the powers of any product matrix which is made up of W and C, since any product matrix corresponds to a relation of a fixed kind.

The inverse of a matrix M is defined by

$$MM^{-1} = M^{-1} M = I.$$

For example, C^{-1} is the matrix that specifies for each clan a son may have what clan his father is in. Thus $(C^{-1})_{ij} = C_{ji}$. Suppose C is of order p; that is, p is the lowest integer such that $C^p = I$, where it was shown above that $p \leqslant n$. Since $CC^{p-1} = C^p = I$, the inverse of C can also be written as C^{p-1}; and similarly for W and for any product matrix. Thus C and W and their product matrices can be used to describe the change in clan in moving from a given person to his ancestors as well as to his descendants. Thus to every possible relation of a person in the society there corresponds a matrix which is some product of repetitions of C and W. We will often use M as a general symbol for such a matrix and call it a *relation matrix*.

There is a final very general restriction implied by Axiom 8 together with Axiom 7. If we calculate the product matrices formed by each of two different sequences of W and C matrices, we often find these two product matrices are equal; that is, the ones and zeros appear in the same places. Let us arbitrarily designate the distinct matrices which result from multiplying W and C in all possible orders and combinations by the symbols $A_1, A_2, A_3,$ .... There are exactly n such matrices, as is clear intuitively since one ego has only n essentially different kin relations, one with persons in each of the n clans, and Axiom 8 requires the structure to be homogeneous.

Axiom 7 states that for any pair of clans k and j there is one of the matrices A_i in which the k, j element is unity. A given matrix A_i has only one unity entry in a row k; there must be at least n matrices A_i. Suppose there is an additional one, A_{n+1}. Then in A_{n+1} the kth row must be identical with the kth row in some A_i, $i \leqslant n$. The kth row of A_{n+1} can be used to specify what the clan is of some one kind of relative of a person in clan k, and similarly for A_i. But two persons related in specified ways to a given person also have a specified relation to each other, and here these two persons are in the same clan. It follows that A_i and A_{n+1} must be equal in each row, for otherwise Axiom 8 is violated. In other words, if two of any set of permutation matrices satisfying Axioms 7 and 8 are equal in one element they are identical. There are therefore exactly n distinct permutation matrices generated as products of any W and C matrices for a society with n clans which has properties 1–8.

There is at least one society satisfying all eight axioms for any n: that with $C = I$, and $W_{i,i+1} = 1$, $1 \leqslant i < n$, $W_{n,1} = 1$, and all other $W_{i,j} = 0$. The n distinct matrices are $W, W^2, \ldots, W^{n-1}$, and $W^n = I$. Another obvious possibility is a society with $C' = I$, $W'_{i,i+2} = 1$, $1 \leqslant i < n-1$, $W'_{n-1,1} = 1$, and

$W'_{n,2} = 1$, and all other $W'_{ij} = 0$; again W', $(W')^2$, ..., $(W')^n$ are the distinct matrices. It is intuitively clear that this second society differs from the first only as to the numbering of the clans.

We will use this description of societies by permutation matrices to classify the societies according to what kinds of relatives are allowed to marry. It is natural to say that two societies described by different pairs of C and W matrices are structurally distinct if and only if there is at least one kind of relative who is allowed to marry ego in one society but not the other. Let $M(C, W)$ be any matrix defined as a product of a sequence of powers of C and W. Then two societies have equivalent structures when $M(C, W) = W$ in one if and only if $M(C', W') = W'$ in the other where M has the same form in both. In the example above $M(C, W)$ can be written as W^m. If $W^m = W$, then $m = jn + 1$ for some integer j. But $(W')^n = I$ also; so $(W')^m = W'$ if and only if $W^m = W$.

Very restrictive conditions thus must be satisfied by the C and W matrices. Many fewer than $n!$ $(n!/e)$ pairs of permutation matrices satisfy these restrictions, and even fewer pairs give structurally distinct societies. However, there is no simple way to count the number of distinct societies with properties 1–8. We shall consider only certain general classes of our ideal-type societies. These classes will be defined by the kinds of first-cousin marriages which are allowed in known primitive societies. To simplify the derivations we need to develop a more abstract view of the A_i matrices.

4. Groups and Societies

Consider the n distinct relation matrices A_i generated by a C and a W matrix for a society with n clans which satisfies Axioms 1–8. The product of A_i and A_j is some A_k for any i and j. We also proved above that one of the A_i is the identity matrix and that for each A_i there is an A_j which is its inverse. Matrix multiplication is associative; that is, $A_i(A_jA_k) = (A_iA_j)A_k$, which is another way of saying, for example, that a man's son's grandson is the same person as his grandson's son. Therefore the set of A_i's constitute a representation of an abstract group. A group is specified by its multiplication table, in which the entry in the ith row and jth column is a_k when $a_ia_j = a_k$.

In the appendix to this chapter we go a step further and show that a regular representation of *any* abstract group generated by two elements constitutes a set of A_i describing an allowed society. The number of elements in the group is called its *order*. One way to begin classifying societies would be by examining all instances of abstract groups of different orders. There is a well-organized and highly developed literature on the properties of abstract groups in which all groups of order less than, say, 32 are examined in exhaustive detail. Unfortunately this approach is not fruitful, for there are usually numerous pairs of elements in a group which will generate the group. Thus the same group can be isomorphic with the set of distinct relation matrices for two very different societies.

It is more efficient to begin by finding all pairs of abstract group generators C and W which have specified characteristics for a given group size n. Then one can construct their regular representation from the multiplication table and diagram each society. These calculations are much simpler, because we can treat C and W and their products as elements in an abstract group algebra rather than as explicit matrices. Once the multiplication table showing all possible products of C, W, and the other $n - 2$ distinct elements is derived, one can write down a concrete matrix for each element. The $n \times n$ permutation matrix which sends the standard list of elements (the row or column headings of the multiplication table) into the ith row of the table is a valid matrix representation of a_i. It was proved that there are the same number of clans as elements, and the numbering of the clans is arbitrary; so the matrix representation obtained from the group multiplication table uniquely specifies a society as long as C and W are explicitly identified in the list of elements.

5. First-Cousin Marriages

It is both logically and empirically appropriate to classify kinship systems on the basis of the kinds of first cousins allowed to marry. There are four possible kinds of first cousins, if one is male and one female. These can be described most easily by a family tree, in which the symbolic convention is:

$\triangle$ for male

$\bigcirc$ for female

—   for sibling relation

| for parent-child relation

=   for marriage relation

The arbitrary convention of referring all relations to a male ego will be used throughout. When the girl cousin is the male's father's brother's daughter, the relation graphically is as shown in Fig. 1; this girl cousin is written FBD. When the two siblings who are parents of the first cousins are of the same sex, the latter are termed *parallel* cousins, otherwise *cross* cousins. When the parent of male ego is female, the cousins are said to be *matrilateral* cousins; male ego and the girl are *patrilateral* cousins if it is the father of male ego who is a sibling of one of the girl's parents. In Fig. 1 the boy and girl are patrilateral parallel cousins. When the father of the boy is the brother of the girl's mother and also the mother of the boy is the sister of the girl's father, they are said to be *bilateral* cross cousins.

A fundamental question to be answered is: What kinds of relations can marry in a society specified by given C and W matrices? Begin with Fig. 1. The matrix $C^{-1}C$ specifies in a row i by a unity entry the column for the clan of the girl who is a patrilateral parallel cousin of male ego in clan i. The clan of the boy's father, say j, is specified in the ith row of C^{-1}, the father's brother is in the same clan, and the latter's children are in the clan specified in the jth row of C, that is in the clan specified in the ith row of $(C^{-1}C)$. In this case it is easy to see directly from Axioms 2–5 required for all societies considered here that the boy and girl cannot marry, and $CC^{-1} = I$, as it should.

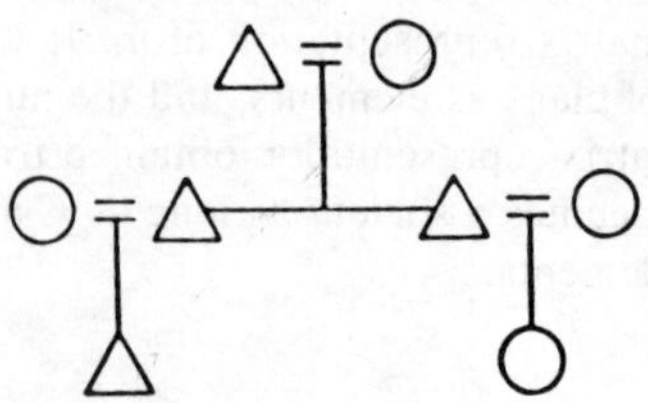

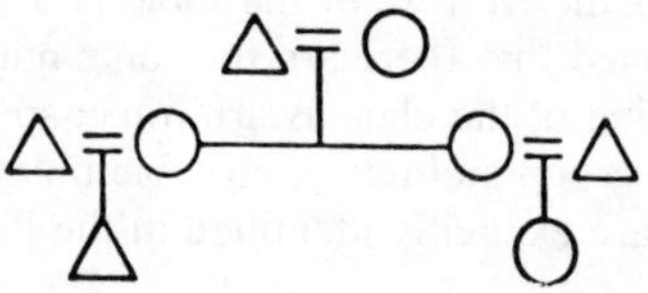

$$M_2 = C^{-1}WW^{-1}C$$

Fig. 1. Patrilateral parallel cousins.

Fig. 2. Matrilateral parallel cousins. M is the relation matrix, in which the girl's clan is specified by the column in which a unity entry appears in the row specified by the boy's clan.

If a boy can marry a girl, her clan must be that indicated by a unity entry in a row of W corresponding to the boy's clan. In symbolic terms, if M is the matrix describing the clan of a girl relation of male ego (for Fig. 1, $M = C^{-1}C$), then

$$M = W$$

is the condition that must be satisfied if the girl is to be a legitimate marriage partner of the boy, whatever his clan. By Axiom 6, $W \neq I$, ever, so in no society satisfying Axioms 1–8 can a boy marry his female patrilateral parallel cousin.

Marriage between matrilateral parallel cousins (see Fig. 2) is also forbidden, since there

$$M = C^{-1}WW^{-1}C$$

or $M = I$, using the associative law. Just as the conversion of husband's to wife's clan is specified by W, the conversion of wife's clan to husband's clan is given by W^{-1}.

The other two kinds of cousins, matrilateral and patrilateral cross cousins, can marry for some W and C matrices. (See Figs. 3 and 4.) Matrilateral cross cousins can marry if and only if

$$W = M = C^{-1}WC.$$

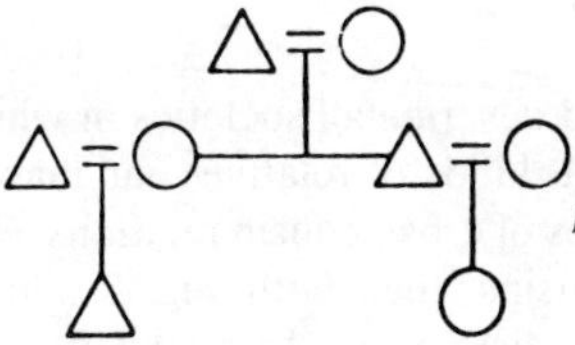

$$M_3 = M_4^{-1}$$

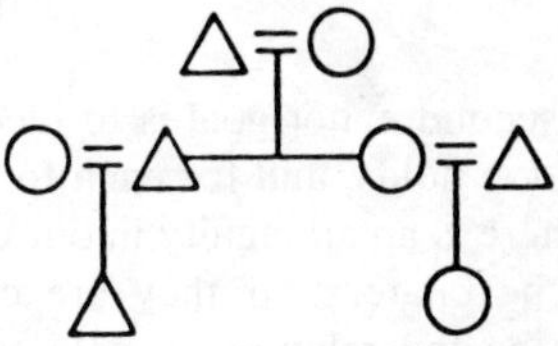

$$M_3 = C^{-1}WC$$

$$M_4 = C^{-1}W^{-1}C$$

Fig. 3. Matrilateral cross cousins.   **Fig. 4.** Patrilateral cross cousins.

If we premultiply both sides of the equation by C, we have $CW = (CC^{-1})WC$, or

$$CW = WC$$

as the necessary and sufficient condition. In other words, the order in which W and C are multiplied does not affect the product matrix; that is, W and C commute. Since all relation matrices are generated as products of W and C, it follows at once that all n distinct matrices A_i for a given society must commute with each other if matrilateral cross-cousin marriage is allowed.

Male ego is allowed to marry many other kinds of relations than matrilateral cross cousins in a society described by a commutative group of matrices, and there are several different subtypes of such societies. The first major goal will be to specify and analyze all such societies. It proves more orderly to define subtypes by simple algebraic conditions on C and W than by what other types of relatives marry.

From Fig. 4 it can be seen that patrilateral cross-cousin marriage is allowed if and only if

$$W = M = C^{-1}W^{-1}C.$$

Again premultiplying both sides of the equation by C, we have

$$CW = W^{-1}C$$

for the necessary and sufficient condition. This can be called the semicommutative condition. An alternative form is obtained by first postmultiplying both sides of this equation by W^{-1}:

$$C(WW^{-1}) = W^{-1}CW^{-1} \quad \text{or} \quad C = W^{-1}CW^{-1},$$

and then premultiplying both sides by W:

$$WC = CW^{-1}.$$

The second major goal is to identify and describe all societies in which this equation holds, and for each to find what kinds of relatives can marry.

There is an ambiguity in our categories of cross-cousin relations. Cousins may be bilateral; if they are cross cousins, then both Fig. 3 and Fig. 4 describe the relation of male ego to his girl cousin. In a society in which bilateral cross cousins may marry, both $WC = CW$ and $CW = W^{-1}C$ must apply. But then

$$W^{-1}C = WC$$

if we combine the two equations. If we postmultiply by C^{-1}, then

$$W = W^{-1}$$

is a necessary condition for bilateral cross-cousin marriage. An alternative form is

$$W^2 = I;$$

that is, the order of W must be two.

Furthermore, bilateral cross cousins cannot exist in a society unless $W^2 = I$. From Fig. 3,

$$M = C^{-1}WC$$

must describe the girl's clan by columns for the boy's clan by rows; but by Fig. 4,

$$M = C^{-1}W^{-1}C$$

must also describe this transformation of clans. A given girl can be in only one clan; so

$$C^{-1}W^{-1}C = C^{-1}WC$$

is required if there is not to be a contradiction. But this can be reduced to the equation $W = W^{-1}$.

On the other hand, in any society there can be bilateral parallel cousins. In both Fig. 1 and Fig. 2 the relation matrix between the boy and girl cousins is just the identity. Bilateral parallel cousins can never marry but can exist in any society; bilateral cross cousins exist only in societies in which $W^2 = I$ and can marry if and only if in addition $WC = CW$.

The condition $W^2 = I$ has a very simple interpretation: there must be an even number of clans in the society, and each clan must swap women as wives with another clan. The basic typology of societies will be

    I. *Bilateral marriage,* in which $W^2 = I$ and $WC = CW$.
   II. *Matrilateral marriage,* where $WC = CW$, but $W^2 \neq I$.
  III. *Patrilateral marriage,* where $WC = CW^{-1}$, but $W^2 \neq I$.
  IV. *Paired clans,* where $W^2 = I$, $WC \neq CW$.
   V. *Residual.*

In the first three names "cross cousin" is omitted, since parallel first cousins can never marry. Only in I and IV societies can there exist bilateral cross cousins. Observe that any two of the three conditions imply the other: for example, if

$$WC = CW^{-1} \quad \text{and} \quad W^2 = I$$

then

$$W = W^{-1} \quad \text{and} \quad WC = CW.$$

Efficient and Viable[1] Organizational Forms

Jacob Marschak   *University of California, Los Angeles*

IF SEVERAL PERSONS AGREE TO FOLLOW A CERTAIN SET OF RULES, WE shall say—just for the purpose of this paper and without quarreling with other existing definitions—that they are members of an *organization*. We shall call this set of rules the *organizational* form or *constitution*.

The rules that the members are supposed to obey deal with their actions, mutual communications, and observations. Typically such a rule (also called "role" by sociologists, I believe) states what a given member *should do* when he receives *information*.

---

[1] *Viability* stems from French *vie* not from Latin *via:* see Webster.

A draft version of the paper, prepared under a contract of the Office of Naval Research with the Cowles Foundation for Research in Economics at Yale University, was presented at a Symposium of the Research Committee on Organization Planning of the American Institute of Industrial Engineers, New York, March, 1958. The paper was expanded and completed when the author was visiting research professor at the Carnegie Institute of Technology, 1958–1959.

Doing means here either:

1. impinging on the world outside of the group of people forming the organization; we call this *action;* or
2. sending to or receiving a message from another member; we call this *internal communication* (and for brevity often omit the word "internal"); or
3. receiving messages from the outside world; we call this *observation.*

For example, an action may consist in adding fuel to a heater, in driving a truck, or in writing to a client. A communication may consist in giving an order to a subordinate, a report to the boss, a speech at the board meeting. An observation may consist in reading a newspaper, a client's letter, the report of a market-research agency.

It is convenient to extend the term "communication with another member" to "communication with one's own memory": committing a received message to one's memory ("filing"), or digging out past information. A cross section of what is being done within an organization during a given period of time is schematically represented by a matrix (Table 1) which may clarify the logic of our concepts.

Table 1

A Matrix of Actions, Observations, and Internal Communications

Receiver

		0	1	2	
	0	(0, 0)	(0, 1)	(0, 2)	· · ·
	1	(1, 0)	(1, 1)	(1, 2)	
Sender	2	(2, 0)	(2, 1)	(2, 2)	
	·				
	·				
	·				

The cell (1, 2) would be filled with the description of messages sent by member 1 to member 2; the cell (2, 1) would contain messages in the opposite direction. The row and the column marked "zero" represent the outside world; hence the observations being made by member 1 would be entered in the cell (0, 1), and the actions of member 1 (interpreted as "messages to the outside world") would be entered in

(1, 0). Each diagonal cell—(1, 1), (2, 2) . . . —is filled with communications between a member and his memory; with the exception of the cell (0, 0), which naturally summarizes all those external events that do not impinge upon, nor in any way reflect, the organization's doings.

In general, an organization member acts or communicates or observes in a given period of time in response to some "message" that he has received from the outside world or from a member (possibly himself), in the preceding period(s). As we have indicated at the beginning, the organizational form consists of rules that prescribe "who should do what in response to what information?" Schematically, the rules state that if the cells of the matrix in Table 1 had certain contents during a given week, they should be filled in a certain fashion in the next week.

The workings of an organization might be better understood if, instead of the usual "organizational chart," one could have the description—if only very rough—of "who does what in response to what information?"

A description of the rules of action and communication that are in actual use in a given organization (though possibly not the officially proclaimed ones) would also help to *improve* them. The set of rules can be good, less good, bad. One set of rules is better—or *more efficient*—than another if, *on the average,* it is more conducive to achieving certain *goals.*

Let us discuss in more detail this evaluation of rules—and hence of organization forms—according to their efficiency. As so often, it helps to begin with a simple, limiting case: the one-man organization, the rules for a single decision-maker. They prescribe what he shall do in response to a given information. One rule is more efficient than another if, *on the average,* it is more likely to further the decision-maker's goals.

I have just said *"on the average"* because the outcome of a person's doings depends, of course, on the chance events of the outside world, and not only on his manner of acting. No soldier or farmer claims the gift of prophecy. Every businessman knows that business involves gambling. He acts on the basis of more-or-less well-founded ideas of how likely it is that the demand for his product will rise or fall; or how likely an invention is to succeed or to fail; and so on. In short, he acts on the basis of some approximate knowledge of, or some hunches about, the probabilities of possible events. More or less consciously he estimates, in effect, the *probability* with which a given decision of his will lead to one result rather than to another.

The decision-maker cannot control the external events, such as the public's demand in a widely competitive market, or the government policies that lead to inflation or deflation; he can only estimate the probabilities of such events. But he can control his own decisions. He chooses, from among several decisions open to him, that decision which—measured on his goals—leads, on the average, to better (or, at least, not worse) results than other possible decisions. One calls such decisions good, or more technically, *optimal*, decisions (avoiding the term "best decision," since two decisions may be equally good); or *efficient* decisions. We shall use *decision* and *action* interchangeably.

The description just given presupposes the simple, but rather exceptional case of *"one-shot decisions"*: the case when no consideration is given to the fact that today's decision may affect the outcome of tomorrow's decision. Yet little thought suffices to extend the concept of efficient decisions also to the more interesting, more usual, and more general case when the phrase "sufficient unto the day is the evil thereof" is not valid. In this more general case one makes "decisions about future decisions," one chooses "maxims of behavior," also called "sequential decisions," strategies, or, in our terminology, *decision rules*. Faced with an unknown sequence of future events, the decision-maker chooses not only what to do today, but also (more or less roughly) how to respond to each of the various possible events of tomorrow and of the day after, and of a still later day. In this choice he is guided by some (more-or-less vague, more-or-less conscious) estimates of probabilities; so that, again, an efficient decision rule is one that, on the average, produces good results, in terms of the decision-maker's goals.

Clearly this is an idealized picture, a *norm*, a piece of logic not of psychology. To prefer efficiency to inefficiency is itself a norm. Is it therefore a useless exercise? I don't think so. Psychologists tell us how often, and by what kind of people, certain logical—or, for that matter, arithmetical—errors are made; this does not make arithmetic and logic useless. In fact, we do try to teach children arithmetic. We are concerned when our students lack logic. And, I suppose, teachers of Business or of Miliary Art are rather anxious to inculcate the ability of efficient decision.

Our picture of efficient decision-making is unpsychological in another important way; it is not true that a man has consistent goals, or values (on which to measure efficiency). It is an idealization to say that a businessman (as such) tries to make, on the average, a large profit, and that the military man tries to act so as to make victory as probable as possible. Again, I believe this idealization is not useless (measured on the goals of those who try to improve the workings of businessmen or of generals).

We now return to the general case, the several-man organization. The extension to this case of the concept of decision rules just defined for the special case, the one-man organization, is obvious: the "rule" is replaced by a "set of rules" (one for each member); and the concept of internal communication is widened to the scope given it at the very beginning of the paper. It is the concept of the *goals* (or values) that seems to present difficulties. If, psychologically, even a single man may lack consistency of values, what to say of a group of several?

Nonetheless, it is possible to evaluate the efficiency of an organizational form, for a *given* goal. A business concern may be inefficient in profit-making but efficient in making its executives love each other. Once the goal is stated, the same logical tools apply. If the goal is defined by an "aspiration level" we can say that the decision's outcome has two values: 0 if "failure" (below the aspiration level); 1 if "success" (above the aspiration level); and the *average* value of the outcome = (1 × Probability of success) + (0 × Probability of failure) = Probability of success.

One empirically useful approach is to estimate the efficiency of an organizational form by taking as the goal a high *chance of survival*. A census of existing organizational forms in some centuries-old field (e.g., that of religious organizations, or of small handicraft, or of family farming), may confirm that certain rules of action and communication, in this particular field, are more viable than others; they have, in the anthropologists' language, a higher "survival value." Such empirical confirmation on evolutionary grounds is, however, true only if one has the right to assume that the environment (that is, the probability distribution of the relevant external conditions) has not changed significantly in the course of time.

Whether the investigator chooses viability or some other goal as the criterion to compare the efficiency of organizational forms in a given field of activity, this goal need not coincide with the goals of any of the members of the organization. Such coincidence is improbable, if only because the individual goals are, in general, not identical among themselves.

This independence of the organizational goal (as chosen by the investigator) from the individual goals does not, by any means, make the efficiency judgments meaningless. It is certainly possible to judge the efficiency of a business corporation in terms, say, of its aggregate profits over the next two generations, without postulating this to be the goal of any of the executives or stockholders. Nor does the frequent praise of the efficiency of the Roman Catholic Church necessarily imply that it has served well the individual aims of all its popes, bishops, and laity.

This raises the problem of *incentives*. Organization rules can be devised in such a way that, if every member pursues his own goal, the goal of the organization is served. This is exemplified in practice by bonuses to executives and the promise of loot to besieging soldiers; and in theory, by the (idealized) model of the *laissez-faire* economy. And there exist, of course, also negative incentives (punishments).

I shall have to leave the problem of incentives aside. In what follows, we shall not be concerned with individual goals. If they still lurk in your mind, inhibiting our understanding of each other, you may make the assumption (actually unnecessary for what follows) that the members of the business organization I am going to discuss are partners sharing the profits equally, or that some perfect system of incentives is operating. In short, you may think of a *team*. My main purpose is to illustrate how various organizational forms can be compared, and an optimal one chosen, given a goal.

Suppose a shipbuilding firm has *two docks:* an old one and a new, mechanized one. The former has higher operational costs (mainly labor) and the difference depends on the dockworkers' wage rates, assumed to be the same in both docks. Suppose further the firm has *two sales representatives*, each in a different market. We shall call the two markets East and West. Each representative receives *price* offers (orders for ships) in his market: this is his piece of information. The production manager on the other hand, knows the current wage rate and hence the production *costs*. Suppose the operational costs per ship are

> in the new dock: 20
> in the old dock: 35

(we neglect capital charges and other non-operational, fixed costs as they must be paid in any case and therefore cannot affect the choice of a decision). Suppose the *prices* offered by a client to a salesman are

> in the East: 29
> in the West: 21.

Clearly if the production manager and the two sales representatives sit in conference they will take the following decision as the best one: use the new dock for the Eastern client (making a profit of $29 - 20 = 9$), reject the Western offer, leave the old dock idle. Instead of having a conference, they might also reach this same decision by each salesman's first reporting the local price to the production manager and then receiving from him the instruction to accept or reject the offer.

But conferences and other forms of extensive *communications take time and money*, especially in the form of salaries to busy executives. We ask therefore: Is it always best to "centralize" all decisions, i.e., base them on *all available information* collected at some conference or headquarters? Under what circumstances is such centralization justified? When is it, on the contrary, more economical to let the local, or the specialized, persons go ahead on the basis of their own *limited information* even if this may involve occasional risks? And what should this limited information be? Should, in our example, a sales representative be constantly informed of the fluctuations in production cost, though not of the fluctuations in markets other than his own? Or could one leave him without even the cost information? Furthermore, each type of information can be used in a variety of ways, applying different *rules of action*. For example, if each salesman knows the production costs in both docks and has the power to accept or reject offers in ignorance of prices in markets other than his own, at what prices should he accept offers, so as to minimize the risk of forcing the firm into the use of the old dock at too small a profit or even at a loss?

In spite of its artificial simplicity, our example may throw light on a fairly large class of practical problems. These arise whenever several decision-makers share the same limited facilities, and the unit cost to the firm increases with output. Instead of two docks, one might think of several plants; or one can replace the "new dock" by "operations during the normal working day of the wage earners," and the "old dock" by "overtime work at extra pay." Also, instead of "local prices" one might think, for products like bread, of "expected local demand" (as with the sales organization of bakeries, a problem that has been studied by C. B. McGuire[2] at the Cowles Foundation, Yale University, and that has in part suggested the example I use here). Thus, many aspects of our "shipyard" example carry over into other fields.[3]

To return to our problem: We want to find, for each system of com-

[2] Mr. McGuire has also helped to revise the final version of this paper.

[3] In collaboration with Roy Radner, now at the University of California, the author has attempted to classify various models of teams on the basis of their mathematical properties. Such models are relevant to many aspects of business, such as production, promotion of sales, speculation, etc. A book on the economic theory of teams is being prepared. See also the author's "Elements for a Theory of Teams" in *Management Science*, 1, No. 2 (January, 1955); and "Towards an Economic Theory of Organization and Information" in *Decision Processes* (Thrall, Coombs, and Davis, eds.), Wiley, New York, 1954.

munications, an optimal set of rules of action for the sales representatives, i.e., that set of rules of action which results in the highest average profit attainable with this communication system. We may call this the *maximum average gross profit*. Deducting the average communication cost (i.e., mainly the executives' salaries chargeable to communications) necessary to maintain and operate the particular communication system, one obtains the *maximum average net profit* of the organizational form that is characterized by the communication system.

If, for example, the average profit of a "centralized" decision system is only slightly higher than that of some "decentralized" system (assuming that appropriate optimal rules of action are used in each case), then the centralized system will have to be rejected, unless the added communication costs that it requires are also slight.

To illustrate, assume that the operational costs in the two docks (20 and 35, respectively) are constant; it is only the prices offered that vary. To figure out in advance the best rules of action, one needs to have an idea of the likely price situations. For simplicity, assume that the prices in the two markets obey the law of chance of Table 2.

Table 2

Probability Distribution of Prices Offered in Two Markets

| | | East | | |
		High ($= 39$)	Low ($= 21$)	Total probability
West	High ($= 31$)	.4	.1	.5
	Low ($= 29$)	.1	.4	.5
	Total probability	.5	.5	1.0

	Average price	Price spread
East	30	18
West	30	2
Correlation coefficient $= .6$		

That is, with probability .4 both prices are high; with probability .4 they are both low; with probability .1 the Eastern price is high and the Western low; finally, with probability .1 the price is high in the West and low in the East. (Thus markets are supposed to be more likely to move in the same than in opposite directions.) We have further supposed that while the average price is the same ($=30$) in both markets, the Eastern price jumps more violently: from the "low" of 21 to the "high" of 39; whereas the Western "low" is 29 and its "high" is 31 (no intermediate prices in any market; this simplifies the arithmetic).

Under the centralized system the head office will clearly choose the following rule as optimal: a ship will be built in the new dock, for the Eastern client if his price is high, for the Western client if the Eastern price is low; the old dock will lie idle (at least as long as the assumed costs remain unchanged). This rule and the resulting profits are shown thus:

Table 3
Optimal Decision Rule in a Centralized Firm

Prices: East	West	Offer Accepted	Profit	Probability
39	31	East	$39 - 20 = 19$	.4
39	29	East	$39 - 20 = 19$	.1
21	31	West	$31 - 20 = 11$	.1
21	29	West	$29 - 20 = 9$	.4

Average Profit: 14.2

The average profit $= (19)(.4) + (19)(.1) + (11)(.1) + (9)(.4) = 14.2$. It is easy to see that any other rule, under a centralized system, will yield a lower average profit.

Now, assuming the same cost and price conditions, consider the following form of a *"decentralized"* system: each sales representative accepts or rejects local offers in ignorance of the price in the other market. Clearly there are four possible rules for each sales representative: (1) accept only if the price offered to you is high; (2) accept only if that price is low (a paradoxical yet reasonable rule, as we shall see!); (3) accept at either price; (4) never accept—i.e., go fishing. Hence there are $4 \times 4 = 16$ possible pairs of rules for the pair of salesmen. For each pair of rules one can compute, as before, the average profit.

It may seem a *paradox*, but the following pair of rules turns out to be optimal: the Eastern salesman should accept offers at the high price only; but the Westerner should accept offers *at the low price only*.

With these rules, the average profit is $(19)(.4) + (13)(.1) + (0)(.1) + (9)(.4) = 12.5$, computed as follows:

Table 4

Optimal Decision Rule in a Decentralized Firm

| Prices: | | Offer | | |
East	West	Accepted	Profit	Probability
39	31	East	$39 - 20 = 19$	.4
39	29	East and West	$39 + 29 - 35 - 20 = 13$	.1
21	31	None	0	.1
21	29	West	$29 - 20 = 9$	.4

Average Profit: 12.5

Similar computations show that the next-best pair of rules is for the Easterner to accept at high prices only and for the Westerner to accept in any case (average profit $= 12$). The rule that ranks third (with average profit $= 10$) is: either the East or the West agency should close shop, the other should accept an offer at any price. The ranking of such rules would turn out to be a different one if I had not purposely chosen numbers that lead to a "paradox"—i.e., to a correct solution that may not seem right at first sight. It serves to illustrate the need for some formal thinking and reckoning. The solution becomes plausible if you remember that under our assumption a low Western price of 29 is likely (with odds as high as 4:1) to be accompanied by a still lower Eastern price of 21; while a high Western price of 31 is likely (with high odds again) to be accompanied by a still higher Eastern price of 39. This justifies, on the average, the Westerner's acceptance of a low-price offer to insure that the efficient dock will be used, and his rejection of a high-price offer to diminish the risk of forcing the firm into using the second, inefficient dock at a loss.

We thus find that the "decentralized" system (as defined) yields, under the best rules, an average profit that is 1.7 ($= 14.2 - 12.5$) below the highest average profit attainable under the "centralized" system. Therefore, if the additional *communication* cost implied in the centralized system exceeds 1.7, we shall reject it; if it is less than 1.7, we accept centralization.

The answer to every problem depends on the "givens" of the problem. In every team problem, the "givens" are: (1) the *"payoff func-*

tion," i.e., the formula that shows how profit depends on the decisions (in our case the decisions to accept or reject an offer) and on the external states (in our case the two prices) as shown, for example, in the "profit" column of my two tables; (2) the *probability function* which states the probabilities with which the various possible external states are likely to occur; and (3) the *organization cost function* which attaches a cost to each of the organizational forms under consideration.

With regard to the *payoff function,* one can say, in general, that more communication is justified when the payoff function involves "*complementarity*" between the members' actions, in the following sense: the effect of one member's action depends on what his colleague is doing. This was certainly so in our example, because of the high production cost in the old dock. If the two docks were equally efficient the need for communication and, hence, the advantage of centralization would be smaller. There is a high complementarity, and therefore strong need for communication, among the stationmasters of a railroad; but, I presume, little complementarity between the branch managers of Sears Roebuck.

Another property of the payoff function which, if present, calls for communication is the existence of "*multiple optima.*" It is equally good for all to drive on the right side of the road, or for all to drive on the left side (as they do in England); but someone has to play the role of a *coordinator.* Time-schedules for group work are often of the same nature; we needed an organizer to have all participants of this symposium to come to this place at this time, although some other place and time might be equally good.

In our case, I had mentioned a pair of rules of action under which one of the two salesmen—*regardless of which*—should accept all offers (at least as long as production costs remained as they were), while the other should not accept any. This pair of rules ranked third, but it would become an optimal one under different numerical assumptions. But then there would be actually two pairs of rules to choose between: either the Westerner or the Easterner should be the one always to accept offers. Thus a coordinator is needed because there are two equally good solutions.

We have also seen how the *probability distribution* of non-controlled events (prices, in our case) affects the solution. Our "paradoxical" solution was due to a high correlation between the two prices and to the fact that one of them had a higher spread or variance than the other. Common sense can add a few more guesses about the way in which the nature of the probability distribution affects the choice between various forms of communication. I am willing to pay a lot for information on future prices of stocks, not of bonds; for the higher the *variability* of a thing, the more useful it is to learn about its state. Further, I am not willing to pay much for special information about the price of a stock, if it is strongly *correlated* with some other price which I know anyhow.

To obtain other useful theorems about the way in which the payoff function and the probability distribution may affect the ranking of various organizational forms, one has to dig deeper, gathering factual knowledge about live organizations (see my earlier remarks on the deficiency of mere "organization charts") and interpreting it logically and mathematically.

One important gap has to be closed: our ignorance of the *communication costs*. We need measurements of the executives' efficiency in using their time—a subject on which, I think, psychologists are working. What we need is something corresponding to, but more appropriate than the I.Q. We need a special "E.Q." (executive quotient). The I.Q. scale is essentially nothing but the statistical distribution of a large sample of American children with respect to their performance of certain tasks. For example, "I.Q. $= 100$" is a set of tasks that fifty percent of all children can perform (the "median" performance). We need, similarly, a statistical distribution of American executive abilities, as measured by performance truly relevant to efficient communication and decision-making.

On Figure 1, the three *given* functions—the probability function, the payoff function, and the organizational cost function—are represented by boxes: they are "operators" transforming "inputs" into "outputs" as indicated by arrows. These three functions, or operators, are *given*; that is, they are not controlled by the organizer. But two other operators (boxes)—the information rule and the action rule— are *chosen* by him, rather than given to him; the investigator can compare them with other rules for greater or smaller efficiency. Each input or output is an element of some set, represented by a circle. For example, a particular "external state" is operated upon in three places: first, together with a particular "action" it determines the particular gross payoff, depending on the payoff function; second, the external state has its probability depending on the given probability function; third, depending on the chosen information rule, the external state will result in a given state of information. The information rule and the action rule can be chosen each out of a set of such rules— represented by dotted circles (thus the two boxes drawn are typical only of other elements of the sets of possible rules of action and information). The two rules are chosen so as to make the *net average*

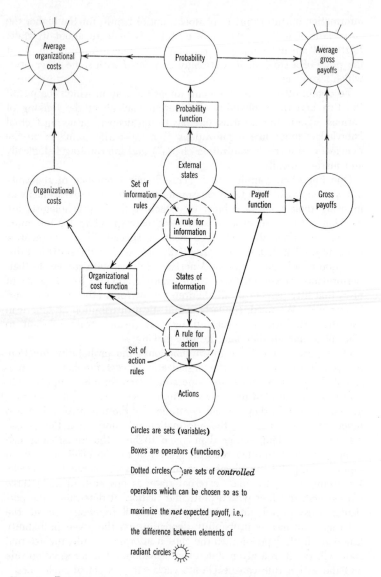

Figure 1.   Determination of average gross payoff and average organizational costs.

payoff as high as possible; it is the difference between *average gross payoff* and *average organization cost;* the circles representing these two variables (sets) are distinguished by an aura to emphasize that they are "goal" variables, in the light of which the efficiency of rules is judged.

There is no need here to expand on the differences between a "model" and the "reality," and on the usefulness of models for both understanding and improving practical solutions. My "shipyard" model is easily made more realistic and more complicated. Its solutions would then transgress simple arithmetic, needed for a presentation like this one, and call for more powerful mathematics and machines. (In fact, the "bakery" problem mentioned above turns out to be one in linear programming.)[4] Even then, the main service one can expect from organization models is to clarify the general logical lines of a practical problem. This clears the ground for the more subtle aspects of the practical problem that escape formalization and call for so-called intuition judgment. Even the best biochemist will not replace a good restaurant chef. Yet biochemical analysis has, in fact, improved our food.

[4] For a different problem, see Roy Radner, "The Application of Linear Programming to Team Decision Problems," *Management Science,* 5, No. 2 (January, 1959).

Party Legislative Representation
as a Function of Election Results*

James G. March *University of California, Irvine*

This article is the report on a study of the relationship between votes and legislative representation in England and the United States. The author describes a process by which the representativeness of democratic institutions may be evaluated.

James G. March is Associate Professor in the Graduate School of Industrial Administration at the Carnegie Institute of Technology.

T HE RELATIONSHIP between election results (i.e., the distribution of votes received by the several parties) and seats gained in the legislative body has long concerned normative theorists of political systems. Patently, one of the foundations of representative democracy is the relationship between votes and seats. Recently, the normative discussion appears to have focused primarily on the arguments for and against strict proportional representation and on the methods by which a strictly proportional allocation of seats can be made with minimum sacrifice to other goals.[1] More generally the object of a normative theorist is to define an optimum method for transforming voting results into a division of legislative seats, the optimality of any system being of course relative to a specified set of goals.

Despite the history of interest in the normative aspects of representation functions, the empirical study of such functions has been relatively neglected in the United States until very recently. Specifically, we can pose the question: What is the relationship between voting results and legislative representation in a two-party, single-member constituency, plurality election system? In his works on electoral prediction, Bean came close to studying this relationship. For example, he considered the relationship between party vote for

* The work on which this paper is based was done in large part at the Center for Advanced Study in the Behavioral Sciences. In addition to the usual published sources of election statistics, the writer has had the advantage of access to unpublished data collected by Robert A. Dahl, Cortez A. M. Ewing, and V. O. Key, Jr., for which grateful acknowledgement is made. He also wishes to acknowledge helpful comments on the manuscript by James S. Coleman and Herbert McClosky and the computational assistance of Susan F. March.

[1] Two of the classics are G. H. Hallett, Jr., *Proportional Representation* (New York, 1926) and F. A. Hermens, *Democracy or Anarchy?* (Notre Dame, 1941). See also, Duncan Black, "Some Theoretical Schemes of Proportional Representation," *Canadian Journal of Economics and Political Science*, Vol. 15, pp. 334-343 (Aug., 1949).

President and seats gained by a party in the House of Representatives.[2] But, at least as far as could be determined, he never published any results relating the aggregate vote for Congress with the distribution of seats in the House. The various commercial organizations that engage in public opinion polling and the prediction of election results in the United States have made predictions regarding the outcome of congressional elections that may (or may not) have been based on calculations of the aggregate distribution of votes to be cast, but again no published treatment of the relationship could be found. Ewing made a detailed study of the results of Congressional elections over a period of twenty-five elections beginning in 1896 and reached a number of conclusions about the character of the relationship between votes and seats.[3] For the present it is enough to note that although he computed a substantial number of statistics which can be pieced together into an approximation, Ewing never focused his attention on an explicit statement of the relationship examined here. Moos in his study of voting for Congress did not consider this question.[4]

Schattschneider in his early work presented an approximate table for relating votes to seats. He stated that with less than 25 per cent of the vote a party would receive a negligible number of seats, that with 35 per cent of the vote it would receive about 15 per cent of the seats, and that 45 per cent of the vote would produce victories in 40 per cent of the seats.[5] Since Schattschneider does not distinguish one party from another, appropriate values above 50 per cent can be exhibited by symmetry.

Recently Dahl has examined the nature of the relationship between seats and votes in the United States.[6] He treated as variables the Democratic proportion of the total two-party vote for the House of Representatives and the Democratic proportion of the total two-party seats in the House and analyzed the data over the period 1928-1954. He found that the relationship between votes and seats was linear (the fit of a linear regression line was exceptionally good) in the range represented by the data. So long as the Democrats gained between .40 and .60 of the two-party vote, the Democratic proportion of seats in the House could be closely approximated by the linear equation

$$y = 2.5x - .7 \tag{1}$$

where y is the proportion of seats won and x is the proportion of votes. Thus, if the Democratic Party received 45 per cent of the total two-party

[2] Louis H. Bean, *How To Predict Elections* (New York, 1948), p. 67.

[3] Cortez A. M. Ewing, *Congressional Elections, 1896-1944* (Norman, 1947).

[4] Malcolm Moos, *Politics, Presidents and Coattails* (Baltimore, 1952).

[5] E. E. Schattschneider, *Party Government* (New York, 1942), pp. 74-75.

[6] Robert A. Dahl, *A Preface to Democratic Theory* (Chicago, 1956), p. 148.

vote for Congress, Democratic candidates would win in approximately 42.5 per cent of the constituencies; if the Democrats received 55 per cent of the vote, they would gain about 67.5 per cent of the seats.

From equation (1) it follows that the equation for the Republican proportion of seats as a function of proportion of votes was

$$y = 2.5x - .8. \tag{2}$$

It will be noted (a) that the equations differ (i.e., that in this sense the electoral system did not treat the parties identically) and (b) that gains or losses in a party's share of the vote were magnified by a factor of 2.5 when they were translated into a distribution of seats.

VOTES AND SEATS

With the exceptions of Schattschneider and Dahl, American students of elections have not attempted to explore in detail the relationship between aggregate votes and seats, although this problem has received considerable professional and popular attention in England. Stimulated by the resurrection in the *Economist*[7] of a "law" apparently first cited by J. P. Smith in testimony before a Royal Commission on Systems of Elections in 1909[8], a number of British scholars have made studies of the votes-seats relationship. Specifically, the focus has been on testing the validity of the following proposition: if the ratio of aggregate votes gained in contested constituencies by the two parties be cubed, the resulting ratio will equal the ratio of contested seats won by the two parties. Strictly speaking, Smith made a less powerful proposition, but current interest has been turned to the equality specified above, which has come to be known as "the cube law."

Since election results are typically given in terms of percentages and the Dahl regression coefficients reflect a specification of a relationship between the proportion of seats and the proportion of votes, it is somewhat awkward to deal with the cube law in terms of ratios as is done in its statement by Smith and most of his discussants. Consequently, it will be transformed here[9] into an equation where, as before, x is the proportion of aggregate votes cast for, and y the proportion of seats won by a given party. The cube law becomes in those terms

[7] "Electoral Facts," *Economist*, Vol. 158, pp. 5-7 (Jan. 7, 1950).

[8] A verbatim report of the key testimony by Smith is quoted in M. G. Kendall and A. Stuart, "The Law of Cubic Proportions in Election Results," *British Journal of Sociology*, Vol. 1, pp. 183-197 (Sept., 1950), at pp. 183-184.

[9] By solving the equation $\left(\dfrac{y}{1-y}\right) = \left(\dfrac{x}{1-x}\right)^3$ for y.

$$y = \frac{x^3}{3x^2 - 3x + 1}.$$ (3)

The graph of the cube law is indicated in Figure 1. Note that the cube law, unlike Dahl's computed regression line, but like Schattschneider's proportions, is the same for both parties. Also unlike the linear regression line, equation (3) has the *a priori* reasonable feature that it passes through the points (0,0) and (1,1).

FIGURE I: THE CUBE LAW

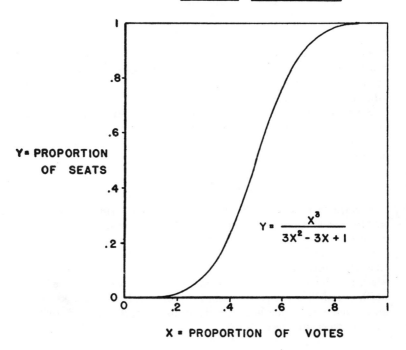

Y = PROPORTION OF SEATS

X = PROPORTION OF VOTES

$$Y = \frac{X^3}{3X^2 - 3X + 1}$$

A striking characteristic of the cubic for present purposes is the fact that it is very nearly linear for a range of values of x from .40 to .60. In that range the cube law can be closely approximated by the first-order equation

$$y = 2.808x - .904.$$ (4)

TABLE 1

COMPARISON OF CUBE LAW AND LINEAR APPROXIMATION FOR x VALUES FROM
.40 TO .50

x	x^3 $3x^2 - 3x + 1$	$2.808x - .904$
.40	.229	.219
.41	.251	.247
.42	.275	.275
.43	.300	.303
.44	.326	.332
.45	.354	.360
.46	.382	.388
.47	.412	.416
.48	.440	.444
.49	.471	.472
.50	.500	.500

Table 1 shows values of y for different values of x (from .40 to .50) computed from the cube law and from the linear approximation. Since both (3) and (4) are symmetric around the point (.5, .5), the comparison for values of x from .50 to .60 is unnecessary.

Since the differences between the cubic and the linear approximation are so slight it will be legitimate to treat them as substantially interchangeable below where it is more convenient to make tests of hypotheses using the linear form rather than the cube law itself.

THE FIT OF THE CUBE LAW

Granted that the cube law has some admirable mathematical and/or aesthetic qualities, its significance lies not in such attributes but rather in the fact that it appears to conform to observed results in a number of countries once the results from uncontested constituencies are eliminated. Kendall and Stuart,[10] Butler,[11] and Cadart[12] have all explored in detail the extent to which British election results fit the model in the five elections since 1935 in which essentially a two-party system has prevailed. If one computes a least squares linear regression line from the British data, the equation (with respect to Conservative seats) is

---

[10] *Ibid.*; M. G. Kendall and A. Stuart, "La Loi du Cube dans les Elections Britanniques," *Revue Francaise de Science Politique,* Vol. 2, pp. 270-276 (April-June, 1952).

[11] D. E. Butler, *The British General Election of 1951* (London, 1952); D. E. Butler, *The Electoral System in Britain, 1918-1951* (Oxford, 1953); D. E. Butler, "An Examination of the Results," in H. G. Nicholas, *The British General Election of 1950* (London, 1951), pp. 306-333. See also Appendices III and IV in R. B. McCallum and Alison Readman, *The British General Election of 1945* (London, 1947) for which the authors give major credit to Butler.

[12] Jacques Cadart, "Les Elections Generales du 26 Mai 1955 en Grande-Bretagne," *"Revue Francaise de Science Politique,* Vol. 5, pp. 799-817 (Oct.-Dec., 1955).

$$y = 2.77x - .87. \tag{5}$$

This is, of course, extraordinarily close to the linear approximation to the cube law. Although some restraint in interpretation is necessary in the light of the small number of elections involved (five), the evidence of the last five British elections is not consistent with rejecting the cube law as an empirical regularity. This fact has been partly obscured by the tendency of British writers to devote a substantial amount of time to explaining minor deviations from the law and implicitly to impose a goodness-of-fit criterion that seems to the present writer inordinately severe. Similarly, the *Economist* reports a close congruence between the law and the results in recent elections in New Zealand.[13]

TABLE 2

COMPARISON OF ACTUAL SEATS WON BY THE DEMOCRATS IN THE HOUSE OF
REPRESENTATIVES, 1928-1954, AND OUTCOME PREDICTED BY THE CUBE LAW

Year	Cube Law	Actual Results
1928	156	166
1930	211	215
1932	298	313
1934	284	315
1936	305	325
1938	240	258
1940	251	261
1942	217	223
1944	240	243
1946	189	188
1948	263	263
1950	239	235
1952	212	213
1954	254	232

Curiously, in the light of the relatively long period of British concern with the cube law, the fit of data from United States elections has not been tested against such predictions. Yet, it would appear from a casual comparison of equations (1) and (4) that the results of American elections may be quite consistent with the cube law. Moreover, both Schattschneider's formulation of the relationship cited above and Ewing's observations concerning the relationship in eastern states[14] bear a close resemblance to the cube law equation. To explore the American experience in detail the fourteen elections from 1928 to 1954 were considered, this being the same period covered by the Dahl analysis. If we apply the cube law to aggregate votes gained in contested constituencies to determine the number of contested seats won by the Democrats and add to the figure thus obtained the number of uncontested

[13] "Electoral Facts," *op. cit.*
[14] Ewing, *op. cit.*, pp. 85, 101.

seats won by the Democrats, we have an estimate of the number of seats the Democrats would have gained if the cube law operated exactly. Table 2 compares such estimates with the actual results. The mean absolute difference between the cube law figure and the actual outcome is 10.4 seats in a legislative body of 435 seats. Whether one considers this error large or small depends somewhat on one's expectations, but it might be instructive to attempt to specify other non-obvious propositions concerning the American political system with as much apparent validity. (Since this paper was written, the 1956 election has provided another test of the cube law. In that election the cube law predicted the Democrats would win 231 seats. They actually won 234 seats.)

Using the data on contested seats only over the 1928-1954 period, one can make a more rigorous comparison of the actual results with the cube law by comparing their linear regression coefficients.[15] The regression line computed from the data is defined by

$$y = 3.331x - 1.143. \tag{6}$$

In Figure 2 the scatter diagram of the fourteen elections is shown along with the computed regression line and the linear approximation to the cubic.[16]

---

[15] Although the regression coefficients are reported in the general form $y = a + bx + \varepsilon$, the actual computations used estimated them for the form $y = a + b (x - \bar{x}) + \varepsilon$. This form has the advantage of making the estimates of the coefficients independent and thus facilitates analysis. The results have been translated back to the more common form simply for purposes of presentation.

[16] The null hypothesis tested is that the data come from a population in which the linear approximation to the cubic (4) holds. The test is an F-test. Since we are somewhat more concerned about rejecting it when it is true than is typical in research, we set the significance level at .10. (Actually, we should like to make the significance level depend on both the power of the test and our evaluations of the "costs" of making the two types of errors, but the problems of statistical decision theory involved in such a procedure have not been sufficiently clarified to warrant its adoption here. As an alternative some data on the power of the test and its implications are presented below.) The computed value for F is not consistent with the null hypothesis. From this we conclude that the data on elections to the House of Representatives are not consistent with the cube law hypothesis.

To explain why such apparently small differences yield a result of statistical significance, we examine the power of the F-test in this case. The power of a test specifies the probability of rejecting the null hypothesis when it is in fact false (i.e., the probability of not making a Type II error). In general, the power of a given test depends on the significance level chosen, the sample size, the population variance, and the magnitude of the error represented by the null hypothesis. In the present case, the significance level is fixed at .10, the sample size is 14, and the populations variance can be estimated from the data. Consequently, we can specify for any ordered pair of coefficients (a, b) the probability of our rejecting the null hypothesis (a_0, b_0) when in fact the true values are a and b. Estimation of the power of the test is based on charts provided in E. S. Pearson and H. O. Hartley, "Charts of the Power Function for Analysis of Variance Tests, Derived from the Non-central F-Distribution," *Biometrika*, Vol. 38, pp. 112-130 (June, 1951) and on computational forms in J. L. Hodges, Jr., "On the Non-central Beta Distribution," *Annals of Mathematical Statistics*, Vol. 26, pp. 648-653 (Dec., 1955). I am indebted to Professor I. Richard Savage for his help on this problem.

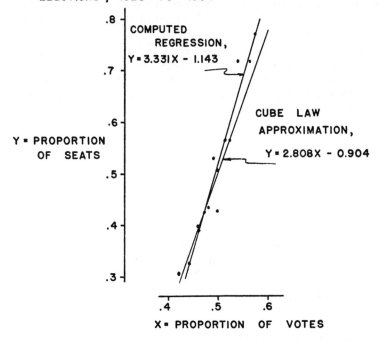

FIGURE 2

OBSERVED RELATIONSHIP BETWEEN DEMOCRATIC PRO-
PORTION OF AGGREGATE TWO-PARTY VOTE AND
DEMOCRATIC PROPORTION OF TWO-PARTY SEATS IN
CONTESTED CONSTITUENCIES, U.S. CONGRESSIONAL
ELECTIONS, 1928 TO 1954

COMPUTED REGRESSION, $Y = 3.331X - 1.143$

CUBE LAW APPROXIMATION, $Y = 2.808X - 0.904$

Y = PROPORTION OF SEATS

X = PROPORTION OF VOTES

In Figure 3 the results of such an investigation are presented. The ellipse represents a probability of .90 of not accepting the null hypothesis when it is false. For any pair of coefficients (a, b) outside the ellipse the probability of accepting the cube law when a and b are the true coefficients is less than .10. The extraordinary power of the F-test indicated by this figure stems primarily from the extremely small standard error of the observations around the regression line.

We can conclude, therefore, that the cube law does not hold in a strict sense in the United States but that it is nonetheless a close approximation. Given the present state of knowledge concerning political behavior, it is difficult to imagine a theoretical explanation of why the cube law might hold that would not also serve as a reasonable explanation for most of the observed relationship between votes and seats in the United States. Here, as in the British case, it is probably unwise for some purposes to establish an extreme goodness-of-fit criterion since that tends to focus attention on the nuances of the relationship before the grosser attributes are suitably explained.

There is another method for testing the goodness-of-fit of election data to the cube law that has generally been used in the English treatments of the law. At the cost of making one not unreasonable assumption, it permits a test for fit over the entire range of possible vote outcomes rather than being restricted to the range available in actual elections. Suppose we assume that shifts in popular support for a party will be approximately homogenous throughout the country, specifically that they will be independent of the level of party support in a constituency.[17] Then, the cube law plotted in Figure 1

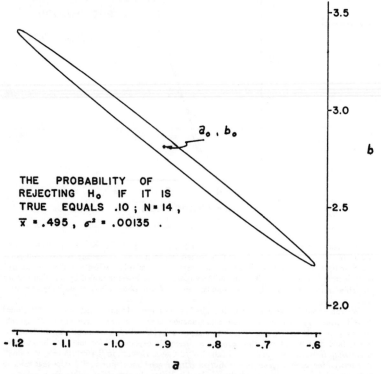

FIGURE 3 : POWER OF THE F - TEST

VALUES OF a AND b IN THE EQUATION $Y = a + bX$ WHICH IF THEY ARE THE TRUE POPULATION PARAMETERS THE PROBABILITY OF REJECTING THE NULL HYPOTHESIS (H_0: $a = -.904$, $b = 2.808$) IS EQUAL TO .90.

a_0, b_0

b

THE PROBABILITY OF REJECTING H_0 IF IT IS TRUE EQUALS .10 ; N = 14, $\bar{x} = .495$, $\sigma^2 = .00135$.

-3.5

-3.0

-2.5

-2.0

- 1.2   - 1.1   - 1.0   -.9   -.8   -.7   -.6

a

---

[17] There is some empirical evidence that this is not always strictly true. See Cadart, *op. cit.*; Philip Williams, "Election Analysis," *Socialist Commentary*, pp. 210-211, 228 (July, 1955).

can be viewed as a distribution function of constituencies according to party strength and the observed distribution for any election can be compared with the distribution defined by the law. It would appear the cube law was originally based on some such analysis since that is the basis both for Edgeworth's pioneer paper[18] and for the work of Martin[19] on which presumably Smith (and/or MacMahon) based their conclusions. As Kendall and Stuart point out, the distribution function defined by the cube law is almost identical to the distribution function of a normal distribution with mean .5 and variance .0187.[20] That is to say that if the homogeneity assumption is met and if $a/a+b$ (where a and b are the votes received by the two parties in a constituency) is distributed normally with the indicated mean and variance, the cube law follows. Moreover, so long as the election outcome is not extreme (say, that one party's total vote does not exceed 65 per cent of the total) balanced abnormality at the tails of the distribution or moderate shifts in the variance will still yield results consistent with the cube hypothesis. For a full discussion of the fit of the British data to the cube law, the extended literature on the subject should be consulted.[21]

Kendall and Stuart considered briefly, but indecisively, the fit of Congressional election data to this distribution function. We have considered the distributions in four elections, 1928, 1944, 1948, 1952. The frequency distributions are indicated in Table 3 for all constituencies in which each party received more than 10 per cent of the vote. In effect, we treat constituencies in which one party received more than 90 per cent of the vote as *de facto* uncontested. An inspection of the table will indicate that the American dis-

TABLE 3

DISTRIBUTION OF DEMOCRATIC % OF THE TWO-PARTY VOTE, U. S. CONGRESSIONAL
CONSTITUENCIES, 1928, 1944, 1948, 1952

Democratic % of two-party vote	1928	1944	1948	1952
10–19	9	0	0	0
20–29	41	6	1	19
30–39	98	73	51	97
40–49	105	103	104	87
50–59	55	83	91	74
60–69	20	50	54	37
70–79	13	21	25	17
80–89	14	11	20	6

[18] F. Y. Edgeworth, "Miscellaneous Applications of the Calculus of Probabilities," *Journal of the Royal Statistical Society*, Vol. 61, pp. 534-544 (Sept., 1898).

[19] R. B. Martin, "The Electoral 'Swing of the Pendulum,'" *Journal of the Royal Statistical Society*, Vol. 69, pp. 655-707 (Dec., 1906).

[20] Kendall and Stuart (1950), *op. cit.*

[21] See footnotes 7-12, *supra*.

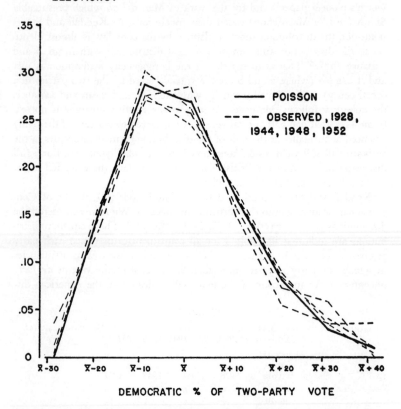

FIGURE 4

THEORETICAL (POISSON) DISTRIBUTION AND ACTUAL
DISTRIBUTION OF CONSTITUENCIES IN FOUR
ELECTIONS.

—— POISSON

——— OBSERVED, 1928,
1944, 1948, 1952

DEMOCRATIC % OF TWO-PARTY VOTE

tribution is not normal. In fact, it appears to be more nearly a Poisson distribution.[22] In Figure 4, the observed frequencies are compared with theoretical frequencies derived from a Poisson distribution with mean and variance equal to 1.87 and class intervals equal to .1.[23] Some reasons why the

[22] Discussions of the Poisson distribution can be found in almost any elementary statistics text. For example, G. Udny Yule and M. G. Kendall, *An Introduction to the Theory of Statistics*, 14th ed. (London, 1950), pp. 189-194.

[23] This, of course, makes the standard deviation equivalent to that cited above for the normal distribution. The frequencies used for the figure are derived in the following way. In each observed distribution the observed mean is computed. Then by interpolation in Table 3 a new

United States distribution should approximate a Poisson rather than a normal distribution are indicated below. Here it may be enough to observe that a Poisson distribution with mean 1.87 has a distribution fairly close to that of the normal with variance .0187, as indicated in Table 4.[24] Consequently, results close to the cube law will be observed if the distribution is a Poisson with mean 1.87 and changes are substantially homogeneous.

TABLE 4

A COMPARISON OF DISTRIBUTION FUNCTIONS FOR THE CUBE LAW, NORMAL DISTRIBUTION, AND THE POISSON DISTRIBUTION

Democratic proportion of two-party vote	Democratic proportion of two-party seats under		
	Cube Law	Normal	Poisson
0	0	.000	.003
.1	.002	.001	.010
.2	.015	.014	.032
.3	.073	.072	.093
.4	.229	.232	.229
.5	.5	.5	.461
.6	.771	.768	.742
.7	.927	.928	.945
.8	.985	.986	1.
.9	.999	.998	1.
1.	1.	1.000	1.

In general, whether one uses the observed outcomes over the 1928-1954 period or the distribution of constituencies in a given election, the results in the United States are not as clearly consistent with the cube law hypothesis as are the recent elections in Britain; but they do not deviate much from the results that would obtain under the cube law. The fact that the cube law fits election results with this much accuarcy both in Great Britain and the United States is enough to stimulate the interest of both laymen and professional students of political systems.

Perhaps partly because of this high curiosity value, professional interest in the relationship has been subjected to some criticism as being superficial.[25]

distribution is determined in which the class intervals are .1 as above but the boundaries are defined in terms of the mean rather than in absolute terms. This is equivalent to viewing the distribution as displaced on the scale without change in configuration. As is clear from the figure, the similarities between the theoretical and the observed distributions are striking despite the fact that the theoretical mean is determined without reference to the observed distribution. The differences between the three recent elections and the Poissons are not significant at the .05 level by Fisher's variance test. In the case of the 1928 election the error on the tail of the distribution makes it possible to reject the hypothesis of a Poisson, but again we are dealing with a very powerful test, and the differences are not great.

[24] Linear interpolation is used to compute the distribution function for the Poisson.

[25] For example, Samuel J. Eldersveld, "Polling Results and Prediction Techniques in the British Election of 1950," in *British Election Studies 1950*, ed. Pollock (Ann Arbor, 1950), pp. 54-78.

Briefly, the import of the complaint is (a) that the cube law does not "fit" and (b) even if it did fit, it would be a freak with little predictive utility and less theoretical importance.

As in all cases of fitting empirical data to theoretical equations, the fit can be judged as "good" or "poor" only in terms of a set of expectations that presumably vary from one investigator to another. It is true that the cube law is not the best estimator of the outcome in the United States over the 1928-1954 period. A prediction based on the linear regression equation specified in (6) would predict the outcome in contested districts with somewhat greater accuracy than would the cube law, although the differences are not of very great magnitude. The point, however, is not that the cube law rather than some other quite similar law holds but that the relationship is quite regular and that the true parameters of the relationship, whatever they are, are not far from the parameters specified by the cube law. Once this is granted, it is reasonable to ask why the relationship holds and why one party's percentage of the two-party vote has the approximate distribution indicated above in political systems such as those of Great Britain and the United States.

THE CONSTITUENCY DISTRIBUTION PROBLEM

One of the problems in providing an interpretation for the relationship between votes and seats in a two-party, single-member constituency, plurality election system is that of defining a frame of reference for comparison. If one starts from an implicit standard of proportional representation, the major problem appears to be that of explaining why the system provides a bias in favor of the majority party in the range around 50 per cent so that an increase of 1 per cent in the party's voting strength results in an increase of approximately 3 per cent in the party's strength in the house.[26] Looked at in another way, the problem is perceived as that of explaining why the variance is as small as .0187. As Rustow has pointed out, instituting anything approaching proportional representation in a single-member constituency, plurality election system is virtually impossible.[27] Consequently, although it has been the implicit approach of some students of the cube law, comparison of the observed results with a normative proportional representation model tends not to be particularly fruitful insofar as one is interested in empirically-grounded theory.

[26] Butler tends to operate from this model, for example. See the works cited in footnote 11, *supra*.

[27] Dankwart A. Rustow, "Some Observations on Proportional Representation," *Journal of Politics*, Vol. 12, pp. 107-127 (Feb. 1950).

On the other hand, it is possible to approach the constituency distribution problem from the point of view of sampling theory. This is the method used originally by Edgeworth[28] and more recently by Kendall and Stuart.[29] Anyone using a sampling model is struck not by the smallness of the variance but rather by its largeness. If constituencies were samples drawn randomly from a parent population, the variance of the Democratic proportion of the two-party vote would be extremely small. In fact, under such conditions if the Democrats received 51 per cent of the vote, they would be expected to win all of the seats in the House of Representatives. It is true that under the central limit theorem random sampling would yield a normal distribution, but some other models are necessary to explain the magnitude of the variance in this case.

Kendall and Stuart suggest two different stochastic models that would explain the outcome. Their first suggestion is a Markoff process in which there exists a high correlation between successive trials or drawings. Thus, imagine that voters are assigned to constitutencies under a scheme in which the probability of the next person assigned to a given constituency being a Democrat or a Republican depends only on whether the previous person assigned was a Democrat or a Republican. Then, if the probability of the voter being a Democrat given the previous voter was a Democrat is very high (nearly 1.0) and the probability of his being a Republican given the previous voter was a Republican is also very high (nearly 1.0), the observed variance can be explained. The level of correlation between successive drawings is, as Kendall and Stuart comment, improbably extreme under this model. In fact, the probability of the next drawing being the same as the previous one must be greater than .999 for both Democrats and Republicans.

Perhaps more important in view of the data presented in this paper is the fact that the parameters of the Markoff model estimated from the British data will not explain the United States data. This follows from the fact that although the variance in the United States case is approximately that found in Britain, constituency sizes are larger by a factor of about four. Moreover, the size of constituency in New Zealand, the other country in which a fit for the cube law has been reported, is less than one-third the size of the constituencies in Great Britain. The tendency for the variance among constituencies to be independent of constituency size suggests that perhaps the constituency *per se* is a meaningful unit and that sampling explanations (being typically dependent on sample size) must be at least partially modified in order to account for the observed result.

The second Kendall and Stuart suggestion suffers less from the sample

28 Edgeworth, *op. cit.*
29 Kendall and Stuart (1950), *op. cit.*

size problem. Suppose that we conceive of a number of populations (perhaps conforming to more or less identifiable socio-economic groups) such that the probability of a voter chosen at random being a Democrat is different in different populations. And suppose that each of these populations contributes equally to the total number of voters and that each constituency is drawn from one and only one of the populations. Then the variance of constituencies will (given the sample sizes we are dealing with) be substantially independent of sample size. However, one of the assumptions of the scheme represents another form of the sample size problem. If we are to assume that each constituency is drawn from only one population, we need to offer some rationale for believing that the demography of a country and the size of its constituencies will be functionally related. This assumption seems unrealistic, but an approximation to it can be achieved. Suppose that we identify basic socio-economic groups in New Zealand, Great Britain, and the United States, considering them as our statistical populations. Suppose further that the variance of proportions among these populations is the same in the three countries. Finally suppose that we conceive of ourselves as drawing sub-constituencies of say 20,000 voters at a time from one population in each country. By this device we make the demography of the country and the sample size independent. In order to produce a result in which the variations due to sample size will be small, it is only necessary to impose the condition that in drawing successive sub-constituencies to complete a given constituency the probability of drawing from a given population decreases rapidly as the difference between the proportions in the previous population and the given one increases. This means that two successive drawings will ordinarily be from quite similar populations and thus the effect on the variance of increases in sample size will be restricted.

Patently, this scheme of sampling leaves something to be desired as an explanation of the result. Nevertheless, its assumptions are not so unlikely as to be rejected cavalierly. If the cube law can be explained in these terms, it is worth careful consideration. In fact, however, the second scheme suggested by Kendall and Stuart can at best provide only a partial explanation of the phenomenon. In particular, it does not provide explanations for why the distribution of proportions among the several populations is approximately normal in Great Britain and approximately a Poisson in the United States. Kendall and Stuart suggest that the scheme will explain the observed normality in the distribution of constituencies in Great Britain, but this does not appear to follow independently of the distribution of population proportions. In fact, under such a scheme and large sample sizes, the distribution of sample proportions will be almost exactly the same as the distribution of population proportions, and the scheme does not specify that distribution. Secondly, the Kendall-Stuart scheme depends, as do other sampling models, on an assumption of approximately equal constituencies. We would not expect results from elections to the United States Senate to follow the cube law since the sizes of senatorial constituencies are notoriously varied. Nevertheless, Dahl reports[30] an extremely good fit to the 1928-1954 data on Senate elections of a linear regression equation

$$y = 3.02x - .95. \tag{7}$$

As can be seen by comparing (7) with equation (4), the results in Senate elections are close to the cube law approximation. Finally, if the explanation of the result lies in the geographic distribution of voters (as is implied in a sampling explanation), there should be no difference between the distribution of constituencies according to the Democratic proportion of the two-party vote in the vote for President and the vote for Congress in the same year. However, in each of the four elections on which data are available on this point (1940, 1944, 1948, 1952)[31], the variance of the distribution for Congressional elections is significantly larger than is the comparable distribution for Presidential elections (the ratios ranging from 1.45 to 1.65). The vote for President is less disperse than the vote for Congress.

In the light of the limitations of our present knowledge concerning political behavior, it is probably not realistic to expect a precise explanation of these phenomena until further research is completed. The most that will be attempted here is an indication of some processes that, combined with a sampling procedure would give results approximating the observed outcomes. We will focus on two processes for which here is some empirical evidence and/or reasonable rationale. First, we will consider the entrepreneurial aspects of the behavior of political parties in organizing coalitions. Second, we will consider the intra-constituency processes of activation and persuasion and their effects respectively on the probability of a voter voting and the probability of his voting for a given party.

I am aware that there are more elegant ways of presenting the theoretical explanations I should like to make in the next sections. A model with equilibrium properties consistent with the cube law undoubtedly can be developed in a number of ways. I think such model construction would be extremely valuable. However, at the present stage of our knowledge, some discussion in

[30] Dahl, *op. cit.*, p. 149.

[31] The data for 1940, 1944, and 1948 are taken from Moos, *op. cit.* The 1952 data are from the *Congressional Quarterly*. In the analysis, only constituencies in which there was a contest in the congressional election were considered. For present purposes, Moos' data are incomplete in two respects. First, he did not include any southern states. Since many of the constituencies in the south are uncontested, this is not a serious disability. Second, he does not present a breakdown of the Presidential vote within metropolitan areas. In lieu of a reason for believing that this bias is systematically related to the comparison under analysis (and particularly in the light of the 1952 results which include the metropolitan and contested southern districts), it has seemed reasonable to believe that the relationships found in the 1940, 1944, and 1948 samples are characteristics of the whole population of districts for those elections.

general terms of the political processes by which distributions such as those described above might be generated seems to me a more pressing need.

Can we imagine what the distribution of contested constituencies would be if we could eliminate all major effects except negotiations by political parties with interest groups to form coalitions? Although this could be formalized in terms of game theory, we will not attempt to do so here.[32] It will be enough to note that if the political parties are "rational," they will be willing to "pay" more for alliances that will give them control (i.e., over 50 per cent of the seats) than for other alliances. In general, they will not be willing to pay much for alliances that will give them additional seats once they have a majority.[33] This will be reinforced by the fact that the other party will be willing to pay more for such seats (and be in a position to do so). Thus, both parties want to have either 51 per cent of the vote or none of the vote in a given constituency. Since the major payments the parties can offer are in the form of public policy decisions, there are constraints placed (a) on the coalitions that are feasible (some demands are mutually exclusive) and (b) on the precision with which even a "rational" politician can achieve exactly 51 per cent of the vote in exactly 51 per cent of the constituencies and no vote anywhere else.[34]

Assuming roughly these pressures, it is reasonable to anticipate that inter-party negotiations will tend to produce a modal value for the distribution of .50 with monotonic decreases to zero on both sides of the mode. Moreover, it is reasonable to expect that the curve will be concave on both sides of the mode since the inter-connections among constituencies are likely to be such that the pressure toward .50 will keep most constituencies close to that figure. For the same reason, we expect the variance to be fairly small.

For the sake of an example, and without the intention of taking the actual numbers too seriously, suppose that the distributions resulting from this political negotiation pressure toward .50 are as indicated in Figure 5 for Britain. We will consider this as a very rough approximation to what would happen if there were no intra-constituency processes operating.

[32] For a formalization of a related question, see L. S. Shapley and Martin Shubik, "A Method for Evaluating the Distribution of Power in a Committee System," *American Political Science Review*, Vol. 48, pp. 787-792 (Sept., 1954).

[33] This point has been made by Schattschneider. E. E. Schattschneider, *op. cit.*, pp. 95-96.

[34] In addition, politicians don't behave entirely in the manner specified by the game theorist. Personal motivations complicate "party" motives. Subparty or inter-party coalitions may be of considerable importance. In the face of uncertainty regarding individual loyalties to the party, 51 per cent may not be considered a "safe" objective. All of these factors also tend to prevent a "perfectly rational" solution to the coalition problem.

Now imagine what the distribution would be if only intra-constituency pressures were observed. We can note the following: (a) It is usually argued that the prime force tending to produce party equality in a constituency is something similar to what we have called political negotiation. Implicit in this characterization is the expectation that without such negotiation, there would be a divergent tendency. (b) Variations in the turnout tend to be related to the extent to which there is a contest in the election, and at least at the extremes it is clear that both majority and minority voters tend to withdraw. (c) Such evidence as there is, however, suggests that in the moderate ranges minority voters withdraw proportionately more than majority voters.[35]

The twin mechanisms of despair (by the minority) and confidence (by the majority) affect the motivation to work for a party. If we assume that the probability of an individual shifting from one party to another is a linear function of the pressure exerted on him by other individuals to do so (and the net shift a function of the differences between the two pressures) and that the pressure exerted equals the number of supporters of the party times their motivation to work for the party, we can construct a model that depends simply on the relationship between the size of the existing majority on the one hand and minority despair and majority confidence on the other. We will argue that it is reasonable to assume that the despair and confidence functions are identical and approximately logarithmic. Under such assumptions, the distribution will tend to be bimodal with virtually no constituencies at the .50 point, a substantial number in the moderate ranges (say about .40 and .60), and fewer and fewer constituencies at the more extreme points. Quite aside from the rationale for it provided here, such a distribution has (at least to the present writer) some intuitive appeal.

As in the case of the political negotiation factor, the actual frequencies indicated in Figure 5 are not particularly important. All that is argued is that the form of the curve might be expected to assume approximately this shape in elections in Britain and the United States.

Finally, if we combine these two pressures by assuming (arbitrarily) equality of weights, we generate the combined distribution indicated in Figure 5. This distribution is close to the normal form with variance .0187. To be sure, the precise outcome indicated in the figure is based on the arbi-

---

[35] See Seymour M. Lipset, Paul F. Lazarsfeld, Allen H. Barton, and Juan Linz, "The Psychology of Voting: An Analysis of Political Behavior," in the *Handbook of Social Psychology*, ed. Lindzey (Cambridge: Addison and Wesley, 1954), Vol. 2, pp. 1124-1175, at pp. 1146-47.

trarily chosen frequencies that have been used and those frequencies were chosen partly with an eye to the theoretical goal involved. However, the frequencies are not "unreasonable" on the basis of common sense and available data; they probably come fairly close to the true distributions.

FIGURE 5

HYPOTHETICAL DISTRIBUTION OF SEATS RESULTING FROM PROCESSES OF POLITICAL NEGOTIATION AND INTRA-CONSTITUENCY PRESSURES (GREAT BRITAIN)

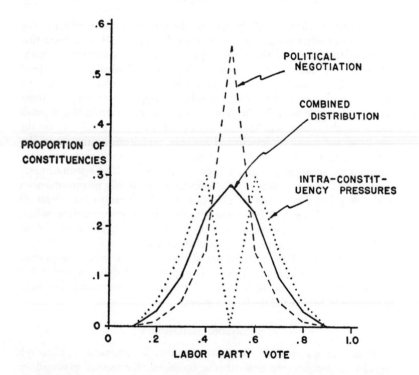

Of much greater importance, however, is the fact that if we use the same basic parameters and apply them to the American situation, we obtain the observed distribution in the United States. In Great Britain, we have assumed that the mode and median of the distribution are the same and equal to .50. This is a reasonable approximation when the uncontested districts are equally shared by the two parties since we then expect the two parties to tend toward equality in contested seats. In the United States, one party has much the greater share of uncontested seats and, therefore, requires less than half of the contested seats to achieve a majority. Under such conditions, we expect the mode to be .50 as before since inter-party competition will still be concentrated at that point; but because one party (Republican) requires a greater number of victories in uncontested seats than the other, the distribution will not be symmetric around the mode. In Figure 6 distributions for the United States comparable to those in Figure 5 for Britain are indicated. It is assumed that one-fourth of the seats are won by the Democrats without contest. This exaggerates the true situation only slightly and is arithmetically convenient. Thus, the frequencies on one side of the mode are cut precisely in half. Note that otherwise the distributions (in frequency terms) are the same as in Figure 5. This results in a combined distribution that is very close to the observed distribution for United States constituencies. Compare the solid line in Figure 6 with the distributions in Figure 4.

With all appropriate qualifications stemming from imprecision in present knowledge, there is a certain plausibility to an explanation that follows the lines outlined here. We cannot claim anything more than that for it. It offers some reasons for a normal distribution of constituencies in Great Britain and a Poisson distribution in the United States. In addition, it makes reasonable the fact that the variance among constituencies in the vote for President is significantly less than the variance among the same constituencies at the same election in the vote for Congress and that the data for elections to the United States Senate "fit" the cube law. In the case of the vote for President, some of the internal constituency processes are damped considerably because the constituency is not an electoral unit. Similarly, political negotiation is based on statewide rather than simply congressional district considerations. Both of these factors operate to make the variance in the vote for President less than that observed in the vote for Congress.

That the Senate elections fit the cube law follows from the above model. If we consider politicians as bidding for support in order to achieve a majority in the legislative body, the value of a voter is a function of his control over a winning majority.[36] In a system of equal constituencies, each voter is formally equal in this sense. In a system of unequal constituencies such as the United States Senate, we can specify blocs of voters that are equal, and a "rational" politician will offer no more to 100 voters in New York than he will to one voter in Nevada insofar as he is attempting to influence the election of a majority in the Senate. That this is approximately how the system

[36] See Shapley and Shubik, *op. cit.*

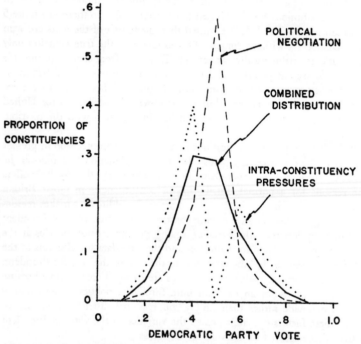

FIGURE 6

HYPOTHETICAL DISTRIBUTION OF SEATS
RESULTING FROM PROCESSES OF POLITICAL
NEGOTIATION AND INTRA-CONSTITUENCY PRESSURES
(UNITED STATES)

operates is frequently alleged. Thus, the processes outlined above should operate in senatorial elections as well as in elections to the House of Representatives, and the distributions of electoral districts should be approximately the same. However, if one party were to specialize in gaining support of voters in states having small populations (a perfectly feasible strategy), the cube law would not follow. What deters a party from such specialization is, of course, the fact that elections to the Senate are only one of several elections to be contested for control of the national government; and there are (at best) only slight advantages of small state specialization to balance against the disadvantages stemming from the interdependence of voting preferences on the part of individual voters.

CONCLUSION

We have attempted to provide an explanation for some of the similarities and differences between the distribution of party vote in constituencies in the United States and Great Britain and particularly to provide possible reasons for the approximate fit of the cube law to those data. Our model specifies rough parameters for two underlying mechanisms: political negotiation and intra-constituency interaction. These parameters appear to be consistent with present knowledge concerning such factors, although that knowledge is scarcely so precise as to permit great confidence in them. They are also consistent with the observed results in Great Britain and the United States. Beyond that we can claim only that the amount of freedom we have allowed in constructing a model to explain the data has been substantial but not unlimited. For example, once we specify the distributions in Figure 5 for Great Britain, we have also specified them for the United States.

Before anything more can be said about the present rough model, additional testing in other electoral systems is indicated. Particularly fruitful would be further tests in systems in which the electoral necessities are different for the two parties. State and provincial legislatures in the United States, Canada, and Australia provide possible sources of data for such tests; although there may be some problems in meeting the two-party[37] and single-member constituency[38] prerequisites. Another possible source of data is voting in non-governmental organizations. The processes specified above are presumably not restricted to governmental institutions, and tests of the hypotheses suggested here in other representative institutions should be possible.[39]

[37] See Joseph A. Schlesinger, "A Two-Dimensional Scheme for Classifying the States According to Degree of Inter-Party Competition," *American Political Science Review*, Vol. 49, pp. 1120-1128 (Dec., 1955); Austin Ranney and Willmore Kendall, "The American Party Systems," *American Political Science Review*, Vol. 48, pp. 477-485 (June, 1954).

[38] See Maurice Klain, "A New Look at the Constituencies; The Need for a Recount and a Reappraisal," *American Political Science Review*, Vol. 49, pp. 1105-1119 (Dec., 1955).

[39] For example, James S. Coleman (Chicago) has recently been considering the distribution of votes in union locals in a labor union having a well-developed two-party system.

Games Decisions and Industrial Organization†

Martin Shubik   *Yale University*

A survey of the current relationship between the many different problem areas investigated by means of Game Theory and the study of Industrial Organization is presented. Several examples are provided to illustrate the nature and relevance of work on (1) two-person constant-sum games; (2) the extensive form of a game; (3) theories of solution for n-person games; (4) theories of solutions for games against nature; and (5) theories of solution for dynamic games. The nature and state of the current applications of game theory to organizational problems and to parts of the behavioral sciences are summarized.

1. Introduction

Approximately 15 years ago, with the publication of the book by von Neumann and Morgenstern[1], the theory of games came into being. There had been previous publications which indicated that both von Neumann and Morgenstern considered problems which eventually led to this theory many years before. There are also historical references as far back as the early 18th century[2]; nevertheless, it was not until 1944 that the theory of games emerged as a formal discipline.

Since that time over a thousand papers and articles have appeared under the general classification of the theory of games. The latter part of the title of the first book, *"The Theory of Games and Economic Behavior,"* indicates that game theory was conceived of as an applied mathematics with economics and possibly other behavioral sciences as the substantive fields for application. How well has it lived up to this? The work by von Neumann and Morgenstern contains disappointingly little economics. Among the articles, papers and other books which have been written, most are strictly mathematical, a number are applied to military problems and a few deal with other areas of application. There have been almost no direct applications of game theory to problems in the behavioral sciences or in business in the same way as there have been applications of linear programming to refining, mixing and scheduling problems.

In spite of the lack of direct applications, the influence of game theory has been considerable. In this paper problems concerning the application and the nature of the influence of game theory are examined.

---

† The author is indebted to W. W. Cooper and to R. Vaswani for valuable comments and criticisms.

[1] von Neumann, J., and O. Morgenstern, *Theory of Games and Economic Behavior*, Princeton, New Jersey: Princeton University Press, 3rd. ed., 1953.

[2] Harold Kuhn has noted that in a letter between Montmort and Nicholas Bernouilli appearing in *Essay d'Analyse sur les Jeux d'Hazard* (1713) mention is made of the concept of a mixed strategy by the English mathematician Waldgrove.

2. Methodologies and Theories of the Solution of Games

Before one is in a position to understand fully the possibilities for the application of game theory it is desirable to distinguish among five very different developments. They are, respectively:

1. The theory of solution for two-person constant-sum games,
2. The description of the extensive form of a game,
3. The theories of solution for n person games (where $n \geqq 2$ for non-constant-sum games; $n \geqq 3$ for constant-sum games),
4. The theories of solution for games against nature (games in which the rules are not completely specified), and
5. The theories of solution for dynamic games.

3. Two-Person Constant-Sum Games

Perhaps owing to a formal relationship between the mathematics required for the solution of a two-person zero-sum game and that required for the solution of a linear program this part of game theory has been the most familiar to those not working directly in the field.

The class of two-person constant-sum games is naturally divided into those games where both players have a finite set of *pure strategies* and those where at least one player has an infinite set of pure strategies. Board games, such as Chess, Checkers and Go, as well as two-person card games belong to the first class. Most "dueling" problems give rise to games of the second type.

The first are referred to as matrix games. All their relevant features can be

TABLE 1

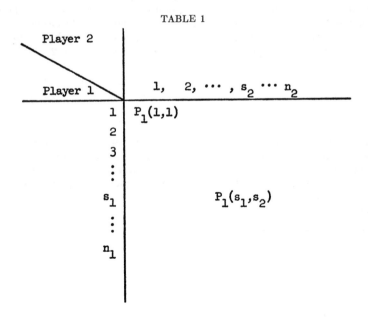

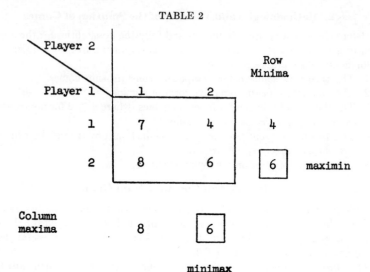

TABLE 2

represented by a payoff matrix. Let S_1 and S_2 be the set of pure strategies for players 1 and 2 respectively. Let $s_1 \, \varepsilon \, S_1$ and $s_2 \, \varepsilon \, S_2$ represent specific strategies chosen by players 1 and 2 from the sets of strategies they have available. We define a payoff function $P_1(s_1, s_2)$ for player 1. This function assigns a value to the outcome of the game for the first player if the strategies s_1 and s_2 are played.

Suppose that the first player has n_1 and the second player has n_2 pure strategies. The payoff matrix in Table 1 completely describes the values of the outcomes to the first player for all possibilities where $s_1 = 1, 2, \ldots, n_1$ and $s_2 = 1, 2, \ldots, n_2$.

By definition, as the game is two-person and constant-sum the payoff for the second player is the negative of that for the first, except for a constant.

$$P_2(s_1, s_2) = -P_1(s_1, s_2) + K$$

There is one commonly agreed upon concept of solution for two-person constant-sum matrix games and a complete theory for their solution[3].

The behavioristic assumption for the play of two-person constant-sum matrix games is that of *minimax*. The game in Table 2 illustrates this. For simplicity, in our examples we set the constant $K = 0$.

The worst that can happen to Player 1 if he uses his first strategy is that he obtains 4 if Player 2 uses his second strategy. The worst that can happen if he uses his second strategy is that he obtains 6. The best that he can obtain is 8 if Player 2 uses his first strategy and 6 if the second strategy.

[3] For a detailed exposition of the concept and method of solution for a two-person constant-sum game, the reader is referred to J. C. C. McKinsey, *Introduction to the Theory of Games*, New York: McGraw-Hill, 1952, Chapter 2.

TABLE 3

Player 2 Player 1	1	2	Row Minima
1	10	-5	-5
2	-15	10	-15
Column maxima	10	10	

By utilizing his second strategy, the first player can guarantee that he obtains at least 6. Similarly, by utilizing his second strategy the second player can guarantee that he will lose at most 6. We note that the maximum of the minima that the first player can win is 6. Furthermore, the minimum of the maxima of the second player's losses is 6. For this matrix we can state:

$$\text{min. max. } P_1(s_1, s_2) = \text{max. min. } P_1(s_1, s_2)$$
$$\quad {}_{s_1} \quad {}_{s_1} \qquad\qquad {}_{s_1} \quad {}_{s_1}$$

The game in Table 3 does not have the *saddlepoint* property that the minimax equals the maximin. However, if, instead of limiting a player to pick a *pure strategy* we allow him to utilize a probability mix over his alternative plans for action this property is restored. Suppose Player 1 uses his first strategy with a probability of 5/8 and the second with a probability of 3/8. If the second player uses his first strategy the first will expect to win

$$5/8(10) + 3/8(-15) = 5/8.$$

If the second plays his second strategy, the first player will win

$$5/8(-5) + 3/8(10) = 5/8.$$

By utilizing the *mixed strategy* characterized by (5/8, 3/8) the first player can guarantee a win of 5/8 for himself. Similarly, by using the mixed strategy of (3/8, 5/8) the second player can guarantee that he will not lose more than 5/8.

The fundamental theorem[4] of two-person constant-sum games establishes that for all games of this type there will be a saddlepoint at which the first player can guarantee a minimum gain for himself. The second player can simultaneously guarantee that the maximum the first player will win is precisely that minimum.

The assumption that the behavior of the players can be described by the conscious application of the minimax rule is based on possibly a peculiarly "ra-

[4] *Ibid.*, Chapter 2.

tionalistic utilitarian" view of the players. It can be interpreted as a normative assumption telling individuals how they should behave in such a situation.

There are a few situations or organizations which can be characterized successfully by means of two-person constant-sum games. Several attempts have been made to draw the analogy between situations involving competition in advertising[5]; however, although they are of value, the problems of formulation are great. Several applications have been made to problems in the oil industry[6].

The second type of constant-sum game, involving at least one player with an infinite set of strategies, includes games of search and duels. The concept of solution is the same for these as for the matrix games; however, the mathematical difficulties are much greater and in some cases solutions may not exist. These games have considerable value to military work. The games of search have direct applications to defense systems and the dueling games are of use in the evaluation of new weapon systems.

In summary, to date there appears to be direct application of two-person constant-sum games to problems of the military but little direct application to economic, social or industrial organization.

4. The Description of the Extensive Form of a Game

The first part of the work of von Neumann and Morgenstern[7] was devoted to a detailed description of the anatomy of a game, or the *extensive form* of a game. This framework has provided a language for modern decision theory and a basis for investigations of organization theory.

In the context of the description of a game, the words *move, play, information set, strategy, payoff, rules of the game* and *perfect information* are defined.

The matrix game portrayed in Table 3 can be represented by a *game tree*. This is done in Figure 1.

The vertices in this game tree represent choice points. The branches indicate alternatives. The vertices are labelled with the name of the player to whom they belong. Thus, at the vertex 0, which is also labelled with P_1, the first player is called upon to make a choice between two alternatives. These are the branches originating from this vertex and labelled 1 and 2.

At the two vertices labelled P_2 the second player is called upon to make his move by choosing between two alternatives. After each player has made his move the game reaches a terminal point of the game tree and each player obtains his payoff. For example, if both players select their first alternative the game terminates with payoff $(10, -10)$.

---

[5] Charnes, A. and W. W. Cooper, "A Constrained Game Formulation of Advertising Strategies," *Econometrica*, October, 1954. See also L. Friedman, "Game-Theory Models in the Allocation of Advertising Expenditures," *Operations Research*, 6: 5, September–October 1958.

[6] Symonds, G. H., *Linear Programming: The Solution of Refinery Problems*, Esso Standard Oil Company, New York: 1955, Chapter 5.

Bennion, E. G., "Capital Budgeting and Game Theory," *Harvard Business Review*, 34, 1956.

[7] von Neumann and Morgenstern, *op. cit*, Chapter II.

The two vertices labelled with P_2 are enclosed by single curve. This indicates that these choice points belong to the same *information set*. The matrix game in Table 3 is a simultaneous move game. The two players select their strategies without knowledge of each other's actions. Thus, in the game tree, although the first player selects between his two alternatives first, in effect the second player is not aware of the choice, hence he cannot tell if he is making a choice at the vertex x or y.

The game illustrated in Figure 2 is a different game inasmuch as the *information* conditions have been changed. The vertices x and y no longer belong to the same information set. The first player's move is disclosed to the second player prior to his own move. This game does not give rise to the same matrix game

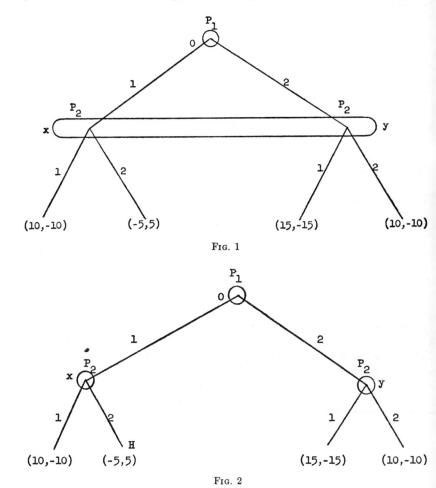

Fig. 1

Fig. 2

TABLE 4

Player 1 \ Player 2	(1,1,;2,1)	(1,1;2,2)	(1,2;2,1)	(1,2;2,2)	Row min
1	10	10	-5	-5	-5
2	-15	10	-15	10	-15
Column max	10	10	-5	10	

as the other. The equivalent matrix game still has two strategies for the first player but has four strategies for the second. These are illustrated in Table 4.

These two examples illustrate the use of a precise language for decision-making in games.

The *rules of the game* specify the complete structure of the game. They indicate the span of the alternatives faced by a player at any point during the play, his information state and the payoffs resulting from any play.

A *play* of a game is a path followed down the game tree. In Figure 2 such a path is denoted by $0 \times H$. This results when the first and second players make their moves by selecting their first and second alternatives, respectively.

The *payoff* is the resultant allocation from the play of a game. In chess this is the value attached to a win, loss or draw, in poker it is money.

A *strategy* is a complete plan of action for a player. It contains instructions to handle all contingencies. For example, the third strategy of the second player indicated in Table 4 is $(1, 2; 2, 1)$. This states: "If Player 1 uses his first alternative my move will be to select my second; if he uses his second my move will be to select my first."

A *move* is the selection of one among a set of alternatives at a choice point in a game. In a game in which each player has a single move and these are made simultaneously, a strategy and a move are equivalent. The players have no contingencies to plan for.

The game illustrated in Figure 2 has *perfect information*. Each *information set* is a one element set. This implies that at any point in the game any player is perfectly informed about all moves made up to the time of his move.

Possibly one of the most important contributions of the Theory of Games to date has been this language to aid in the study of decision-making.

Paradoxically, the power of this notation has enabled those working in the behavioral sciences to isolate and specify some of the major weaknesses in the theories of solutions to games and in the other economic theories invoking "rational behavior."

Once an attempt is made to study a game of moderate complexity in the extensive form, such as chess, the difficulties concerning theories of "rational choice" are highlighted. The first two moves in the game of chess can occur in 400 ways. By the tenth move there are many billions of alternatives!

It is evident that humans do not search through millions of alternatives, but they have various methods to limit their search in a relatively successful manner. Consideration of this has led Shannon, Simon, Newell, Samuel and others[8] to construct chess and checker-playing computer programs based on "heuristics" which are general rules or principles that serve to cut down the alternatives to be examined to a manageable number.

Closely tied to the work on chess playing is work on other "search processes" and on learning. M. M. Flood and others[9] have experimented directly with game learning situations.

Of more direct influence upon industry has been the direct effect of the terminology of Game Theory on operations research and planning work. The Payoff Matrix is now common terminology in many parts of U. S. industry. And with it are the concepts of contingent forecasting, strategic planning and sensitivity analysis. Obviously, the growth of linear programming, sequential decision theory and other mathematical techniques have also had influence. They, too, apart from specific applications, have played their cultural role of preparing the "climate" in industry for the scientific study of decision processes.

5. Theories of Solution for n-Person Games

To those only slightly acquainted with the Theory of Games the title of the book by von Neumann and Morgenstern is misleading in several ways. The authors wrote, in effect, three books under one cover. The first book deals with the description of a game in extensive form. The second offers a theory for the solution to two-person constant-sum games. It has been argued with considerable effect that the mode of behavior suggested by von Neumann and Morgenstern is very reasonable and that people "should" play in the manner suggested by their theory[10]. This, to some extent depends upon the acceptance of the von Neumann and Morgenstern concept of utility which can be regarded as a major contribution by itself.

The third book presents a theory of behavior for players in a variable sum n-person game ($n \geq 2$). This theory has not been found to be satisfactory to

[8] Friedberg, R. M., "A Learning Machine: Part I," *IBM Journal of Research and Development*, 2: 1, January 1958.

——, B. Dunham and J. H. North, "A Learning Machine: Part II," *IBM Journal of Research and Development*, 3: 3, July 1959.

Newell, Allen, J. C. Shaw and H. A. Simon, "Chess-Playing Programs and the Problem of Complexity," *IBM Journal of Research and Development*, 2: 4, October 1958.

Samuel, A. L., "Some Studies in Machine Learning Using the Game of Checkers," *IBM Journal of Research and Development*, 3: 3, July 1959.

[9] Flood, M. M., "On Game-Learning Theory and Some Decision-Making Experiments," Chap. X of *Decision Processes*, Thrall, Coombs and Davis (eds.), New York: Wiley & Sons, Inc., 1954. See also Wm. K. Estes, "Individual Behavior in Uncertain Situations: An Interpretation in Terms of Statistical Association Theory," *Ibid.*, Chap. IX.

[10] There are some who disagree. See for example D. Ellsberg, "The Theory of the Reluctant Duelist," *American Economic Review*, 46, 1956.

TABLE 5

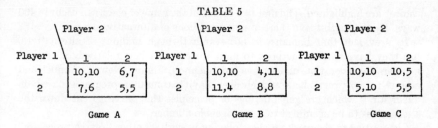

	Player 2			Player 2			Player 2	
Player 1	1	2	Player 1	1	2	Player 1	1	2
1	10,10	6,7	1	10,10	4,11	1	10,10	10,5
2	7,6	5,5	2	11,4	8,8	2	5,10	5,5
	Game A			Game B			Game C	

most behavioral scientists. It does not appear to provide solutions that match even casual observations. Furthermore, the concept of solution only provides for a very weak type of prediction for the outcome of a game.

At this time there are about twenty different theories for the solution of a variable sum n-person game. Most of them are described by Luce and Raiffa[11].

The multiplicity of solution concepts indicates how little we know about behavior in different situations involving group conflict. Perhaps it would be wise at this time to consider several solution concepts, each applying to a specialized area such as

A. Behavior within the firm

B. Small group behavior

C. Conflict situations involving two individuals

D. Markets

and so forth. In this manner some of the groundwork necessary to the eventual construction of a general theory of organization could be done.

At this point a fundamental analogy between two aspects of the Theory of Games and two aspects of industrial organization can be made. The description of a game, its extensive form for example, is equivalent to a description of *market structure* in an industry or organizational structure in a firm. The specification of a solution concept is equivalent to the description of *market behavior* or behavior within a firm.

It is highly desirable to distinguish clearly between structure and behavior, especially when investigating the meaning of several concepts which are crucial to an understanding of socio-economic organization. These include the concepts of competition, collusion, power, centralization and decentralization.

Three simple 2×2 non-constant-sum games and three different concepts of solution, shown in Table 5, serve to illustrate the interplay between structure and behavior.

In the payoff matrices in Table 5 the double entries stand, respectively, for the payoff to the first player and then to the second. Thus, for example, in Game B the result of the play in which Player 1 uses his first strategy and Player 2 his second is 4 to Player 1 and 11 to Player 2.

Although highly simplified, the matrices can be regarded as representing *market structure*. Thus, Game A may portray a rationalized industry where the

[11] Luce, R. Duncan and Howard Raiffa, *Games and Decisions*, New York: Wiley & Sons, 1957.

first strategy for each player is a commitment to a high price *provided* his competitor maintains the high price, together with an intent to meet any cut if the price is not maintained. The second strategy for each is a price cut.

This particular payoff matrix reflects a hypothetical situation in which, if both maintain a high price, they both profit considerably. If one leads off with a cut he may obtain a temporary advantage but eventually both do not do as well as previously. If both begin with price cuts neither does very well. Such might be the case in a dying industry.

The strategies in Game B can be interpreted as decisions concerning advertising and distribution. The first strategy is a decision to spend little on advertising and distribution. The second calls for a large expenditure. Here the matrix reflects the market properties to be expected in a situation where the total sales cannot be heavily changed by advertising or distribution but shares may be radically effected. Furthermore, if one firm establishes a market lead there is little hope for the competitor to retaliate effectively by a "me too" strategy.

The third game represents, in the terminology of economics, a purely competitive market. This will be discussed after some solutions are examined.

The von Neumann and Morgenstern solution to the general n-person game calls for the players to *jointly maximize* and then work out some manner to share the proceeds between themselves. There are other cooperative solutions which suggest joint maximization[12].

Using the notation of section 3, joint maximization calls for the players to select strategies s_1 and s_2 such that

$$\underset{s_1 \varepsilon S_1}{\text{Max}} \ \underset{s_2 \varepsilon S_2}{\text{Max}} \ (P_1(s_1, s_2) + P_2(s_1, s_2)).$$

Another concept of behavior postulated in order to obtain a solution to a game is so called non-cooperative behavior. John Nash has developed the theory which gives non-cooperative equilibrium points as the solutions to games. The type of equilibrium proposed is one familiar to all economists and is directly related to the equilibrium solutions put forward by Cournot, Chamberlin and many others.

Expressed mathematically, a pair of strategies $(\bar{s}_1, \bar{s}_2)$ gives rise to an equilibrium point if the following conditions are simultaneously satisfied:

$$\underset{s_1 \varepsilon S_1}{\text{Max}} \ P_1(s_1, \bar{s}_2) \rightarrow s_1 = \bar{s}_1$$

$$\underset{s_2 \varepsilon S_2}{\text{Max}} \ P_2(\bar{s}_1, s_2) \rightarrow s_2 = \bar{s}_2$$

In words, if Player 1 attempts to maximize his payoff on the assumption that Player 2 will use his strategy $\bar{s}_2$, then Player 1 will use his strategy $\bar{s}_1$ and vice versa.

A third theory of behavior giving rise to another solution concept would be that the players each assume that their opponents are "out to get them." This

[12] For example: Nash, John, "Two-Person Cooperative Games," *Econometrica*, 21, 1953.

is a paranoid world in which it is necessary (as the French view it) that "*on se défend*." Such behavior calls for a maxmin strategy regardless of the type of game. It is the behavior of the highly cautious and pessimistic individual. If both players follow this behavior their actions will be characterized by

$$\underset{s_1 \epsilon S_1}{\text{Max}} \underset{s_2 \epsilon S_2}{\text{Min}} P_1(s_1, s_2)$$

$$\underset{s_2 \epsilon S_2}{\text{Max}} \underset{s_1 \epsilon S_1}{\text{Min}} P_2(s_1, s_2)$$

We now apply the three different behavior concepts to each of the three games. The entries in Table 6 are the strategy pairs which are the solutions to the games. For example, the equilibrium solution to Game B is obtained when both players use their second strategies and the payoff to each is 8.

An inspection of the three games yields the Joint Maximization solutions immediately. For all the games the strategy pair of (1, 1) produces the joint maximum of 20.

The equilibrium solution to Game A is obtained by the following argument. Player 1 observes that if Player 2 uses his first strategy Player 1 will be likewise motivated. Furthermore, placing himself in the position of his competitor he can carry out a similar argument. The solution can be tested in the formal equations given previously in this section.

In Game B if Player 1 presumes that his opponent will use his first strategy he will switch to his second. Carrying this type of argument further, the pair of strategies (2, 2) is the equilibrium solution.

It was noted that Game C represents a purely competitive market (following the terminology of economists). An inspection of the matrix shows that the strategy sets of the players are not interlinked in the sense that the actions of one player have no influence on the payoff for the other. For example, a change in the price of hamburgers by a diner near Philadelphia will have no effect on the trade of another independent diner near Boston.

Because there is no interlinkage between the fates of the players it is not surprising that in a game of this structure all the forms of behavior postulated lead to the same solution. In other words, given the structure in Game C, it is not possible to *identify* the behavior of the players by observing the solution.

TABLE 6

STRUCTURE

BEHAVIOR	Game A	Game B	Game C
Joint Maximum Solution	(1,1)	(1,1)	(1,1)
Equilibrium Solution	(1,1)	(2,2)	(1,1)
Maxmin Solution	(1,1)	(2,2)	(1,1)

In Game A, even though the payoff to each player depends strongly on the actions of both, the structure is such that most forms of behavior lead to the same result. The maxmin behavior produces possibly the most paradoxical result. The extreme caution and pessimism of each player brings them a jointly optimal result.

In Game B, it is possible to distinguish different outcomes resulting from jointly maximizing or non-cooperating behavior. Other structures can be portrayed easily in which it becomes possible to distinguish different outcomes resulting from non-cooperative and maxmin or other forms of behavior.

In Games A and C it is not possible to distinguish between competition, collusion or cooperation.

Suppose both players belong to the same organization, and the structure of the joint enterprise were reflected by the matrices of Games A or C. Such an organization would be naturally fully *decentralized*. The structure of the organization is such that under the very weakest of assumptions concerning the motivations of the players, the joint maximum will be obtained. No communication or messages are needed. The sub-systems will be independently controlled in a manner that benefits the organization as a whole.

In Game A decentralization is achieved because both players have considerable incentives to seek a joint optimum and have no incentives to do anything else. In Game C decentralization is actually isolation. The fates of the players are not intertwined.

For the joint maximum to be achieved in Game B the players must exhibit cooperative behavior. This may entail an elaborate system of communication, coordination and policing. A slight deviation in behavior in Game B would destroy the joint maximization. This is not so in the other games.

A system is successfully decentralized with respect to a set of decisions if the independent actions of individuals in control of the actions of sub-systems achieves the same outcome as a single decision-maker making all the decisions.

Decentralization will depend upon both structure and behavior. The less cooperative the individuals are and the more they commit mistakes or change their behavior, the more difficult it will be to design a system that is successfully decentralized.

The more highly the payoffs of the players are correlated, the easier it is to decentralize decision-making.

Possibly the most fundamental concept to Political Science is that of *power*. The study of Political Science can be defined as the study of power. Yet from Sun Tzu[13] to Machiavelli to the present day this concept has been elusive to the best of minds. In an elementary and highly limited way Game Theory analysis serves as a means to clarify, examine and extend some of the concepts of power.

To date even the concept of power in a chess game is not fully understood. However, the formalization of the analyses of games permits an isolation of

[13] Tzu, Sun, "The Art of War," in *Roots of Strategy*, Brig. Gen. Thomas R. Phillips, (ed.), Harrisburg, Pennsylvania: The Military Service Publishing Company.

problems for study. An example of such a formalization is provided in the construction of an index of power in voting systems[14].

The political problems of power merge directly into economic and industrial ones. The measurement of the power or control of a firm over its market is of prime socio-economic importance. The delegation of authority in decision-making systems presents measurement problems concerned with power.

The direct applications of theories of solution to n-person nonconstant-sum games to operating problems of industry have been few. Apart from the investigation of several different aspects of bidding[15] and the allocation of joint costs few others have been utilized. An interesting use of an n-person game model with Nash equilibria has been made by Charles and Cooper[16] in association with the Chicago Area Transportation Study to simulate patterns of traffic flow when the huge size of the problem made ordinary cut-and-tried simulations prohibitive for electronic computer runs.

6. Theories of Solution for Games Against Nature

In Section 4 the description of the extensive form of a game was given. The formalization made use of an implicit assumption that all the *rules of the game* were known. This means that (at least theoretically) it is possible to enumerate every alternative available to the players. All physically and legally possible events are comprehended.

Even in certain board games, such as the Japanese game of Go (and its Chinese predecessor)[17] there have been some difficulties in defining rules to describe the outcome from every eventuality! How much more difficult is the definition of rules concerning industrial or social organization.

The normalized form of the game serves to illustrate the difficulties faced when an attempt is made to construct a model of a market, firm or other institution.

"Game" D in Table 7 portrays a situation in which the first player knows all the strategies available to both sides, he knows his own payoffs, but he does not know the payoffs to his competitor. This is often the case in bargaining and haggling.

In these examples, the word "Game" has been placed in quotes to indicate

[14] Shubik, Martin, "The Uses of Game Theory in Management Science," *Management Science*, 2, 1955.
    ——, and Shapley, L. S., "Method for Evaluating the Distribution of Power in a Committee System," *American Political Science Review*, 48, 1954.
    Shapley, L. S., "A Value for n-Person Games," *Contributions to the Theory of Games*, Vol. II, *Annals of Mathematics*, No. 28, Princeton, New Jersey: Princeton University Press, 1953.
[15] Vickrey, Wm., "Counterspeculation, Auctions, and Competitive Sealed Tenders," mimeographed, 1959. See also Martin Shubik, "Economics, Management Science, and Operations Research," *The Review of Economics and Statistics*, XL: 3, August 1958.
[16] See Charnes, A. and W. W. Cooper, "External Principles for Simulating Traffic Flows over a Network of City Streets," *Proceedings of the National Academy of Sciences*, 44: 2, February 1958.
[17] Murray, H. J. R., *A History of Board Games Other Than Chess*, Oxford, England: Clarendon Press, 1952, Chapter 4.

TABLE 7

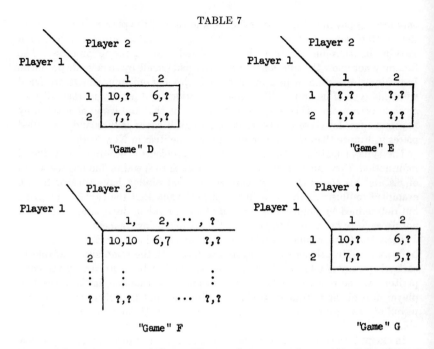

"Game" D

"Game" E

"Game" F

"Game" G

that in the strict sense of Game Theory these examples are *not* fully defined games. However, from the viewpoint of the behavioral scientist these situations involving almost-or pseudo-games must be investigated. The quotes subsequently will not be shown, although the text may imply them.

Experiments have been carried out to study bargaining under varying conditions of information[18]. Even the mathematical analysis of simple and familiar bargaining structures is far from complete, assuming the behavior of the players is known. Vickery[19] has investigated the properties of the usual high bid auction as compared with the Dutch auction.

Many theories of equilibrium in an economic system appear to have the type of game illustrated by Game D as their model. Specific information about one's own payoffs is known, but little is known about the others. An example of an institutional attempt to cope with some of the aspects of ignorance in bidding behavior is to be found in some of the Danish building and crafts trades. After closed bids are submitted, the contract is awarded to the bidder whose tender is closest to a fixed percentage below the *average bid*! In this manner it is hoped that the incompetents whose low bids may be based on misestimates and who might be driven bankrupt while executing the contract will be eliminated. The analysis of this procedure presents several logical difficulties.

Game E illustrates a level of ignorance that is deeper than Game D. Here not

[18] Siegel, Sidney and L. E. Fouraker, *Bargaining and Group Decision Making: Experiments in Bilateral Monopoly*, forthcoming, Macmillan, 1960.

[19] Vickrey, Wm., *op. cit.*

only are the payoffs of the competitor unknown, but the player is not aware of the worth of some of his own payoffs. This corresponds to situations that often exist in multiproduct firms with complicated manufacturing processes. The firm may not know the true contribution to profits made by some of its products. Individuals operating in new markets and with unfamiliar products are faced with this type of ignorance. Thus the art, antique and jewelry markets display great imperfections. This is so to such an extent that the ignorant may easily pay more for Japanese prints in Japan, English silver in England, or period pieces in France than if they purchased the same item in New York.

The type of matrix in Game E brings up problems concerning the value of information. How much should a player be willing to spend to find out the worth of his and his competitors' payoffs? Feeney and Shubik have constructed an example[20] to illustrate that even if the players knew that the payoffs were fixed but determined by numbers drawn from known random distributions, it would not necessarily be rational to "explore the complete environment."

There is a further difficulty which is not illustrated in Game E, but might also be present. Even though the players are aware of the strategies available to each, they may not know which strategy has in fact been utilized by the competitor. As the payoffs are not known, suppose for example, initially the first player uses his first strategy in Game E. He finds out that there is a resultant payoff of, say, $+3$ to him and -3 to his competitor. He may not necessarily be able to tell if this is the result of the strategy pair $(1, 1)$ or $(1, 2)$.

In Game F the players do not know the range of their strategies. It is possible for them to explore for new alternatives. This model confronts the behavioral scientist with the necessity for empirical work on search processes and the need for the development of a theory of search.

Game G illustrates a situation in which the nature of the opponent is not known. He may be "nature," the weather, the tide, a mechanism, a non-human animal, a rat, a psychologist, a sociologist, a Trobriand islander or an ordinary businessman.

In order to "solve" this type of game, i.e., to be able to predict the outcome of a play, or to recommend a form of behavior to Player 1, it is necessary to add some postulates concerning the type and behavior of the opponent. Luce and Raiffa[21] present a comprehensive survey of the many different methods for playing against "nature," which have been suggested.

Many problems dealing with quality control and involving sequential decisions based on statistical sampling are formally equivalent to one-person games against nature. In this sense, it may be said that there has been considerable direct application of this type of Game Theory.

7. Theories of Solution for Dynamic Games

Throughout this article the discussion has proceeded and the examples have been presented as though all game models could be represented by the matrix

---

[20] Feeney, George J. and Martin Shubik, "A Multi-Stage Game with Uncertain Pay-Offs," mimeographed note, February 16, 1960.

[21] Luce and Raiffa, *op. cit.*

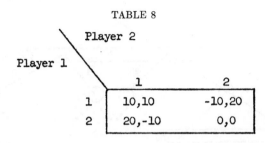

TABLE 8

form. In many instances, especially in the examination of Games A, B and C in Section 5, the discourse had an "almost dynamic" flavor. The dynamics, however, was not made explicit.

The dynamic features of interest can be illustrated by simple examples closely related to the Gambler's ruin problems studies in probability theory.[22]

In Section 4, the extensive form of a game was described. It was implied that any game could be represented by a finite (oriented) game tree. The payoffs from a play of the game in this representation are to be found at the terminal branches of such a diagram. Even though the diagram would be of immense size, such a portrayal of the game of chess is conceivable. Every path from the vertex of the game tree down to a terminal for win, lose or draw will occur there.

The chess analogy does not serve too well for a model of the firm. There are two features which are lacking. Chess, Poker and most other games are of *finite* length with a single payoff at the termination of the game. Theoretically (if not practically) a corporation is immortal. There is no foreseen finite end to the game it plays. Furthermore, it receives payoffs at many times during the game. Sometimes it pays them out as dividends, sometimes it ploughs them back.

If an analogy between a game and the activities of a corporation is to be drawn, corporate activity might be viewed as a non-terminating Poker game in which players occasionally die or are born and furthermore in which there is an inflow of edible poker chips which provide the only food[23]!

Games which have no definite termination cannot be portrayed by a game tree of finite length. The situation of the fanatic gambler playing roulette until he is ruined provides an example of this type of game. Even though the probability may become fantastically small, there is always a small chance that the length of the game will exceed any specific number.

An example of the differences that may be observed between a game of finite length and of indefinite length is illustrated by two closely related games, shown in Table 8. Consider the simple 2 × 2 matrix game that is played for 100 periods. An analysis of the one period game shows that there is an equilibrium point which yields the players (0, 0) and occurs when they both use their second strategies. Initially we might suspect that if the players were to play for 100 periods they

[22] Feller, Wm., *An Introduction to Probability Theory and Its Applications*, New York: Wiley & Sons, 1950, Chapter 14.
[23] I am indebted to Max Woodbury in the formulation of this analogy.

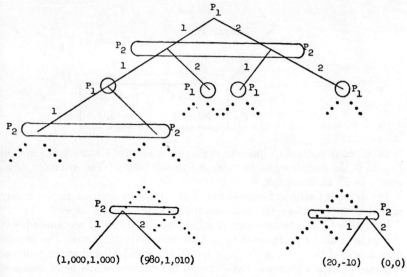

Fig. 3

would not persist in playing in a manner that yielded zero to each on every trial when they have the possibility of obtaining 1,000 each. Yet it can be shown that the equilibrium strategies in the over-all game call for the players to always use their second strategies in the subgames (i.e., in the single period games).

An inspection of the matrix shows that if the game lasts for only one period the players will use their second strategies. Suppose that the game is to be played for 100 periods and that the players have decided each to use their first strategies, thus obtaining 10 each. In the last subgame of the series it will pay each player to "double-cross" his competitor. Both can calculate that they will be forced to the strategy pair (2, 2) on the last game. Each can then reason one stage further back and double-cross each other at stage 99. By continuing the backwards induction it is shown that (2, 2) is always played.

The game tree of the 100 stage game is as indicated in Figure 3. Experiments with this type of game have been run and the evidence to date points towards the type of behavior where the joint minimum is obtained[24].

The closely allied game that is now examined is one in which the period by period subgame is precisely the same; however, at every period there is a probability of p that the game will terminate at the end of that play. The expected duration of the game will be:

$$p + 2(1 - p)p + 3(1 - p)^2 p + \ldots + n(1 - p)^{n-1} p + \ldots$$

[24] Scodel, A., J. S. Minas, P. Ratoosh and M. Lipetz, "Some Descriptive Aspects of Two-Person, Non-Zero-Sum Games," *Conflict Resolution*, II: 2, June 1959.

which represents the probabilities that it lasts exactly one, two, three, ... periods multiplied by the length of the period. This sums to:

$$1/p$$

hence if this game is to have an *expected* length of 100, p can be obtained by setting

$$1/p = 100$$

giving $p = 0.01$ to three figures of accuracy. This game now only differs from the first inasmuch as its expected duration rather than fixed duration is the same as the finite game. All else is identical. Yet now there will exist strategies in the over-all game which cause the players to utilize their first (sub) strategies in the period by period subgames.

Suppose the first player were to adopt the following policy:

"In every subgame I will use my first strategy as long as I observe that Player 2 has utilized his first strategy. As soon as my information tells me otherwise, I will switch to and maintain my second strategy in every subsequent subgame."

If the second player knew of this strategy and tried to maximize his payoff, given this information his over-all expected payoff would be at most

$$10p \sum_{t=0}^{\tau-2} (1 - p)^t + 20p(1 - p)^{\tau-1} + (0)p \sum_{t=\tau}^{\infty} (1 - p)^t .$$

This is obtained on the assumption that at any time, say at period τ, he utilized his second strategy in a subgame. If he only utilized his first strategy his expected payoff is:

$$10p \sum_{t=0}^{\infty} (1 - p)^t.$$

The difference between following the latter policy or the former is always positive for $p = 0.01$; hence the policy of adhering to the first strategy will always be preferred, rather than the second. Similarly, if Player 2 "threatens" Player 1 with the same type of reprisal if he deviates from his first strategy in any subgame, Player 1 will be motivated to play only his first strategy in every subgame.

In the finite game neither side had an effective threat as was shown by their inability to carry out a reprisal against a double-cross at the play of the last of the subgames. In the infinite game, at any play of a subgame, the length the game is still expected to last remains constant and is always long enough to make some reprisals effective.

Referring back to Games A, B and C in Section 5, they can be rephrased in fully dynamic terms and studied accordingly. The details of market structure such as time lags, degree of fixed investment, flexibility in advertising, research or pricing policy all will effect the maneuverability of the firms and their ability to enforce stability in a market.

A further modification to a game of indefinite length can be obtained in the construction of a Game of Economic Survival[25] as a model of the corporation. A simple example illustrates the construction of this type of game and provides the analogy between it and the corporation. In the ordinary Gambler's Ruin Game, the gambler commences with an amount x and plays until he has won a specified amount or the game terminates with his ruin.

In a Game of Economic Survival the player has two accounts, a *corporate account* and a *withdrawal account*. If the assets in the corporate account fall below a specific amount the game terminates and the player is bankrupt. There is a discount rate ρ where $0 < \rho < 1$, which must be used when evaluating income payed into the player's withdrawal account. Every period the player plays in a subgame. This subgame may represent the current market. He received a payment as a result of having played the subgame. This enters his corporate account. He then has a financial move which is to rearrange his assets by shifting money between his corporate and his withdrawal accounts.

By means of this type of model, entry and exit or the birth and death processes of the firm can be portrayed explicitly. Furthermore, different goals or objectives of the firm can also be displayed and studied. Formal models giving emphasis on paying out dividends to stockholders, speeding the growth of the firm, or minimizing the risks of being driven out of business may be examined.

The complete portrayal of a simple, one-person game of Economic Survival is given below:

$$W(0),\ C(0),\ \rho,\ B,\ L, \begin{pmatrix} -1 & 1 \\ 1 & -1 \end{pmatrix}, \qquad (p,\ 1-p).$$

$W(0)$ is the initial value of the withdrawal account.
$C(0)$ is the initial value of the corporate account.
ρ is the discount rate.
B is the bankruptcy level which has effect as soon as $C(t) \leqq B$.
L is the liquidation value or worth of the corporate account of the firm if it is forced to liquidate.
$((a_{ij}))$ The matrix of the subgame represents the payoffs obtained for the corporate account after each play of the subgame. Here, the matrix is specialized to a very simple form.

As this is a one-person game, we assume that the opponent or competitor is "Nature" who is employing a known strategy. This is indicated by $(p,\ 1-p)$ where $0 \leqq p \leqq 1$.

The player could attempt to maximize the discounted expected value of his withdrawal account. Alternatively he may wish to maximize the probability of survival for his firm subject to fixed requirements on the dividend policy. The optimal policies under both of these circumstances have been obtained[26, 27].

[25] Shubik, Martin, *Strategy and Market Structure*, Wiley & Sons, 1959, Chapter X.

——, and G. L. Thompson, "Games of Economic Survival," *Naval Research Logistics Quarterly*, 6: 2, June 1959.

[26] *Ibid.*

[27] Shubik, M., *op. cit.*, pp. 260–264.

In the first instance, the optimal policy is such that the firm will eventually be ruined with a probability of 1. This is not surprising when finances are viewed in terms of inventories. Under an optimal inventory policy, unless out-of-stock costs are infinite, the firm will run out of stock sooner or later.

The type of game described here is closely related to processes that are dealt with by dynamic programming[28].

As it is for most of Game Theory, little claim can be made for direct application of dynamic games. They appear, however, to provide a framework in which many concepts of importance to an understanding of markets, firms and other organizations can be studied. Viability, flexibility, maneuverability, ability to survive, power of threat, ability to retaliate, and sensitivity to information are all examples of concepts which lie in the penumbra between the vague and ill-defined and the clear and well-defined. An understanding of these aspects of the study of strategy are as important to the knowledge of industry and bureaucracy as they are to the knowledge of international affairs, politics or war.

[28] Bellman, Richard, *Dynamic Programming*, Princeton, New Jersey: Princeton University Press, 1957.

Theories of the General Interest, and the Logical Problem of Aggregation

G. Th. Guilbaud   *University of Paris*

[EDITORS' NOTE: In the introductory pages of his essay the author traces the history of what he calls the problem of collective decisions. He shows how, for a long time, this was not distinguished from the distinct problem of choice under uncertainty. He feels that the French philosopher and mathematician Condorcet was the first to see the problem clearly, and that K. J. Arrow was the first to give it an exact formalization. The examples with which the translation begins were taken from a work published by Condorcet in 1785, nine years before his execution during the French Revolution.]

The Principle of Condorcet

The principle of Condorcet motivates us to reduce every opinion to its *simplest components,* but to know "the will of the majority" it is not necessary to have multiple ballots: if we ask each voter to rank the candidates (or the options) in order of preference, we have all the elements necessary for a complete exposition. In establishing a certain order, for instance:

$$\text{First} \ldots \ldots \text{A}$$
$$\text{Second} \ldots \ldots \text{B}$$
$$\text{Third} \ldots \ldots \text{C}$$

the voter affirms (implicitly) the following judgments:

$$\text{A is better than B}$$
$$\text{B} \quad '' \quad '' \quad '' \quad \text{C}$$
$$\text{A} \quad '' \quad '' \quad '' \quad \text{C}$$

which we will express by A > B, B > C, A > C.[1]

---

[1] This is the notation used by Condorcet and later by Lacroix; we find in these authors a clear idea of ordinal structure.

Imagine an electoral body of sixty voters divided in the following manner:[2]

$$23 \text{ have given the order } A > C > B$$
$$19 \quad " \quad " \quad " \quad " \quad B > C > A$$
$$16 \quad " \quad " \quad " \quad " \quad C > B > A$$
$$2 \quad " \quad " \quad " \quad " \quad C > A > B$$

We analyze the voting as follows:

In comparing A with B we have

$$23 + 2 = 25 \text{ votes for } A > B$$
$$19 + 16 = 35 \text{ votes for } B > A$$

Condorcet proposed that the opinion of the majority be

"B is better than A"

In the same way, by comparing A and C, we have

$$23 \text{ votes for } A > C$$
$$19 + 16 + 2 = 37 \text{ votes for } C > A,$$

from which we conclude that the majority prefers C to A. Finally, let us compare B and C:

$$19 \text{ votes for } B > C$$
$$23 + 16 + 2 = 41 \text{ votes } C > B,$$

so the majority prefers C to B.

This analysis leads us to present as "the will of the majority" the three judgments:

$$C > B, B > A, \text{ and } C > A,$$

that is, the order $C > B > A$. If it were necessary to choose only one candidate, we would choose C.[3]

---

[2]Condorcet, "Essai sur l'application de l'analyse à la probabilité des décisions rendues à la pluralité des voix," *Discours préliminaire,* p. 58. Cf. the eleventh hypothesis of the first part, page 119. The same numerical examples are used in later works, in particular in the "Essai sur la constitution et les fonctions des assemblées provinciales."

[3]Condorcet noticed that an ordinary election where each voter puts only one name in the urn would have given 23 votes for A, 19 for B, and 18 for C, and that this vote gives a wrong idea of the real preferences of the collectivity. It is a paradox, noted in these terms in the "Essai sur la constitution et les fonctions des assemblées provinciales" (*Oeuvres de Condorcet,* Arago

Condorcet himself showed the limitations of his method. "There is only one rigorous way of knowing the wish of the plurality in an election. This consists of basing this wish on the respective merits of all candidates compared two by two...but...first, this method is very long...; second, it is possible that none of the candidates will be claimed superior to all the others...."[4]

The first problem, length and difficulty of practical application, is less interesting for us than the second, which indicates the possibility of a situation where there is no valid solution. Let us look at the second numerical example constructed by Condorcet, with the numbers slightly changed.

$$
\begin{array}{rl}
23: & A > B > C \\
17: & B > C > A \\
\text{Vote:} \quad 2: & B > A > C \\
10: & C > A > B \\
8: & C > B > A
\end{array}
$$

$B > C$: $23 + 17 + 2 = 42$; $C > B$: $10 + 8 \quad = 18$
$C > A$: $17 + 10 + 8 = 35$; $A > C$: $23 + 2 \quad = 25$
$A > B$: $23 + 10 \quad = 33$; $B > A$: $17 + 2 + 8 = 27$

By the law of the majority, we should hold three judgments,

$$B > C, \ C > A, \text{ and } A > B,$$

but they are incompatible!

The reason for this failure is easy to detect: the three elementary judgments obtained from an individual opinion are interdependent; if we state $A > B$ and $B > C$, we must have $A > C$. But if we apply the rule of the majority to each of them, nothing can ensure that the three results will

edition, Paris, 1847), Vol. VIII, p. 193: "What do we mean by being elected? Is it not to be judged preferable to the competition? Why do we make this judgment depend on the opinion of the plurality? It is because we think that a statement claimed as true by 15 persons is more likely to be true than the contradictory statement claimed as true by only 10 persons. So, the one who really obtains the preference of the plurality in an election must be the one who seems most superior to his competitors, and thus is the one who has been judged by the plurality as superior to all. But it is possible, if there are only 3 candidates, that one of them will have more votes than the others but that one of the latter, perhaps the one who had the smallest number of votes, will be looked upon by the plurality as superior to each of the others. This assertion seems paradoxical, but one feels that it could be true, if one recalls that when we vote for one candidate, we claim that we believe he is superior to the others but we do not give our opinion on the respective merits of the others; and then the judging is incomplete.... We guessed this inconvenience by a kind of instinct a long time before we proved its reality." Notice that Condorcet uses the word *plurality* when we use *majority* (which, in French, was an Anglicism of the eighteenth century).

[4]*Sur la forme des elections* (Arago edition, Paris, 1847), Vol. IX, p. 305; Brunswick edition (1804), Vol. V, p. 29.

be consistent. In the preceding example there is really a majority for B > C, a majority for C > A, and a majority for A > B; but these three majorities are distinct, none of the voters belonging to all three.

The existence of this phenomenon makes the twofold task of the legislator more difficult: that is, "to know the true judgment of the plurality whenever it exists, and even when such a judgment does not exist" — for example, in the case where the different elementary judgments are not compatible — and "to indicate the choice which should be adopted in order that the risk of error be as small as possible."[5] This is why after having studied the paradox, Condorcet could not resign himself to conclude that it is impossible to attribute any coherent opinion to the electoral body (it would be necessary to claim a kind of "standoff"). He looks for a lesser evil, that is to say, among all *coherent* opinions, the one which is supported by the largest possible number of votes. But, as we will see later, the difficulty is more profound and every attempt at a solution is more or less arbitrary. Condorcet does not ignore this problem and returns to it several times. Daunou, without using mathematics, "presents some very well-founded difficulties with this method of combining statements, and he thinks that in the dubious case there would not be a well-defined majority"; this means that the paradox brought to light by Condorcet is, in a certain sense, impossible to eliminate. It is precisely this ineluctable aspect which K. J. Arrow[6] studied in great detail. Let us spend some time on it.

The Condorcet Effect

Numerical examples cannot hope to make us understand the mechanism of the paradox; a general analysis is necessary. Consider an assembly which has to choose between three options, A, B, and C, and suppose that each member of this assembly has for the three options a consistent set of preferences — that is, he arranges the three options in a given order. Some, for instance, will order in this way:

$$(1) \qquad A > B > C$$

---

[5] "Essai sur les assemblées provinciales," the first work on ways to evaluate the opinion of an electoral body, *Oeuvres de Condorcet,* Arago edition, Vol. VIII, p. 573.

[6] K. J. Arrow mentions the "well-known paradox of voting," without referring to its previous origins. He mentions the "Report on Methods of Election" by E. J. Nanson and attributes to the latter the discovery of this paradox (*Social Choice,* p. 3, n. 3 and p. 95). In fact Nanson published in "Transactions of the Royal Society of Victoria" (Vol. 19, Melbourne, 1883), a study which draws its inspiration explicitly from Condorcet and Borda — known, without doubt, through Todhunter, "A History of the Mathematical Theory of Probability," 1865 — and which does not add anything new to the meaning of the paradox ("These results are well known"). Nanson's aim was to find an election rule of the kind proposed by Condorcet: "In this case (inconsistency) there is no real majority and we cannot arrive at any result without abandoning some one of the three propositions. It seems reasonable that the one which is affirmed by the smallest majority should be abandoned" (*loc. cit.,* p. 213).

This we will call opinion (1). Five other opinions of this type are possible a priori:

(2)	A > C > B
(3)	C > A > B
(4)	C > B > A
(5)	B > C > A
(6)	B > A > C

Thus the members of this assembly are supposed to be divided into six opinion categories or *parties,* which we will designate by the numbers above.[7]

Let N be the total number of voters in the assembly and $N_i (i = 1, 2, \ldots, 6)$ the number of voters in each of the six categories. The search for a collective opinion should be made, following Condorcet's principle, by decomposition: first examine[8] the attitude of the assembly concerning A and B. The six categories are regrouped into two classes:

$$(A > B) = (1) \text{ and } (2) \text{ and } (3)$$
$$(A < B) = (4) \text{ and } (5) \text{ and } (6)$$

and similarly for the other alternatives:

$$(A > C) = (6) \text{ and } (1) \text{ and } (2)$$
$$(A < C) = (3) \text{ and } (4) \text{ and } (5)$$

$$(B > C) = (5) \text{ and } (6) \text{ and } (1)$$
$$(B < C) = (2) \text{ and } (3) \text{ and } (4)$$

The rule of the majority is used to compare the number of voters in two opposed classes.

For instance, if we have[9]

$$N_1 + N_2 + N_3 > N_4 + N_5 + N_6,$$

we will consider $(A > B)$ the collective judgment.

---

[7]Notice that the enumeration of categories has not been done at random: between two contiguous categories there is less difference than between two more distant ones. Clearly the chain closes on itself and (6) and (1) are contiguous; it is possible to represent the categories as placed around a circle.

[8]Either by a simple vote or by the results of a preliminary vote of preference.

[9]The > is used here with its arithmetical meaning "greater than" where, in preceding lines and in the following line, it means "preferred to." But both meanings have the same logical structure—ambiguities are impossible.

The problem is to find out whether the three collective judgments considered can be inconsistent and in which circumstances this could happen.

Inconsistency will occur if we have $(A > B)$, $(B > C)$, and $(C > A)$; or, inversely, if $(A < B)$, $(B < C)$, and $(C < A)$. The first case occurs when we have simultaneously

$$N_1 + N_2 + N_3 > N_4 + N_5 + N_6$$
$$(i) \qquad N_3 + N_4 + N_5 > N_6 + N_1 + N_2$$
$$N_5 + N_6 + N_1 > N_2 + N_3 + N_4$$

Conditions (i') for the second case can be written by inverting the three inequalities.

Conditions (i') are perfectly possible for properly chosen numerical values of the $N_k (k = 1, 2, \ldots, 6)$; we knew already, from Condorcet's example, that application of the decomposition principle and the majority principle could sometimes lead to inconsistency. We can construct as many new examples as we please; for instance — this example is mentioned frequently[10] because it is a simple one — by choosing

$$N_1 = N_3 = N_5 = 1$$
$$N_2 = N_4 = N_6 = 0$$

we satisfy conditions (i). This is an assembly of three persons who hold, respectively, opinions (1), (3), and (5). It would also be sufficient to choose $N_1 = N_3 = N_5 > N_2 = N_4 = N_6$.

Some systems of numbers N_k, that is, some partitions of individuals among the six possible opinions, lead to the situation envisaged by Condorcet. It will be convenient, in the rest of this paper, following the custom of the physical and natural sciences, to call these special situations the "Condorcet effect." It is natural to wonder if these partitions — defined by the systems of inequalities (i) and (i') — possess some other properties more intuitive than their definition, and we wonder whether the Condorcet effect is more or less exceptional. This is not a matter, for the time being, of empirical or historical research, of assemblies meeting to decide on the best of three proposed solutions; in the present state of the subject, psycho-social phenomena more complicated than those we envisage can certainly arise — and, besides, attempts at documentation can only furnish isolated examples[11] with no valid indication of frequency.

---

[10]We shall see, a little further on, the significance of this example.

[11]K. J. Arrow mentions the U. S. Congress deliberations on school appropriations (*Social Choice*, p. 3, n. 3).

It is, however, possible to use the traditional technique of tabulating a priori all possible cases – the results of which can be given in the language of probability theory. In saying that for a die the probability of an ace is equal to 1/6, we are only comparing the ace to the set of faces, that is, to the set of all possible events. In the same way, we can consider all possible partitions of a given number of voters into categories and compute the proportion of those which yield the Condorcet effect. The result can be stated in terms of a probability without necessarily referring to the corresponding game of dice.[12]

Let us begin with a simple case, an assembly of three persons. We can count possibilities: first, all three have the same opinion; second, all three have different opinions; third, two against one. In the first case (unanimity) there is evidently nothing to say, as the ballot problem does not even arise; in the last case a majority obviously exists – no Condorcet effect; but in the second case there are three different opinions, and it is proper to distinguish the several types.

If, for example, the three opinions are

(1)	$A > B > C$
(2)	$A > C > B$
(3)	$C > A > B,$

we see that $(A > B)$ is accepted unanimously and $(A > C)$ and $(C > B)$ by a majority. These three opinions are consistent and lead us to take opinion (2) for the opinion of the majority.[13]

With (1), (2), (4) [cf. p. 265f.] we have the same conclusion: (2) is adopted as the opinion of the majority on each of the three individual ballots. But if the three opinions are (1), (3), (5), the three conclusions are inconsistent,[14] as they are when the opinions are (2), (4), (6). It is possible to verify that these configurations are the only ones which lead to the Condorcet effect.

It would be possible in this case (only three voters) to be satisfied with a summary table of the different possibilities, but we can easily guess that such enumeration will become laborious when the number of voters increases. This is the reason why it is preferable, when the diversity begins to tire the imagination, to replace purely qualitative enumerations with strictly quantitative ones.

To reach this quantitative expression, it is necessary to standardize in

---

[12]This game would consist of throwing a die a certain number of times, N, letting the face obtained represent one voter's opinion, and, at the end, finding the result of this ballot by the Condorcet method. The habit among statisticians of mentioning this kind of game, a specious subordination of statistics to probability, disconcerts the uninitiated; they see obscure intentions in this language and consequently are, with good reason, shocked.

[13]Intermediary in circular ordering.

[14]This is exactly the example already mentioned.

some way: We will consider, for instance, that the first voter can adopt any one of the six opinions, and likewise for the second and third, so that the result is $6 \times 6 \times 6 = 216$ possibilities. Among these 216 possibilities there are twelve[15] which give rise to the Condorcet effect — a little less than 6 percent. A computation of the same type for any number above three would be easy to carry out by the usual methods of combinatorial analysis. We can see that the computed proportion increases slightly with the number of voters:

$$
\begin{array}{lll}
3 \text{ voters} & \ldots \ldots & 5.6\% \\
5 \quad " & \ldots \ldots & 7.0\% \\
9 \quad " & \ldots \ldots & 7.8\% \\
\text{etc.} & &
\end{array}
$$

The limiting value is just under 9 percent.[16]

It appears that, without being rare, the Condorcet effect represents only a small fraction of the possibilities (between 6 and 9 percent); if it occurs much more often than one time out of ten in a long enough run of observations, we can conclude that it is not foolish to look for a specific *cause* which, in the midst of the observed collectivities, orients the antagonistic individual opinions in a way that makes it more difficult for a true majority opinion to emerge.

The key to the whole system is breaking down each individual opinion into simple judgments. Everything is done as if we were determining the opinion of everyone by a battery of three questions, according to the following table, in which the signs + and − mean yes and no, the possible answers to the three questions x, y, and z. Question x, for example, is "Do you prefer B to C?"

Table 1

| | Questions | | | |
	x = (B > C?)	y = (C > A?)	z = (A > B?)	
(1)	+	−	+	A > B > C
(2)	−	−	+	A > C > B
(3)	−	+	+	C > A > B
(4)	−	+	−	C > B > A
(5)	+	+	−	B > C > A
(6)	+	−	−	B > A > C

Opinions (bracketed for rows (1)–(6))

---

[15]These twelve possibilities are (1)(3)(5); (1)(5)(3); (3)(1)(5); (3)(5)(1); (5)(1)(3); (5)(3)(1); and the six analogous arrangements of (2), (4), and (6).

[16]Value given by computing:

$$
1 - \frac{3}{\pi} \text{ arc cos} \left(\frac{1}{\sqrt{3}} \right) = 0.0877
$$

This table does not mention all possible combinations of the signs + or —; two cases are obviously missing, (+++) and (———), because these two systems of answers do not constitute an opinion; they both correspond to three inconsistent elementary judgments.

Once this is done, and once the poll has given us the attitude of each voter, it is possible to construct the table of results by writing in three columns titled x, y, and z the signs corresponding to each ballot. We count in each column the number of votes for (+) and against (—), and finally we compare these two numbers. This amounts to the same thing as performing one algebraic addition and looking at the sign of the result. If the result is positive, it means that there is a majority in favor; if it is negative, there is a majority against.

The table of results for the example we studied first looks like this:

Table 2

	x	y	z
(1)	0	0	0
(2)	—23	—23	+23
(3)	—2	+2	+2
(4)	—16	+16	—16
(5)	+19	+19	—19
(6)	0	0	0
Total	—22	+14	—10
Opinion of majority	—	+	—

We conclude by attributing to the majority the opinion $(-+-)$, that is, opinion (4) or $(C > B > A)$.

In the second example we have

Table 3

	x	y	z
(1)	+23	—23	+23
(2)	0	0	0
(3)	—10	+10	+10
(4)	—8	+8	—8
(5)	+17	+17	—17
(6)	+2	—2	—2
Total	+24	+10	+6
Conclusion	+	+	+

and the result is not a consistent opinion (Condorcet effect).

In general, if the numbers for the six opinions are respectively

$$N_1, N_2, N_3, N_4, N_5, \text{ and } N_6,$$

we have to compute three algebraic sums:

$$x = N_1 - N_2 - N_3 - N_4 + N_5 + N_6$$
$$y = -N_1 - N_2 + N_3 + N_4 + N_5 - N_6$$
$$z = N_1 + N_2 + N_3 - N_4 - N_5 - N_6$$

The Condorcet effect results when the three numbers x, y, z have the same sign.

Now we can give an algebraic form to the Condorcet paradox. It is sufficient to represent each individual opinion by an arrangement of three numbers, each of these numbers taking on the value 1 or -1. Then we have to define a law of composition (or aggregation) combining several opinions into one by adding the columns and replacing each of the results with 1 or -1, depending on its sign.

Symbolically:

$$\hat{x} = \text{Sgn } \Sigma (x_i)$$
$$\hat{y} = \text{Sgn } \Sigma (y_i)$$
$$\hat{z} = \text{Sgn } \Sigma (z_i),$$

(x_i, y_i, z_i) being the opinion of individual i, Σ meaning a sum over all the individuals in the assembly, and Sgn being an operation which consists of replacing every positive number with $+1$ and every negative number with -1; $(\hat{x}, \hat{y}, \hat{z})$ are the resulting opinions.

The Condorcet effect is essentially the following: We define a law for aggregating a set of objects (the triplets of $+1$ and -1); then we see that the fact that some values, $(-1, -1, -1)$ or $(+1, +1, +1)$, are prohibited for component objects is not a sufficient condition for avoiding these same values in the resulting object: the consistency of judgments in each individual opinion is not sufficient to ensure a similar consistency for judgments resulting from the application of the majority rule.

Quételet's Paradox and the Iron Rule

A phenomenon of a more extensive kind can be seen in the Condorcet effect. For instance, we immediately see analogies with the very famous

Quételet paradox. The "average man" theory was strongly criticized for more than a century; but critics often allowed themselves to be drawn in on the ground of sociological science before solving the preliminary question, which is a technical one. It is this preliminary question (and this one only) which will be summarily treated here.[17] As early as 1843, Cournot presented very clearly the fundamental objection:[18] "When determination of the mean (average) is applied to the different parts of a complicated system, great care should be taken to remember that these mean values might be inconsistent with each other, for the system might be in an impossible state if each of the elements took on its mean value, determined separately."[19]

This is a well-known mathematical fact which was clearly recognized by Gauss and Laplace in their theories of errors of observation and their explication of the method of least squares. If one measures several quantities that are not independent, corrections cannot be independent either. Cournot suggests some simple examples inspired by triangulation techniques.

Take some right triangles and compute the means of the lengths of their sides. The three means can be used to construct a new triangle which we could call "average" but *which is not a right triangle*. Here is a numerical example which stresses, by its presentation, analogies with the Condorcet paradox; we have taken four right triangles (the lengths of the sides must satisfy the Pythagorean rule) and computed the three means:

Table 4

	First side	Second side	Hypotenuse
	5	12	13
	15	8	17
	3	4	5
	7	24	25
Sum	30	48	60
Mean	7½	12	15

[17]The best introduction for a reader who wants to know more about the question is the lecture given by Frechet under the title "Réhabilitation de la notion statistique de l'homme moyen" (Les Conférences du Palais de la Découverte, Paris, 1950, 24 pp.). There is also the mathematical memorandum on typical elements by Frechet.

[18]As on many occasions, J. Bertrand satisfied himself by following closely Cournot's text and by adding to the scientific objections his own sprightly style. The result is that Bertrand has been quoted more often than Cournot.

[19]*Exposition de la théorie des chances* (A. A. Cournot, Paris, 1843), p. 213.

The result is not a right triangle, because the sum of the squares of the first two sides is

$$(7\tfrac{1}{2})^2 + (12)^2 = 200\tfrac{1}{4}$$

and the square of the hypotenuse is

$$(15)^2 = 225$$

Here again, by combining several objects, each having the same property, we obtain an object which does not have this property.

More generally, suppose we measure the three sides and three angles of several triangles and compute the mean for each of the six elements. The system of six computed numbers cannot form a triangle unless all the triangles chosen are similar. In this case (similar to the case of unanimity) an average triangle exists.[20]

"Generally, there will not exist any triangle in which the average values for angles and sides correspond. The average of the areas will not coincide with either the area of the triangle based on the average of the sides, and so forth. . . . Thus even if one measures the dimensions of different organs in several animals of the same species, it could very likely happen that the average values would be incompatible with each other and with the conditions for the survival of the species. We insist on this very plain remark because it seems to have been forgotten in work[21] very estimable from another point of view, where the author intends to define and determine the 'average man' by a system of means obtained by measuring the size, weight, and other characteristics of a great number of individuals. The average man so defined, far from being the archetype of the species, would plainly be an impossible man, or at least nothing allows us to consider him possible."[22]

Another famous quarrel has some basic traits in common with the problem raised by Cournot concerning Quételet's text. The invention of

---

[20]For right triangles it is possible to compute quadratic means: the result will be all right. But it is impossible to find a satisfactory operation for ordinary (not right) triangles. Here we touch on the classical problem of aggregation in econometric models, which is very close to the problem we are studying. For instance, one can compare the results of A. Nataf (*Econometrica*, 1948, pp. 232–44) and those of M. Fleming (*Q. J. of Econ.*, 1952, pp. 366–84). The same mathematical structure is discussed.

[21]This is probably Quételet's book, published in Paris, 1835 (Brussels, 1836) with the title *Sur l'homme et le développement de ses facultés, ou Essai de Physique Sociale*. But the "average man" theory already had appeared in an essay of 1831: "Recherches sur la loi de croissance de l'homme" (Nouveaux memoires de l'Acad. R. des Sc. et Belles-Lettres de Bruxelles, Vol. VII, 1932).

[22]Cournot, *Exposition de la théorie des chances* (Paris, 1843), p. 214. Compare the moderation of Cournot with J. Bertrand's tone, "Calcul des Probabilités" (Paris, 1889), pp. 41–43.

printing modified in a very profound way the attitude of the human mind toward the written word; it was probably the necessity to print the Bible which made people aware of the particular nature of problems with the manuscript tradition. The different manuscripts available did not always agree. By the middle of the sixteenth century some scholars recommended authenticity rules which call to mind the rules of popular suffrage, the degree of truth being measured by the number of witnesses. Editions appeared provided with as complete critical apparatus as possible, raising *ipso facto* some problems very close to those of statistical induction. Finally, during the nineteenth century, a transformation of the critics' state of mind occurred which was quite similar to the one already mentioned concerning collective judgments. This corresponded to a kind of strategic retreat approaching careful positivism, at the same time reevaluating the "subjective" as an object of science. With Karl Lachmann a true science of the manuscript tradition was born; it was no longer a matter of starting with value judgments (the authority of the witnesses or even their antiquity) but of determining first the genealogy and relationships. In the same way that scientific criticism of judicial decisions was to lead to some paroxysms so excessive that they would be easy targets for the "subtle minds" who would come later, textual criticism produced, in emulation of Condorcet and Poisson, erudite espousers of "the geometric way" who (perhaps only by the reactions they caused) served philology well. Even more than Lachmann, editor of *Lucrèce* and then of the Greek text of the New Testament (1831), we have to mention Dom Quentin, editor of the Latin version of Genesis who wrote in 1926, "I recognize neither common errors or mistakes, nor good or bad passages, but only different forms of text.... By a method founded on rigorous statistics...I classify manuscripts.... From this classification results a critical canon which imposes an iron rule for the establishment of the text...."[23]

One can imagine the storms raised: "Though it may be possible to compute the movements of machines, it is impossible to compute those of a human will! Scribes were not copying machines!" Dom Quentin's problem or challenge consisted of building an algebra: once the voices of the different witnesses have been weighed and counted, one finally decides by looking at statistics alone, without letting oneself be influenced by a subjective criticism suspected of bias. That is precisely Condorcet's problem. Complication comes from the fact that, for Condorcet, voters were contemporary men, the members of a single assembly, and hypothetically equally right, while in the other case the voters — that is, manuscripts — can be very unequally right depending on how the copy descended. Still, the question is to choose between several divergent opinions for each section of text, and what is wrong with constructing an absolute and acceptable

---

[23]"Essais de critique textuelle" (Paris, 1926), p. 37.

rule which will always permit an appeal to intelligent internal criticism? Repeated application of the rule, whatever it is, does not guarantee the consistency of the final product. A set of preferences constitutes a real opinion, provided that some logical regularities are respected. In the same way, once a Latin or Greek text has been reconstructed, it must show a unity, however difficult to define, of vocabulary, syntax, style, tone, and thought.

In the three cases we have presented, the problem is always to combine several individual representations into a single one and to see if the result satisfies some internal requirements of consistency. Many other illustrations of the conflict between external criticism (which combines the votes) and internal criticism (which examines the product of this combination) could be given; we will see some of them later on. The preceding is sufficient to help us to state the preliminary logical problem in its most general terms. However, the provocative character of the theses of Condorcet, Quételet, Dom Quentin, and their few supporters should be noted; the problems stated are not purely mathematical or logical. It should be very clear that preliminary logical analysis does not allow us to draw conclusions, but it should be evident that drawing conclusions without it is not allowed. This mistake was made by the majority of their opponents. In their eagerness to condemn this psychology or that philosophy, they jumped to conclusions and did not try to understand whether something of the method could be saved. *"Multi pertransibunt,"* Pierre de Fermat liked to repeat, *"ut augeatur scientia."*[24] This implies a lot of waste to gather a little gold.

Means and Associative Operations

The idea of a law of composition is one of the most primitive in mathematics: it occurs naturally in concrete and familiar forms as soon as we start to compute, either with numbers or measurable quantities; addition and multiplication are the two primary examples. Each of the successive extensions of the notion of number has required a parallel extension of the operations. It was quickly noticed that the form of computations and operations could remain the same while the nature of the numerical objects subject to the computation evolved. In this way a kind of general grammar of operations, often called modern algebra (or abstract algebra), was set up.[25] This grammar went back to earlier formal logic, with its combinatorial procedures, which were seen quite early to be similar to arithmetic processes. For instance, the use of the conjunctions *and* and *or* is quite close to the signs $+$ and $\times$. The universal notion which subtends the progress of

---

[24]A contemporary of his would say "Headlong haste and prejudice should be carefully avoided."

[25]Leibniz and even Lulle are precursors. Boole is the initiator: *Laws of Thought,* 1847.

arithmetic as well as that of logic is the law of composition or operation. Consider a set of objects which have no specified nature, and between which relations have been set up in order to define an operative or "algebraic" structure: the setting up of a composition law or *operation* consists of associating with a group of elements called *terms* one unique element called the *result*. In most fields of application, and in particular those we are interested in (composition of votes, judgments, testimonies, etc.), one should be able to apply the operations of composition to a variable number of terms; thus addition for numbers (ordinary or otherwise) or vectors allows us to compute

$$x_2 = a + b$$
$$x_3 = a + b + c$$
$$x_4 = a + b + c + d$$
etc.

In spite of analogies, we take a point of view quite different from that of the definition of a function of several variables. When we write $x = f(a,b,c)$ it indicates that the function f requires three and only three arguments. If we use the functional language, we will have to say that the problem is to define a whole battery of functions such as

$$x_2 = f_2(a,b)$$
$$x_3 = f_3(a,b,c)$$
$$x_4 = f_4(a,b,c,d)$$
etc.

Each function gives a composition law for a definite number of terms. Of course, the set of these functions possesses a certain unity: one must be able to say that, in some sense, the composition law remains *the same* whatever the number of terms being composed.

One of the most frequently used processes in abstract algebra to assure this unity is the recurrence process which defines f_3 by means of f_2; f_4 by means of f_2 and f_3, etc. For instance, as soon as we know how to add two terms in some set, we can, without innovating, add any number of terms just by repetition: addition is said to be *associative*. It is proper to note that in addition the different terms play the same role: in systems where the suffrage is said to be universal, voters are all treated equally and the composition law of the votes possesses the same property of total symmetry as ordinary addition. But this complete indifference to the arrangement of the component terms is not always required; it could be useful to consider cases where the different terms are treated differently, each one having its own role and being unable to change places with another.[26]

The most interesting case of composition by association for this study is the case of the *mean;* as is well known, it is one of the most common processes of statistics, among those which substitute one typical representative object for a set of objects. From the algebraic point of view,[27] which we will take here in order to define the arithmetical mean of a set of objects, we have to know how to write

$$m_2 = \frac{a+b}{2}$$

$$m_3 = \frac{a+b+c}{3}$$

etc.,

that is, to add the objects $a,b,c,\ldots$ and to divide them by an integer.

The operation is really associative, but it is possible to miss this by not computing cautiously. Let us compare the means of five terms: a,b,c,d,e. The associative rule allows us to operate progressively, for instance by computing first the mean of (a,b,c) and then the mean of (d,e) and finally the mean of the two results. Thus we have

$$x = \frac{a+b+c}{3} \qquad y = \frac{d+e}{2}$$

But it is clear that the final mean is not $\frac{x+y}{2}$. The true mean is $\frac{3x+2y}{5}$.

Indeed, there is no such thing as a nonweighted mean, only *equally weighted* means, for every averaging operation implies that a weight is given to each of the combined objects. The previous way of writing is convenient because of its conciseness, but it is fallacious.

---

[26]However, the variety of situations obtained by repeating any binary operation is almost always too large; this leads us to reduce that variety by some restriction. This is the meaning of the associative axiom, which states:

$$f_2(a,f_2(b,c)) = f_2(f_2(a,b),c) = f_3(a,b,c)$$

Modern algebra, which is not too easily freed from numerical models, has surely been a little negligent about studying nonassociative operations.

[27]The idea of the mean has been extensively studied from a topological point of view by Frechet; see, first, "Les éléments aléatoires de nature quelconque dans un espace distancié" (*Annales de l'Institut Henri Poincaré,* Vol. X, fasc. 4, pp. 215–308, Paris, 1948); second, "Une propriété générale des valeurs typiques d'une nombre aléatoire" (*Publications de l'Institut de Statistique de l'Université de Paris,* Vol. 1, fasc. 1, Paris, 1952, 47 pp.); and also, for an elementary and rapid view, the conference at the Palais de la Découverte, mentioned (note 17).

If we write $(a;p)$ to indicate the object a weighted by p (which is a number), the composition law is

$$(a;p) + (b;q) = \left(\frac{ap + bq}{p + q}; p + q\right),$$

which indicates, in addition to the arithmetical rule for computing the mean, $\frac{ap + bq}{p + q}$, the weight that must be assigned to this mean, which is the sum of the weights of the components.

With this convention, the case previously mentioned takes the form

$$(x;3) = (a;1) + (b;1) + (c;1)$$
$$(y;2) = (d;1) + (e;1)$$

and the general mean is $(x;3) + (y;2) = \left(\frac{3x + 2y}{5}; 5\right)$.

Thus the operation of averaging is really associative. It is even commutative, that is, perfectly symmetrical, as is addition. This is not the case for another very common procedure, namely the *median*. It is known that to define a median,[28] it is not necessary to know how to add the objects treated by statistics; it is sufficient to know how to rank them in a "scale," or linear ordering, in order to be able to make meaningful the statement that one object is located *between* two other objects. The operation of determining a median can therefore be used in qualitative areas.[29] If we have a particular set of objects which can be ordered, we shall call the cut which divides the set into two groups with an equal number of objects (or more exactly, of equal weight) the median.[30]

It is clear that (in contrast to the computation of a mean) the determination of a median cannot be made progressively. If the median of a group of seven numerical measures (assumed to be equally weighted) is $x = 15$ and if the median of another group of three is $y = 10$, it is not possible to say very much, as long as we do not have other information, about the median

---

[28]This word was introduced with that meaning by Cournot: *Exposition de la théorie des chances,* pp. 63 and 120.

[29]Strictly speaking, means and medians do not have the same range of application. To consider a mean the set of objects studied must have a structure of the kind called vectorial (possessing an internal addition and multiplication by a body of operators, here the weights, which are ordinal numbers). To consider a median, the set must have an ordered structure. The set of real numbers possesses both these qualities, so that it is possible to speak of mean and median and compare these two composition laws, but this is an exceptional case.

[30]If the number of objects in a collection is odd, the cut consists of one of the objects of the collection itself; if the number is even, it is an interval which might contain objects of the set, but which may also be empty.

of the group formed by combining the ten measures, except that it is somewhere between 10 and 15. When a group increases through the addition of new members, we have to start computing all over again; the operation is not associative.

A third classical procedure leading to the choice of a typical object is the *mode*; in a collection of objects to which weights have been assigned (in statistics, these weights represent the number of observed repetitions), a mode (also called a dominant or most frequent value) is an object which has the greatest weight.[31] The mode corresponds exactly to the rule of the majority; in this case objects do not have to be added or even ordered.

These three methods are all laws of composition which, applied to objects of a specific type, lead to a result of the same type. One could figure out others; in fact, the mean has been generalized (quadratic, geometric, harmonic, etc.). We note that Quételet used means. For philologists the question is naturally more subtle, yet it is possible to relate the critical (external) rules to a process of determining the median; an important reservation should be that testimonies are not ranked in linear order but as far as possible are arranged in a genealogical tree. All efforts are made to find the source or archetype, and it is no longer a matter of choosing an *intermediate* situation like the median but still of choosing some situation defined in a more complex structure. The analytical study of the Condorcet paradox will lead us to see how medians can be defined in partially ordered structures of various types.

Every operation is defined within a certain set: the result of the operation is of the same nature as each of the terms; one does not go outside the set of all objects of the nature considered. Thus the sum of several numbers is a number; the mean of a set of (weighted) numbers is, in the same way, a (weighted) number. But if we restrict in any way the range of variability of component terms, it is not always true that the operation gives a result located in the new restricted range. The sum of several integers is still an integer, but their mean may not be. We will say that the set of integers is closed[32] for addition, but not for the mean.

The problem stated by Cournot with regard to the theory of Quételet is the following: given the definition of the mean of a certain set of objects (triangles or any geometrical objects, or even, as Quételet wanted, numerical descriptions of humans), is this set closed under the operation or will the operation make external, impossible, and absurd objects appear? The Condorcet paradox also consists of observing that a certain operation applied to certain objects (individual opinions in the form of preference

---

[31]Obviously, there will be more than one mode if two weights are equal and greater than all the other weights. This causes certain problems (analogous to a standoff in voting).

[32]*Stable* has the same meaning.

judgments) gives birth to objects which do not have the same form (a set of inconsistent judgments). The paradox in both cases arises because the composition operator has been mathematically defined on a set larger than the set to which it can be effectively applied. The mean of Quételet is applicable to every system of numbers, even if they do not describe any real object; the counting of the votes recommended by Condorcet could be done even if the ballots expressed inconsistent judgments. In one case as in the other, the typical, representative object was not directly defined to be a mean or a mode. In both cases the beginning was the analysis of each of the objects of the collection. According to Quételet, a descriptive card giving a series of measures is set up for each individual of the studied population; anthropometry is the first step, which will reduce our knowledge to a system of numbers, and for each of these "dimensions" or "coordinates" a mean will be set up. From Condorcet, an analogous principle directs us to reduce opinion to a series of preference judgments, answering yes or no to a battery of questions, and it is for each of these "dimensions" that the "will of the majority" is established.

The general frame in which our paradoxes and problems of "aggregation" will be contained takes form by itself. The objects for which we are trying to define composition are complex objects formed by pooling several components. Thus $(x,y,z \ldots)$ is such an object which has for components $x,y,z,$ etc. Given a population $(x_i, y_i, z_i, \ldots)$ $(i = 1, 2, \ldots, n)$, we try to define a mean, median, mode, or any other operation on the complex objects by doing separately such operations on each of the populations of components. If the different components have the same nature (e.g., real numbers), it may seem natural to perform the same operation on each component:

$$x = M(x_1, x_2, x_3 \ldots)$$
$$y = M(y_1, y_2, y_3 \ldots),$$

but it is possible that in some cases we will find it advantageous to do one operation on the x's and another on the y's.

In the case in which all the components are numerical—the ideal case for Quételet's anthropometry—the study of such operations on complexes of numbers is a natural extension of simple algebra. A complex object (x,y,z) can be symbolized by a point in an adequate space, and if the M operation is the arithmetical mean, the point (x,y,z) is the center of gravity of the population of given points.[33] Thus the problem stated by the paradoxes is this: given a part of the space containing points representing real (or possible) objects, does the center of gravity of those points always lie

---

[33]Quételet referred to his average man as a "center of gravity," but for him the word *gravity* had an active meaning (attraction).

in that subspace? In other words, is the possibility space closed for the operation of the mean?[34]

If we take as objects right triangles and for coordinates the lengths of the three sides, we always have $x^2 + y^2 = z^2$. The possibility space is the surface of a cone. It is not closed; the center of gravity is inside the cone. The conditions for closure of the operation of the median or any other technique would be studied in the same way, but we will not linger on it. The study of qualitative, not quantitative, situations will make us better able to grasp the nature of the problems.

The Logical Problem

The problems of abstract algebra arise as soon as we have to compose or aggregate *several* objects into one of the same kind; the two fundamental characteristics of the algebraic game were just outlined. On the one hand, the operation of composition is not a juxtaposition but a real reduction of a multitude of component objects to one, the result having the same nature as each of the terms. On the other hand, the number of component terms should be kept indeterminate; it must be possible to compound any number of terms. These two aspects are obviously present in the voting problem, where the result looks like an individual opinion once it has been announced and the procedure has to be adaptable to any variation in the number of votes cast. That is not all. As was clearly seen by Condorcet, the very nature of the terms and of the result is not strictly defined in advance; it even seems impossible, except in some exceptional cases, to predict the general effect of the forms that the opinions expressed by the voters can take. In contrast, it is certainly possible to consider each individual opinion as a system of judgments, that is, of affirmations or negations, of acceptances or refusals, of a certain number of simple propositions. All that each member of the collectivity may say at the moment of the ballot on a given subject can be represented by the answers yes and no to a series of questions.

Thus the general scheme will be

Questions	Individual Responses				
	No. 1	No. 2	No. 3	...	...
a............	+	−	+	...	...
b............	+	+	−	...	...
c............	−	−	+	...	...
d............	−	+	+	...	...
....	...	...	...	...	...

---

[34]A *convex* part of the space means a closed part of the space.

But, in the same way that the number of individuals must be left arbitrary and rules valid for any number have to be figured out, the number of elementary questions must not be fixed in advance. Thus the algebraic or combinatorial problem comes up in two ways. Condorcet solves this problem by proposing, first, to define a composition rule for every series of simple judgments, a rule which could be applied to every row of the preceding table; and second, to apply this rule to all the rows and to compute in this manner a new column which will be taken as an expression of the collective opinion. Without discussing here the practical applications, let us admit that some institutions fit the model. An assembly, for instance, or a committee, often has to give its opinion successively on several questions:[35] the collective answer for each question is determined separately by a procedure of discussions, votes, or the like, and we often recognize after some time that the different decisions are logically interconnected and should present a consistent appearance. Experience, in fact, proves that this consistency is not always very strong. But can we charge an assembly with "contradicting itself"? The idea of contradiction applies to the logic of the individual: what logic (is it the same?) results from the mechanisms of voting?

Let us first consider what the application of the rule of the majority leads to. Once each individual opinion has been analyzed into simple elements by means of a series of questions (columns of the preceding table), a statistic is established separately for each line and we keep the dominant answer. However, the example already studied (p. 265ff.), in which elementary questions were related to preference judgments, warns us that for each individual opinion there exist certain connections among the different answers. This interdependence, incidentally, is not functional and does not resemble the interdependence used by Cournot in his criticism of Quételet: in a right triangle the three sides are interdependent, meaning that each side is a function of the other two; knowing the lengths of two sides allows us to compute the length of the third side. Here it is different. Knowing the answers to the two questions "A > B?" and "B > C?" does not *always* allow us to predict the answer to the third question, "C > A?" All we can say is that it is impossible to have the same answer (either yes or no) for all three questions. The interdependence of the component elements, or the logical consistency of an individual opinion, is expressed by excluding some arrangements of signs (see Table 1).

The general logic of propositions, a development of part of the older theory of syllogisms, teaches us that the problem is universal. Given several propositions or questions, every logical relation between them can be expressed by establishing the list of possible arrangements of signs and the

---

[35]The procedures of disjunction, of voting "by articles," etc., are of the same family.

list of impossible arrangements.[36] For instance, the implication "A implies B" or, more familiarly, "no A without B" is nothing but the impossibility of the one arrangement $A = +$, $B = -$.

In the same way, the conjunction "A implies B and B implies C," which forms the framework of the traditional syllogism, is equivalent to the impossibility of the four arrangements

$$
\begin{array}{lcccc}
A................. & + & + & - & + \\
B................. & + & - & + & - \\
C................. & - & + & - & -
\end{array}
$$

and the possibility of four others:

$$
\begin{array}{lcccc}
A................. & + & - & - & - \\
B................. & + & + & - & - \\
C................. & + & + & + & -
\end{array}
$$

As a consequence, each time a logical connection among several questions appears, we may be sure that certain arrangements are missing. However, as Condorcet's example shows, the rule of the majority may very well lead to a forbidden arrangement. It is easy to see that this phenomenon does not occur for two propositions, but it can appear as soon as we consider three propositions that are not completely independent.[37] In order to analyze this easily, a geometrical model can be used. The different answers to the three questions can be schematized by the eight vertices of a cube, the first question being represented by the left-right alternative; the second, upper-lower; the third, front-back. Condorcet's method of deriving a collective opinion consists of considering opposite faces and choosing the face having the majority. The *effect* consists of the following: it is possible to distribute a population among the vertices of a cube, leaving empty some corners so that the three majority faces meet at an empty vertex. In spite of the very large number of possible cases, it is always possible to reduce them to combinations of situations analogous to the following:

Individual opinions	Resulting opinion
+ + −	+
+ − +	+
− + +	+

---

[36]See any treatise on logic: for instance, J. Piaget, *Traité de logique* (Paris, 1949), p. 225ff, or J. Dopp, *Leçons de logique formelle* (Louvain, 1950), 2d part, "Logique moderne," Vol. I, pp. 37ff.

[37]With the meaning of formal logic: three propositions are independent if the eight arrangements are a priori possible.

This radical configuration is obtained easily if we start at the empty corner and find the three points joined to this empty point by an edge of the cube; if we put one individual at each of these three points, there will be two individuals (and thus a majority) on each face. It is precisely this configuration of opinions which is always pointed out as an example of the voting paradox. This effect can occur for any number of propositions, provided there are more than two. It can also occur for propositions having more than two values. For instance, it could be assumed that besides the answers yes and no, indifference[38] is a possible response.

In any case, it is possible to state the following result. If the individual opinions are analyzed into elementary attitudes or answers to a series of questions, and if we determine the dominant attitude separately for each question, the system of dominant attitudes may *not be represented* in the population and may even be judged contradictory by universal agreement.

Since in many cases these contingencies (mainly the second one) will be considered serious impediments, the occurrence of the Condorcet effect should be prevented. A first line of research is to note that the Condorcet effect can be produced only by a certain distribution of individual opinions, but experience proves that the distribution (which could be called opinion, in the singular) is not of any particular type. Certain individual interdependencies exist which in fact make up one of the subjects for study in the sociology of opinions. If all the opinions are alike (unanimity), there is no danger. We are led to consider that the distributions which produce the Condorcet effect are those which are the farthest from unanimity, and that the effect itself should be considered a pathological symptom of unusually deep social division. It would be vain to try to remedy this evil through a complicated electoral system. It is an evil which should be prevented before it is manifested in voting. The way Condorcet considered the problem[39] is not very different from what we have just summarily described, which brings to mind Rousseau's theory of the general interest.

But we should realize that although, from a political and social point of view, such views appear reasonable, they leave untouched the fundamental logical problem. We have seen that if the law of the majority is applied to a set of opinions, each opinion consisting of a preference judgment, it can lead to inconsistencies. But let us see if in the population considered there is, besides the universal logical rules,[40] a certain community of view which, while not being unanimous, ensures that we no longer risk the Condorcet effect. We know the role played by logical connections among the com-

---

[38]However, we must carefully distinguish between equivalence and ignorance. A blank ballot can mean either "no opinion" or "the two proposed solutions have the same value."

[39]Of course this way of thinking was mocked. The same people who reproached Condorcet for using mathematics in political and human affairs now reproach him for not using enough mathematics in his conclusions.

[40]Lack of a cycle (A > B, B > C ... Z > A) of any length.

ponents of an individual opinion; the question now is to consider the role that could be played by the connections among the individual opinions and in particular to see whether these new connections could not, at least in certain circumstances, reduce the disturbing effect of the first ones. Let us start by considering an example.

Suppose that an assembly debates, not different propositions of some kind, but the choice of a number—for instance, the amount of credit, expenditure, tax, sale price, or the like. It is very likely that individual opinions will have something in common. If there are three choices, a low, medium, and high figure—say A = 1,000, B = 1,500, and C = 2,000—the voters will be divided naturally into three classes:

(a) Those who prefer the low figure
(b) "   "   "   " medium figure
(c) "   "   "   " high figure

But although it may be all right to subdivide class (b) according to whether A is judged better than C, or vice versa, it is doubtful whether the persons who prefer A would judge C better than B. Thus we can be led (at least under certain circumstances) to exclude a priori some orderings of preference: that is, admit that *subjective* individual opinions are related to the natural and *objective* ordering of the proposed figures.

The same type of considerations will occur each time the options proposed for deliberation have an *objective* order. If there was a fourth option, D = 3000, these orderings would be possible:

$$A > B > C > D \quad | \quad D > C > B > A$$
$$B > A > C > D \quad | \quad C > B > A > D$$
$$B > C > A > D \quad | \quad C > B > D > A$$
$$B > C > D > A \quad | \quad C > D > B > A$$

but others would be excluded, such as B > A > D > C, by the following argument: B is preferred to everything else, and C is closer to B than to D, so C should be preferred to D. It is seen that subjective preference orderings do not directly follow the objective order, but rather certain rules of proximity which derive from this objective order.

Let us treat the general case by designating choices by the letters A,B,C, . . . , X,Y,Z in such a way that the objective order is the alphabetic one. Every opinion will be represented by a complex of simple judgments— A < D, B < F, . . .—but we admit that these simple judgments are not completely independent. Not only must they follow the general logic of preference; they must make allowance for the logical ordering. Thus, when an opinion contains the judgment D < K, it indicates that this opinion locates its optimum either between D and K or at K or beyond K. The result is that all options preceding (objectively) D must be judged inferior (subjectively) to all the options preceding K:

$$C < K \quad B < K \quad A < K$$
$$D < J \quad C < J \quad B < J \quad A < J$$
$$D < I \quad C < I \quad B < I \quad A < I \quad \text{etc.}$$

In the same way, as soon as one allows a judgment which inverts the objective order, H > M, it indicates that the optimum precedes M and as a consequence we must have

$$H > N \quad H > O \quad H > P$$
$$I > M \quad I > N \quad I > O \quad I > P$$
$$J > M \quad J > N \quad J > O \quad J > P \quad \text{etc.}$$

These observations focus attention on a sort of hierarchy of judgments — one judgment dominates several others. This subordination is easy to designate in the form of an ordered network.[41] A triangular table such as the following is constructed:

$$(A < B) \leftarrow (A < C) \leftarrow (A < D) \leftarrow (A < E) \leftarrow (A < F) \ldots$$
$$\uparrow \qquad\quad \uparrow \qquad\quad \uparrow \qquad\quad \uparrow$$
$$(B < C) \leftarrow (B < D) \leftarrow (B < E) \leftarrow (B < F) \ldots$$
$$\uparrow \qquad\quad \uparrow \qquad\quad \uparrow$$
$$(C < D) \leftarrow (C < E) \leftarrow (C < F) \ldots$$
$$\uparrow \qquad\quad \uparrow$$
$$(D < E) \leftarrow (D < F) \ldots$$
$$\uparrow$$
$$(E < F) \ldots$$

Note that the affirmation of any one of these judgments implies the affirmation of all the "consequences": that is, the affirmation of those located either in the same row and to the left, or in the same column and above, and thus of all the judgments located to the left and above.

Analogously, the negation of any judgment in the preceding table implies the negation of all the "antecedents": that is, all those to the right and below.

If affirmation is indicated by a plus sign and negation by a minus sign, the result is that the complete opinion of any individual can be represented by a triangular table like the following:

---

[41]This is a partially ordered structure, called a lattice. The elements of the theory will be found in V. Glivenko, *Théorie générale des structures* (Paris, Hermann, 1938); "Actualités scientifiques," No. 652, 54 pp.; and H. B. Curry, *Leçons de logique algébrique* (Paris and Louvain, 1952, 163 pp.).

	B	C	D	E	F	G ...
A	+	+	+	+	+	−
B		+	+	+	−	−
C			+	+	−	−
D				−	−	−
E					−	−
F						−
...						...

There are two distinguishable regions, one of plus signs and one of minus signs, which can be separated by a border as has been done in the preceding table. This border must respect the symbolic implications: all the arrows of the network that cross the border pass from the plus region to the minus region.*

Now let us see how several opinions of this type can give birth to a collective opinion when the majority rule is applied to each of the component judgments.

Superimposing the different schemata and counting the votes is sufficient: let us take for example the simplest case, that of three voters. The three borders might not cross each other:

	I B	II C	D	III E	F	etc.
A	+	+	+	+	−	
	+	+	−	−	−	
	+	−	−	−	−	
B		+	+	+	−	
		+	−	−	−	
		−	−	−	−	
C			+	+	−	
			−	−	−	
			−	−	−	
D				−	−	
				−	−	

etc.,

*[EDITORS' NOTE: A plus sign in the above table thus indicates that the column option is preferred to the row option by the individual whose opinion the table represents, whereas a minus sign signifies the opposite preference. The supposed objective order of the options and the assumptions about the behavior of the individual respondents ensure that entries above or to the left of a plus sign will be plus, whereas entries below or to the right of a minus sign will be minus. The next step is to consider what happens when the opinions of several individuals who have different patterns of plus and minus signs are aggregated.]

thus determining four regions. In the first there is unanimity (three plus signs), in the second a majority ($+$), in the third a majority ($-$), and in the fourth unanimity ($-$).*

If the law of the majority is imposed, we will institute the plus sign in the first two regions and the minus sign in the last two.

Finally, the majority law leads us to adopt the intermediary opinion represented by the border II, namely, $C > B > A > D > E > F$ etc.

Thus we obtain two important results: first, majority law leads to the adoption of a set of judgments which possess the same consistency as the components of each individual opinion; and, second, this same law permits the definition of a "median" or "intermediate" opinion as the collective opinion. It would not be difficult to show that the situation is the same if we compound five, seven, or any odd number of individual opinions. For an even number, exact balances of the number of votes "for" ($+$) and "against" ($-$) may occur. But whatever decision is taken with regard to these litigious cases,[42] the result is always the same: the result still deserves the name *opinion* because of the consistency of its component elements and the epithet *intermediate* because of its location. The first conclusion to draw from this examination[43] is the lack of any Condorcet effect. If the individual opinions respect, with the indicated meaning, the same *objective* order, the law of composition by majority leads to an opinion which has the same form. The set of opinions taken into account is *closed* for the composition law adopted: there is no risk of having to leave this set.

The second conclusion is just as important. The problem is to understand the reasons for the vanishing of the Condorcet effect. The name "median" or intermediate opinion presented itself very naturally during the analysis because the set of opinions that we have studied possesses a certain order, at least partial, which is a direct consequence of the partial order present in the set of component judgments, and is symbolized by the triangular network (lattice) drawn earlier (p. 286).

Let us briefly describe the structure which prevails in the set of acceptable opinions. First, there are two extreme opinions:[44] the alphabetic order ABCDE and the inverse, EDCBA.

---

[42]For example, a preponderant voice to the president, or any other analogous rule.

[43]This result was recognized by Duncan Black, "The Decisions of a Committee," *Econometrica,* **16,** 1948, 245–61. For a deeper analysis, the work of the same author can be consulted: D. Black and R. A. Newing, *Committee Decisions* (London, Hodge, 1952), p. 59. See also K. J. Arrow, *Social Choice,* pp. 6, 75–80.

[44]Let us limit ourselves to seeing the phenomenon in the example of choosing between five options: A, B, C, D, and E. Nevertheless, the conclusions are general.

*[EDITORS' NOTE: The three signs in each cell of this array indicate the opinion of each of the three voters. For instance, the $^+_-$ in row A and column D indicates that voter number 1 prefers D to A, whereas voters 2 and 3 prefer A to D.]

Then, given any opinion—for example, CBDAE—it is possible to construct an opinion which is intermediate between this one and one of the two extremes; for instance, ABCDE affirms all the elementary judgments, and CBDAE affirms only

$$AE, BD, BE, CD, CE, DE$$

and negates all others.

The opinion BCADE will be intermediate, since it affirms *more* than CBDAE and *less* than ABCDE. These different kinds of relations can be symbolized by an oriented network on which we will verify that BCDAE is really on one of the paths which lead from CBDAE to ABCDE:

```
                                              BACDE → ABCDE
                                                 ↑
                                  CBADE → BCADE
                                     ↑         ↑
          DCBAE → CDBAE → CBDAE → BCDAE
             ↑        ↑        ↑        ↑
          DEBEA → CDBEA → CBDEA → BCDEA
             ↑        ↑
          DCEBA → CDEBA
             ↑
EDCBA → DECBA
```

Using this schema, it is possible to interpret the construction of the collective opinions based on some given individual opinions. If the various individual opinions are located on the same chain, the ordinary definition of the *median* is satisfactory; otherwise it is a generalized median.

We know now that there are two cases where the Condorcet effect does not occur and the application of the majority law will never lead to absurdity.

The first case is when no combination of affirmations and negations of the elementary propositions is a priori impossible. If all combinations of plus and minus have meaning, it is clear that the resulting opinion will be acceptable. The example we just studied belongs to the second case, where the individual opinions are restricted to a preferential set which has been defined here by referring to an "objective" value; in order to explain that this set is closed, it is sufficient, as we have seen, to note that the set is ordered and that the majority law is equivalent to the choice of an *intermediate* opinion. The two cases are actually very similar, in spite of appearances. The first can be put in the form of the second, and vice versa.

Let us begin by presenting the second case in a form analogous to the first. Again take the example of the five options A,B,C,D,E. Here an opinion consists of an order of preference established among the options, but not just any order: we have supposed that the subjective preferences are subordinate to an objective order and that there are only sixteen possible orders (the orders of the network on page 289).[45] To know an opinion it is not necessary to ask all the questions "A > B?", "A > C?", ..., "D > E?". There is a more economical way to conduct the inquiry. Begin by asking if the option put in the last place is A or E. The answer to this question is seen to divide the table of opinions in half. Proceed by asking if the option put in last place and the one before it are naturally contiguous (as for CBADE) or not (as for CBDAE). Then ask if options put in two successive places in the subjective opinion are contiguous in the objective order. There are four questions whose answers are absolutely independent; therefore the opinions are represented by all possible combinations of yes and no. This is the same form as the first case.

Inversely, the first case (answers completely independent) can be presented in the form of the second (ordered system of opinions). The set of all obtained opinions can be ordered by arranging the plus and minus signs in all possible ways. Begin by choosing two extreme opinions that we will call, respectively, the "first" and the "last." It is sufficient that they be contradictory—for instance, if the first opinion is the one that answers no to all the questions, the last will be the one that answers yes to all. To go from the first to the last, we can construct different chains or sequences of opinions so that each opinion is inferred from the preceding one by a "concession," replacing a no with a yes:

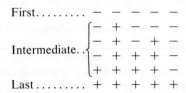

$$
\begin{array}{ll}
\text{First.}\ldots\ldots & -\quad-\quad-\quad-\quad- \\[4pt]
\text{Intermediate.}\left\{\begin{array}{l} \\ \\ \\ \\ \end{array}\right. &
\begin{array}{l}
-\quad+\quad-\quad-\quad- \\
-\quad+\quad-\quad+\quad- \\
-\quad+\quad+\quad+\quad- \\
+\quad+\quad+\quad+\quad-
\end{array} \\[4pt]
\text{Last.}\ldots\ldots & +\quad+\quad+\quad+\quad+
\end{array}
$$

For two elements of such a chain it is possible to talk of antecedents and consequences; the result is again an oriented network. So we perceive what we will call the *reasons* for the Condorcet phenomena. The system of acceptable opinions must show an internal consistency linked to the two images of order and completeness. It is not necessary to go further into the algebraic technique,[46] but it is important to underline the significance of the fundamental logic.

Condorcet clearly saw that the majority rule seems to be an improve-

---

[45]Generally, for *n* options, there will be $2n - 1$ acceptable orders.

[46]It would be necessary to clarify the relations between the "lattice" structures and the "ring" structures.

ment on the statistical determination of a typical element which, by itself, has the greatest weight.[47] If the majority opinion were chosen, a large part of the information given by the vote (or statistical survey) might be neglected. In fact, very often the "palette" of opinions is not totally devoid of structure: one feels that one opinion is more or less "close" to another. Why do we not recognize the elements of the vote which, being common to the minority opinions, may have more real importance than the majority opinion considered alone? Thus the whole problem consists of beginning to be conscious of what we vaguely called the structure of the palette of opinions. It is interesting to see that the analysis of an opinion as responses of yes and no to a series of questions, followed by the adoption of the opinion built up from the majority responses, leads us to define this structure as *partially* ordered and to recognize that the collective opinion finally adopted is a generalization of the *median* of a *completely* ordered linear set.

If the elementary questions were independent, every combination of responses would be possible: the set of all these combinations is ordered, but if a part of this set is not allowed (because of some criterion of internal consistency) then the rest of the set has to possess the same type of structure — all the cases which can occur can be predicted by looking for those parts of a structure which have a structure analogous to that of the whole.

A certain internal harmony of the *possible* opinions is the general form of the conditions imposed in order for a series of decisions taken by the majority of votes to form a unique consistent opinion. It should be recognized that voting and majority rule are often used to resolve conflicts which are too profound to depend on this procedure. By examining the vote closely enough, we would be led to some useful reflections on majorities which are "more or less strong." It is not the strength of numbers which gives more or less weight to a voted decision, but whether the vote has revealed little diversity of individual opinion: then we are undoubtedly closer to the ideal conditions which allow the application of the majority law. Voting operates at first as a test of the degree of unity in the electoral body.

By the way, it can be seen that the usual language does not adequately express the questions we raise here; it is tempting to say — and it is said sometimes — that a series of decisions made by the majority of voters cannot claim to represent a true collective opinion if the individual opinions are too deeply divergent: for aggregation to be allowed, the variety of opinions must not be too large. But this is not the point: if the variety is the largest possible, if all the combinations of yes and no are acceptable, then the majority law performs its task and correctly determines a median opinion.[48]

---

[47]The other meaning of *mode,* the maximum density of probability, is relevant to a completely different logic. In order to speak of density, the distribution has to have a certain internal consistency.

[48]It is meaningful.

But if a gap occurs, if an opinion is forbidden, then all the logic collapses; and if we want to restore this coherence, it is necessary to restrict the variety even more until it takes on a stable form. Thus it is not a question of the magnitude of the ideal population of possible opinions. To know whether it is stable and whether it has a meaning, we should not wonder whether it is too numerous or not numerous enough — we should find and mark the forms and wonder if they have the property of stability (or if they are closed). These forms are set off from each other by profound gaps — it is not possible to go from one to the other through a series of stable positions, but we must "jump" from one to the other. We are in the realm of discontinuity,[49] of quantification, to use the modern jargon. In this way the particular nature of the problem is revealed. It is nowadays called "algebraic," a term which does not appeal much to the imagination, but is dedicated to, and designates the study of, operational and combinatorial structure.

What Is a Majority?

The preceding analysis indicates only what is required for one to be able to apply the rule of the majority without danger of contradiction. When opinions are arranged in order of preference, we know that there is a danger if the preferences are free, but that this danger vanishes if the preferences refer to a universal objective order. But we can ask for more. In the case of preferences, for instance, could we not, by *abandoning the majority rule,* find a law of composition of individual opinions which always gives an acceptable result? In other words, if there is a danger of contradiction, why blame the heterogeneity of individual opinions rather than the rule of the majority?

We have seen that it was possible to consider the contradictions revealed by the Condorcet effect symptoms of the social division which made it impossible to form a stable collective opinion. But one could say that it is the instrument used to detect collective opinion which is too crude. Replace the rule of the majority with a more minute examination of the state of opinion and perhaps a noncontradictory resultant opinion would appear. *Non numerentur sed ponderentur* has been repeated everywhere about the quest for testimonies — it being well understood that the pondering required is not the brutal pondering of the modern statistician, but "weighing" [*pesée*] which is also "thinking" [*pensée*], a qualitative and personal appreciation.

---

[49]The name that would be the most suitable here would be "harmony" — in all its connotations and echoes. This text — "a distribution of colors ... system ... complete problem ... closed group of relations which has its own logic, its own operations ... it is a whole which can exist by itself ..." — and many others by Valéry evoke this science, so sadly called algebra. (P. Valéry, "Lettres à quelques-uns"; Paris, N.R.F., 1952, p. 142.) The wonderful papers of Herman Weyl, *Symmetry* (Princeton Univ. Press, 1952, 168 pp.), should be read also.

Now we should see whether other laws of composition of individual opinions can be constructed in such a way as to escape the threat of the Condorcet effect.

Although some research in formal logic has approached this fundamental problem, thus unconsciously providing useful material, the first results seem to have been reached by the economists' studies on the general interest. The great contribution of Arrow lay in discerning a logical problem in the literature of welfare and bringing it out as clearly as possible.[50]

Let us consider a set of individuals whom we will continue to call voters, because we try to learn their wishes by asking each of them a series of questions. The answers of all the voters to all the questions can be arranged in a rectangular table, where a row is assigned to each question and a column to each individual.

For each row or question, we try to construct a global response. The set of global responses will constitute the resultant opinion. We must now study the different possible ways of aggregating. The point which especially interests us is this: Assuming that all the individual opinions obey some logical constraints — that is, some combinations of answers never appear in any column — is it possible for these forbidden (or "absurd") combinations to appear as the resultant opinion, as happens, according to Condorcet, for the majority rule? Are there not, on the contrary, rules better adapted to avoid absurdity?

A very important theorem has been proved by Arrow which establishes the impossibility of a rule of composition of opinions when they are preference judgments and the rule is chosen in a well-defined way. We will come back to this result again in a little while; however, the statement and proof of the theorem are presented by their author in a negative form. It is quite laborious to talk in an indeterminate way of a rule that will eventually be proved to be nonexistent; the reduction to absurdity which is sometimes necessary is not the most enlightening method of mathematical logic.

In what follows, a "constructive" style has been sought systematically — perhaps at the cost of ponderousness in the progress of ideas, but with a guarantee of comprehension.

Let us search for a method of *building* an acceptable rule of composition. Such a rule must allow us to arrive at a "global" opinion in all cases where the individual opinions are known. This rule must also guarantee that absurdities never arise in the global opinion.

For each question, if the individual answers are known, it must be possible to "compute" the global opinion. If for question A the response of

---

[50]Once the logical problem is solved, if that is possible, it is clear that this would only prepare the ground for the economic analysis.

individual i has been a_i, the global opinion, $\hat{a}$, will be determined by the different a_i:

$$\hat{a} = R_A(a_1, a_2, \ldots, a_n)$$

Consider first the case (to which all others can be reduced) where the responses can only be yes or no. Then the rule R_A consists of saying which $\hat{a}$ results from each combination of the signs for a_i. For two individuals, a rule R_A can easily be written in tabular form.

	$a_1 = +$	$a_1 = -$
$a_2 = +$		
$a_2 = -$		

Here we will write in each of the four cells the value $\hat{a}$ chosen to represent the set (a_1, a_2). If we do not want to leave out any possibilities, we should consider all the possible choices, all imaginable rules R_A. There are $2 \times 2 \times 2 \times 2 = 16$ ways to fill four cells with plus or minus signs, and thus there are 16 possible rules for two individuals. Their enumeration is easy. To shorten the writing, it is convenient to condense the preceding table. We will write in sequence the four values of $\hat{a}$ taken in a conventional order, say:

1	3
2	4

Thus the symbol $(+ - + -)$ means:

$$R(++) = +$$
$$R(+-) = -$$
$$R(-+) = +$$
$$R(--) = -$$

The complete list of all imaginable rules is:

1. $(++++)$	7. $(+--+)$	13. $(--++)$
2. $(+++-)$	8. $(+---)$	14. $(--+-)$
3. $(++-+)$	9. $(-+++)$	15. $(---+)$
4. $(++--)$	10. $(-++-)$	16. $(----)$
5. $(+-++)$	11. $(-+-+)$	
6. $(+-+-)$	12. $(-+--)$	

We could then study the significance of these diverse ways of compounding two answers given by two persons. Rule 1 and rule 16 consist of not taking into account individual answers and imposing an answer a priori. Rule 4 consists of adopting the point of view of the first voter, rule 6 the point of view of the second; while 13 and 11 do the exact opposite, respectively, of 4 and 6. Rule 7 consists of saying yes when the two voters agree and no otherwise; 10 does the opposite; and so on. But once the family of 16 rules for two voters has been detailed, we pass to the case of three voters. Now every rule must specify a function of three individual responses:

$$\hat{a} = R(a_1, a_2, a_3)$$

There are therefore eight values to examine. We consider these in an arbitrary order; for example:

a_1	+	+	+	+	−	−	−	−
a_2	+	+	−	−	+	+	−	−
a_3	+	−	+	−	+	−	+	−

Each rule will be well defined by a sequence of eight signs. For instance, according to this convention the rule of the majority would be expressed by the sequence $(+++-+---)$.

Similarly, the rule consisting of taking into account only the first voter if his ballot is positive and otherwise using the ballot of the second voter (an imaginary example) would be denoted by the sequence $(++++++--)$.

If we want to enumerate *all* the rules which are possible a priori, however, we have to form all possible combinations of eight plus or minus signs: there are $2^8 = 256$ of these. Establishing the complete list would be very troublesome, and the interpretation of each rule would take too long.[51] There would be some 65,000 rules for four voters. Even if we had the patience to write the list,[52] we would wonder how to use it. And do not speak of the four billion cases for five voters.[53] Let us console ourselves by realizing that five

---

[51]The list of ternary operations of two-valued logic must be constructed. A summary enumeration can be found in M. Boll, *Manuel de logique scientifique* (Paris, Dunod, 1948), pp. 92–93, 108–9, 139–61; and a more thorough description in J. Piaget, *Essai sur les transformations des opérations logiques; les 256 opérations ternaires de la logique bivalente des propositions* (Paris, P.U.F., 1952). Compare this point of view with that of the theory of switching functions in, for example, *Synthesis of Electronic Computing and Control Circuits* (Harvard Univ. Press, 1951), pp. 15ff., 259ff.

[52]Which would fill four or five fascicules comparable to the present edition of *Economie Appliquée*.

[53]Each time we increase the electoral body by one unit, the number of rules is squared: $16 \cdot 16 = 256$; $256 \cdot 256 = 65,536$; etc.

is still a very small number of voters!

Complete enumeration is certainly impractical. Anyway, we would like to know if there exists any privileged rule among this gigantic multitude which avoids contradictions. Better, we will look for all such rules.

An Example of the Resolution of the Problem of Noncontradiction.

Suppose we had chosen a rule composing the responses of a large number of voters. Then we would have a list such as

x_1	x_2	x_3	$\cdots$	$x_i \cdots x_n$	$\hat{x}$
$+$	$+$	$-$		$+ \quad -$	$+$
$-$	$+$	$+$		$- \quad -$	$-$

Represent each row by x, a set of individual answers x_i, followed by the global response $\hat{x}$ prescribed by the rule. We write

$$\hat{x} = R\ (x) = R\ (x_1, x_2, \ldots x_n)\,.$$

Let us now ask two questions A and B. We will obtain two ballots a and b and the rule[54] will give two answers $\hat{a}$ and $\hat{b}$. If the two questions are independent – that is if each voter is free to choose among the four "opinions" –

$$\begin{cases} a_i = + \\ b_i = + \end{cases} \quad \begin{cases} a_i = + \\ b_i = - \end{cases} \quad \begin{cases} a_i = - \\ b_i = + \end{cases} \quad \begin{cases} a_i = - \\ b_i = - \end{cases}$$

we do not have to fear any contradiction. But what if the two questions are related? Condorcet, who was interested in juries, chose this example:

A. Is it proven that the defendant is guilty?
B. Is it proven that the defendant is not guilty?

For this example the answers

$$\begin{cases} a_i = + \\ b_i = + \end{cases}$$

must be rejected.

The problem is then the following: What precautions have to be taken in the construction of the rule R so that when the response

---

[54]We suppose that we use the same rule for both counts of the vote. See below for the more general case.

$$\begin{cases} a_i = + \\ b_i = + \end{cases}$$

cannot occur on a single ballot, the resulting opinion

$$\begin{cases} \hat{a} = + \\ \hat{b} = + \end{cases}$$

cannot occur.

There are four cases to consider, according to which of the opinions is proscribed:

3) $a = +$	1) $a = +$	2) $a = -$	4) $a = -$
$b = +$	$b = -$	$b = +$	$b = -$
(incompatibility)	(implication of B by A)	(implication of A by B)	(disjunction)

We will start with the cases of implication which are homologous to each other and easier to translate into ordinary language.

If the opinion

$$a = + \\ b = -$$

is forbidden, it means that when going from question A to question B, none of the voters who had answered yes can switch to no, but switching the other way is allowed. The yes party does not lose any of its members and has a chance to gain some. In other words, the "partisans of A" constitute a party which is contained[55] in the party of the "partisans of B."

We will write:[56]

Partisans of A $\leqslant$ Partisans of B.

It will be convenient to use a summary symbolism to designate the two "parties" on a ballot.

From now on we will write a^+ to designate the set of individuals who have voted $+$ in the ballot, and a^- for the others.

---

[55]According to the mathematical convention, this word includes the extreme case in which the yes party would not gain any member. Thus the symbol $\leqslant$ is used, not $<$.

[56]Note that this is not a numerical relation between the number of members in each party: of course the party of B cannot have fewer members, but we mean by the preceding symbol every person of A is a member of the party B. The relation is essentially qualitative; it will be seen even more clearly in what follows. This is the third distinct use that we have made of the same sign.

We can conclude in these terms:

> If proposition A implies proposition B—that is, if it is impossible to answer no to B after having answered yes to A—then every opinion

$$a_i = +$$
$$b_i = -$$

> is impossible and consequently[57] we have $a^+ \leq b^+$, "the party in favor of A is included in the party in favor of B."

Let us return to the rule of composition of individual answers. To each system x, there corresponds a unique answer $\hat{x}: \hat{x} = R(x)$.

This is equivalent to dividing the set of all possible x (that is, the set of all possible ballots or sequences of plus and minus) into two classes, those which give $\hat{x} = +$ and those which give $\hat{x} = -$, the positive and negative ballots. But we have just seen that when the A proposition implies the B proposition, the positive party a^+ is "contained" in b:

$$a^+ \leq b^+$$

On the other hand, there would be a contradiction if, when A implies B, we nevertheless obtain the result

$$\hat{a} = +$$
$$\hat{b} = -$$

The contradiction that we wish to avoid consists of the simultaneous occurrence of

1) $a^+ \leq b^+$
2) $\hat{a} = +, \hat{b} = -$

For a rule to avoid this contradiction, it is necessary and sufficient that the "plus" party of a positive ballot never be contained in the "plus" party of a negative ballot.

One would treat the three other cases in the same manner. If it is B which implies A, we have necessarily

$$a^+ \geq b^+$$
$$(\text{or } a^- \leq b^-),$$

and we want to avoid the rule saying that $\hat{a}$ is negative when $\hat{b}$ is positive.

---

[57]We could just as well say "$a^- \geq b^-$."

If two yes responses[58] are forbidden (case three), we have

$$a^+ \leqslant b^-$$
$$(\text{or } a^- \geqslant b^+),$$

and we want to avoid having $\hat{a}$ and $\hat{b}$ both positive. Finally, if the relation between the propositions A and B excludes two no responses,[59] we have

$$a^+ \geqslant b^-$$
$$(\text{or } a^- \leqslant b^+),$$

and we want to avoid having $\hat{a}$ and $\hat{b}$ both negative.

Finally, if we want to avoid simultaneously the four risks of contradiction, we have to make it impossible for the following four results to appear at the same time:

1) $\hat{a} = +, \hat{b} = -$ and $a^+ \leqslant b^+$
2) $\hat{a} = -, \hat{b} = +$ and $a^- \leqslant b^-$
3) $\hat{a} = +, \hat{b} = +$ and $a^+ \leqslant b^-$
4) $\hat{a} = -, \hat{b} = -$ and $a^- \leqslant b^+$

If these four kinds of simultaneous occurrences are impossible, we are sure that the rule will avoid contradiction whenever two ballots are related in one of the four ways considered.[60]

We now have to determine the rules satisfying these exigencies. First of all, such rules certainly exist. We have only to think of the trivial solution where we would decide to adopt the opinion of one of the voters and would always stick to this opinion without taking into consideration the opinions of the other voters. It is clear, indeed, that the rule will then respect all the logical connections of the opinion of the chosen voter. But the question is to find out whether there are other rules which satisfy the requirement of contradiction and whether it is possible to know all of them.[61] Let us call a rule

---

[58]Incompatibility.

[59]This is the logical "disjunction."

[60]We could introduce other types of relations which would forbid not one joint opinion, but two, but it can be easily established that these types do not raise new problems.

[61]We could state this problem in terms of a network in the following way: Consider the set of possible ballots. The rule divides this set into two parts, positive and negative. On the other hand, the eventuality of a relation between the two questions sets up certain relations between the ballots (such as the mutual inclusion of the positive or negative parts). The problem is then to demand that the partition made by the rule conform to the structure revealed in the relation. The graphic image appears at once. Let us represent the ballots by small circles drawn in a plane and the relations by arrows linking the circles; the question is then to divide the set into two categories — white circles and black circles — in such a way that none of the arrows of the first category goes from white to black, none of the arrows of the second category goes from black to white, etc.

acceptable if it never leads to a contradiction, avoiding the kinds of events mentioned above.

If a rule states that a ballot, say a, must lead to a positive decision $R(a) = \hat{a} = +$, we may say that this rule decides *in favor* of the positive party, a^+: that is, in favor of the individuals who have voted yes ($+$). But if the same individuals have voted no ($-$), or if we consider the ballot b in which b^- is identical with a^+ (the ballots a and b are contradictory), we then have simultaneously

$$b^- \leqslant a^+$$
$$a^+ \leqslant b^-;$$

but as $\hat{a} = +$, it is necessary, if we want to avoid contradiction (see case three above) that we have $\hat{b} = -$.

Thus, if the rule is acceptable, and the decision is in favor of some coalition if it votes yes, then this rule will also decide in favor of this coalition whenever it votes no. Such a coalition will be called efficient.

If e is efficient, $a^+ = e$ has for a consequence $\hat{a} = +$ and $b^- = e$ has the consequence $\hat{b} = -$.

Consider now a coalition which contains $e: f \geqslant e$. If we state that $c^+ = f$, we will have

$$c^+ \geqslant a^+ \qquad \hat{a} = +$$
$$c^+ \geqslant b^- \qquad \hat{b} = -,$$

and in order to avoid the contradictory simultaneous occurrences (1 and 4), the rule must say

$$\hat{c} = R(e) = +.$$

Thus the coalition f is efficient.

As we might have expected, one of the conditions of noncontradiction is the following: An efficient coalition does not cease being efficient if new members are added.

It can be easily proved that if e is efficient, the complementary coalition (which groups all the voters who are not contained in e) is *not* efficient. Then, if g is not efficient, it will not become efficient if it loses members. Finally, the coalition which contains all the voters is surely efficient.

We are led to the following conclusions: If a rule is *acceptable,* the efficient coalitions which this rule defines are such that—

Every coalition which contains an efficient coalition is efficient.
Every coalition contained in a nonefficient coalition is nonefficient.
The complementary coalition of an efficient coalition is nonefficient, and inversely.

On the other hand, it is easily proved that these conditions are sufficient. Any set of individuals can be divided into two parties in a number of ways. If for each partition one states arbitrarily which of the two parties will be the efficient one, a rule for determining a resultant opinion is set up, and this rule will be *acceptable* (free from contradiction) if, first, unanimity is efficient; second, every efficient party does not cease to be efficient by adding new members; and third, every inefficient party does not cease being inefficient by losing members.

It is clear, indeed, that the four simultaneous occurrences to avoid (p. 299) all state that the efficient party must not be contained in an inefficient party.

It is easy to enumerate, for each case, the rules which satisfy the preceding conditions—that is, to find the *acceptable* rules.

In the case of two voters, since one of the two must be efficient by himself, we come to the rule: always take the opinion of one of the voters (always the same one, evidently). It is clear that we thus avoid any contradiction, and the rule is trivial.

In the case of three voters, we must distinguish between two cases: First, if one of the three voters is efficient by himself, call him (1), then the coalition (2,3) is not efficient, nor (2) nor (3)—but clearly (1,2), (1,3), and (1,2,3) will be efficient. The solution is given by the trivial rule: take the opinion of Primus.

Second, if none of the three is efficient, then every coalition of two is efficient and we arrive at the rule: take the opinion of the majority.

For four voters, if we discard the trivial solution, none of the voters can be right by himself; thus three voters are always right against the fourth. As for the coalitions of two voters, they cannot all be efficient or all inefficient, being complementary two by two. It is then necessary to decide in one way or another: for example, between coalitions (1,2) and (3,4). If the first is declared to be efficient, it is then necessary to choose between (1,3) and (2,4), and then between (1,4) and (2,3). If we enumerate all the possible choices, we observe that they are of two types. Either the three coalitions of size two which are efficient all contain a common voter—that is the well-known rule giving the deciding vote to one particular member in case of a tie—or the three inefficient coalitions have a common member. This means an analogous but opposite rule: in case of a tie, the value of one of the votes is diminished or, what would have the same result, a louder voice is given to three of the four members of the jury.[62]

We can continue the analysis: for five voters, the diversity is greater. The trivial solution being discarded, as well as the solutions which do not take into account the vote of one or two particular voters,[63] and the well-

---

[62]The fourth has, in some sense, a "consulting" voice.

[63]But not of three, for only two voters would remain, and there is no other rule acceptable for two, as we have seen, except following the opinion of the same voter.

known solution of the ordinary majority (where every three-member party is efficient), there remain three types of new rules in which some parties of two voters can be efficient (either only one of this kind or all except one, or only two). If we examine these new solutions, we perceive a close relation with the usual majority rules. For instance, it is possible to choose as efficient coalitions

$$(1,2) \qquad (1,3,4) \qquad (2,3,4)$$
$$(1,3,5) \qquad (2,3,5)$$
$$(1,4,5) \qquad (2,4,5)$$

and it could be said that, in this system, each of the two privileged individuals (1 or 2) is "worth" two of the others, since the coalition $(1,3,4)$ has the same "strength" as the coalition $(1,2)$.

In this case we could get the same result by giving two votes to 1 and 2, and one vote to each of the others.

But we should beware of believing that this is always the case. With six voters some rules appear which *cannot be reduced* to a numerical weighting. It is still possible to speak of a weighted majority (but not of a plurality). It is a matter of basically qualitative structures, and one can say that the opposed forces are no longer measurable. Let us give a curious example of this.

Suppose that in a committee of seven voters it has been decided that five votes always outweigh the two others—but the two losing members can reverse the situation if they form a coalition with a third voter, chosen so as to form a "harmonious" trio. It is sufficient to write the list of these winning trios. A and B being any two members, they need a third, say C: ABC is an efficient coalition. D being one of the other four, it is necessary to be able to form a trio with A,D and another, say ADE; the same for BDF and CDG. It then is clear that AFG is a winning coalition; likewise for BEG and CEF. Thus there are[64] seven winning trios,

ABC, ADE, BDF, CDG, AFG, BEG, CEF,

and it can be seen that the set is constructed in such a way that it is impossible to say that any member is privileged—or even that any pair is privileged. Only the trios have a real existence. It is impossible to attribute the strength of such a trio to the sum of the strengths of the individual components. It is impossible to give numerical weights to each individual.

---

[64]It would also be possible to present the system by beginning with three elements which do not form a trio, for instance ABD: it will be said that C, harmonizing A and B, is "intermediary" between A and B, and likewise F lies between B and D, and E between A and D; this looks like harmonious colors. It is possible to associate in a trio the three intermediates CEF or an intermediate and its "complement" along with the seventh element, G (which plays the role of the color white).

We have to introduce a definition of the concept of majority, beyond that usually conceived, which will include all the usual cases and also some other significant cases.[65] We will say that a decision is a majority decision (in the broad sense) when, in a collectivity, the efficient coalitions have been fixed in advance, that is, for each "partition" we know which one of the two parties outweighs the other; the several "majorities" chosen in this way will satisfy the conditions of consistency which could be summarized by the axiom: No majority is *contained* in a minority. With this definition it is possible to state the following theorem: If we wish to compose the opinions of several voters into one, guarding against any contradiction between two successive votes, we have to use a rule of majority in the broad sense, and this is sufficient (as long as it can be guaranteed that the various opinions of a particular voter will not be contradictory).

The Inevitable Contradictions

The law of the majority, so expanded, gives all the solutions to the problem stated: *two* decisions could be made by the majority, and whatever the logical relation existing between the two questions asked on the two ballots, we can be sure that if each of the voters respects this relation, the result will also respect it.

But, as we know, consistency between *two* ballots is not always enough. If the successive ballots carry judgments of preference, any two ballots are logically independent. It is possible to answer as we please to the two questions "A < B?" and "B < C?"; but if we have answered yes twice or no twice, then we find ourselves restricted on the third question, "A < C?"

Consideration of the binary relation is not sufficient, for there are logical relations which are essentially ternary. On the other hand, if we want to respect all the ternary relations, we have first to respect all binary relations which are a part of ternary relations. Thus it is among the laws of the majority (in the broad sense) that we must search.

We already know that the law of the ordinary majority or plurality is not suitable. It does not respect the ternary relations, and this is precisely the Condorcet effect. But one can legitimately wonder whether among the other majority laws (which we have seen are very diverse) there would not be any which would respect the ternary relations (or even relations of higher order).

---

[65]These schemata are found in theory of what O. Morgenstern and J. von Neumann have called *Simple Games*. See their work *Theory of Games and Economic Behavior* (Princeton, 1947), pp. 420–70. The authors discard, a priori, the solutions that we have called trivial, in which a single individual can constitute a majority.

Given three questions A,B,C, let us suppose that we have obtained, after composition, the resultant responses:

$$\hat{a} = +$$
$$\hat{b} = +$$
$$\hat{c} = -$$

This means that a "majority" answered yes to A, a "majority" (the same or another) answered yes to B, and a "majority" answered no to C. It can be concluded that any individuals whose opinions conform to the resultant opinion belong simultaneously to all these three majorities. The same result is verified for any number of questions: in order that the collective opinion (which results from the application of a majority rule) be the opinion of a given individual, it is necessary and sufficient that this individual belong to all the majorities. Thus the Condorcet effect manifests itself as soon as the majorities on the several questions have *no common elements*: for then the majority opinion is the opinion of no one.

We are back to a question of structure. Among all the laws of majority that can be imagined, do any exist for which any three majorities always have at least one common element for which any number of majorities have at least one common element?

Let us examine the singular law, valid for an assembly of seven voters, which we have already mentioned and which is defined by majority trios.

ABC forms a majority (against DEFG)
but also

$$\text{ADE,ADF,CDG}$$

and finally

$$\text{AFG,BEG,CEF}$$

are majorities.

If we add that there are no other groupings where three are efficient, the law is completely known.[66] But any two majorities must have a common member,[67] as:

$$\text{ABC}$$
$$\text{ADE}$$

and by adding a third "majority coalition" we obtain either A in all three:

---

[66]Every coalition of five members contains a majority and is itself a majority, and so every coalition of two is a minority; for the coalitions of four, it is sufficient to distinguish those which are complementary to majorities of three, as DEFG, which is a minority, and those which contain a majority, like ABCD, and so are a majority.

[67]And, in the present example, never more than one common member.

ABC
ADE
AFG
(A in common)

or no member in all three majorities, for example:

ABC
ADE
BDF

This last eventuality proves the possibility of Condorcet effects. If, for instance, three questions are asked which cannot all be answered in the affirmative, then we only have to form a majority of yes on each question in order to end up with an absurd result.

A	B	C	D	E	F	G	Majority	Result
+	+	+	−	−	−	−	(ABC)	+
+	−	−	+	+	−	−	(ADE)	+
−	+	−	+	−	+	−	(BDF)	+

In order to construct a law of the majority which excludes every Condorcet effect, we have to make another arrangement. Return to the case of any number of voters. Notice first that two majority parties must necessarily have members in common; indeed, if in the assembly

ABC, ..., XYZ

ABC is a majority, then DE, ..., Z is a minority and consequently every fraction of this party is a minority, DEF for instance. It would be absurd to state that ABC and DEF are both majorities.

Then, given two distinct majorities:

ABCDEF
ABCKLMN

what can be said about their common part (ABC)? If it is a minority, its opposite (DEF ... XYZ) is a majority and we have three majority parties without common members:

ABCDEF
ABCKLMN
DEF, ..., XYZ

and so the Condorcet effect may occur.

To avoid the Condorcet effect it is necessary that the common part of two majority parties be itself a majority coalition. Therefore the set of *all* majority parties must have a common part which is itself a majority, and, being contained in every majority coalition, represents in a certain way the minimum or limiting majority. But this is not sufficient, for, once a majority has been found, say ABC, to decide whether it is a minimum we have to examine whether its fractions, for example AB, are minorities. But if AB is a minority, CED, ..., Z is a majority and the two majorities ABC and CDE... have a common part C which must be a majority.

Thus either AB or C is a majority. By repeating the same reasoning it is seen that there is no other way to operate than the following: choose a single member who by himself constitutes a majority.

Thus the only majority laws which completely avoid the Condorcet effect are the trivial ones, according to which a single voter constitutes the "majority,"[68] that is, the opinion of one member determines the opinion of the collectivity (the same member, of course, for all questions asked). It is clear that consistency is assured in that case. We can state the following result:

If we want to avoid having the collective opinion take a form not chosen by any of the voters, the only universal rules valid for all imaginable circumstances are those which give the privilege of deciding to a single individual chosen once and for all.

[EDITORS' NOTE: To summarize Guilbaud's final section, on the irreducibility of the general interest:

The problem of defining in a formal way what is to be meant by "social utility," or the general interest, has been considered by many authors. In particular, Pareto's conception of the general interest was in terms of something that is advantageous for *everyone,* or at least is not disadvantageous for anyone. The problem of how to define this concept when unanimity does not occur was not solved.

Modern writers have tried to complete this definition while holding to Pareto's strictures that an individual's preferences should be measured only in terms of an ordering of the various alternatives. This is, of course, impossible, in the light of Arrow's theorem and the discussion earlier in this paper. The dilemma is reduced to this statement:

Either (1) the general interest is not something that can be constructed from the individual interests which are taken as nondecomposable (i.e.,

---

[68]These are the solutions that K. J. Arrow calls "dictatorial."

the general interest is *something more* than the mere aggregation of what is best for the individuals);

or (2) each individual interest must be supposed to have something more than a simple ordinal structure.

However, Guilbaud concludes, it is not realistic to suppose that collective decisions do respect the autonomy of every individual; when there is neither slavery nor unanimous harmony, then the general welfare arises out of a struggle. Individual interests do not "combine" with one another to form a general will: the actions involved in discussion, debate, and bargaining are the integral parts of this struggle. In this context the appropriate mathematical model for the study of these phenomena is seen to be the theory of games.]

Suggestions for Further Reading (Section Four)

ABELSON, ROBERT P. "Mathematical Models of the Distribution of Attitudes Under Controversy," in *Contributions to Mathematical Psychology,* eds. NORMAN FREDERIKSEN and H. GULLIKSEN. New York: Holt, Rinehart & Winston, 1964. Assuming that the attitude can be represented as a point in a continuum, interaction between individuals with different attitudes tends to change both attitudes. Different assumptions about how these changes occur lead to different mathematical models. Abelson explores several of these, finally moving to a complex simulation model of the behavior that takes into account many interacting factors, including (1) interest in the issue, (2) attitude toward each other *individual* in the group, and (3) attitude toward the *arguments* that may be proposed in favor of, or in opposition to, the issue. This model has been applied to studies of community controversy, in particular to the issue of fluoridation.

FAGEN, R. "Some Contributions of Mathematical Reasoning to the Study of Politics," *American Political Science Review,* 1962, pp. 888-900. A review of mathematical work in political science.

LUCE, R. DUNCAN, and ROGOW, A. A. "A Game Theoretic Analysis of Congressional Power Distribution for a Two-Party System," *Behavioral Science,* 1956, 1, 83-95. Taking the American two-party system as an example of a "stable" system, the authors examine the possible distributions of power that could lead to such stability, taking into account only the party of each legislator and whether he is a diehard or a potential defector. They list the coalitions that can control power under different circumstances, and are able to derive some nontrivial conclusions about the exercise of legislative power.

NAGEL, E. "A Formalization of Functionalism," Chap. 10 in his *Logic Without Metaphysics.* Chicago: Free Press, 1956. Nagel draws on the mathematical formalization of functional systems in biology in order to clarify Merton's codification of the concepts and aims of functional analysis in the social sciences (Robert K. Merton, *Social Theory and Social Structure;* Chicago: Free Press, 1957). In this way he is able to distinguish problems that can be dealt with within the framework of the theory of functional systems from those which are specific to the particular subject matter considered by Merton.

RAPOPORT, ANATOL. "Lewis F. Richardson's Mathematical Theory of War," *Journal of Conflict Resolution,* 1957, 1, 244-99. In this perceptive essay Rapoport examines the role of mathematical models, especially with regard to the "scientific" search for causal relations and the nature of deterministic models. His review of Richardson's "Mathematics of Arms Races" shows how systems of differential equations are used to describe the interaction between competing countries. The work of Lotka and Rashevsky in mathematical biology involves similar uses of mathematics, wherein the existence of stable or unstable equilibriums is of great importance. (See Simon's paper in this volume.) Rapoport also comments on the work of Richardson, of Zipf, of Simon, and of Mandelbrot in developing "explanations" of why and how certain statistical distributions arise. (See Mandelbrot's paper in this volume.) Rapoport's *Fights, Games, and Debates* (Ann Arbor: Univ. of Michigan Press, 1960) is in part an expansion of this article.

SHUBIK, MARTIN. *Game Theory and Related Approaches to Social Behavior.* New York: Wiley, 1964. This valuable reader of articles on game theory, power, bargaining, and gaming contains a bibliography of books and articles in these fields.

Section Five **Models
Analyzing Processes**

Some Possible Effects of Birth Control on the Human Sex Ratio

Leo A. Goodman*   *University of Chicago*

INTRODUCTION

A number of authors have commented upon some of the possible effects of birth control on the sex distribution of the children born. These authors include, among others, Winston (1932), Slater (1944), Gini (1951), Robbins (1952), Edwards (1958), and Weiler (1959). The articles by Winston, Robbins, and Weiler discussed the possible effects of birth control on the sex ratio, while some of the other authors were concerned more with its possible effects on other aspects of the sex distribution of the children born. In the present article, we shall be concerned primarily with the sex ratio and how it might be affected by birth control.

Winston (1932) has suggested that, for the particular group of families he has studied, 'the prevalence of the desire for male offspring on the part of...parents, together with their knowledge of methods of birth control, appears to be significant in relation to the high sex-ratio...' observed in that particular group. Robbins (1952), in a mathematical investigation which he states was suggested by Winston's attempt 'to explain an observed preponderance of male children in a certain group of families by the hypothesis that whereas the probability of a male birth may be approximately 1/2, male children are regarded as more desirable, so that parents are more likely to stop having children when a male child is born', proves that an expected preponderance of male children can *not* be explained by the use of birth-control methods, even though there may be a preference for male offspring on the part of the parents, if it is assumed that the probability of a male birth is 1/2, that the sexes of the children born are statistically independent, and that the expected family size is finite. The results presented by Robbins tend to suggest that the sex ratio will be *unaffected* by the preference for male offspring. Weiler (1959) states that Winston's 'conclusion...is...fallacious' and he proves that the sex ratio will be, in fact, either *decreased* or unaffected by the preference for male offspring, if certain assumptions can be made concerning the way in which this preference affects the parents' decisions as to whether or not to have another child; e.g. one of the assumptions made in Weiler's proof is that, if the parents' first child is a girl, this preference would lead them to desire a boy as the second child, and they would therefore decide to have another child. In the present note, we shall prove that, if a preference for male offspring does exist, it might actually *increase* the sex ratio (as suggested by Winston but contradicted by Robbins and Weiler), the sex ratio might be unaffected by this preference (as suggested by the results presented in Robbins's paper), or the sex ratio might be decreased by this preference (as suggested by Weiler), depending on the particular assumptions that can be made concerning the ways in which this preference might

* Part of this research was carried out at the Statistical Research Center, University of Chicago, under the sponsorship of the Statistics Branch, Office of Naval Research, and of the Social Science Research Committee, University of Chicago. A part of this work was done while the author was at the Statistical Laboratory of the University of Cambridge under a National Science Foundation Senior Postdoctoral Fellowship and a John Simon Guggenheim Memorial Foundation Fellowship.

affect the parents' decisions as to whether or not to have another child (assuming that they make such decisions). The assumptions made in the present note are similar to some of the assumptions made by Robbins (1952), Edwards (1958), and Weiler (1959).

It is of some historical interest to note that in 1819 Laplace discussed the attempts that had been made still earlier to explain the excess of the births of boys over those of girls by the general desire of fathers to have a son. His results suggest that the sex ratio will be unaffected by this general desire. Gini, in 1951, making somewhat different assumptions than those made by Laplace, suggested that this desire would decrease the sex ratio. For further references to this literature, see the article by Gini (1951).

The results here presented are intended to further clarify some of the factors involved in an analysis of the possible effects of birth control on the sex ratio. Besides the factors introduced here, other factors might also play an important role; but, in order to keep the present discussion simple, and still indicate some of the important complexities of the actual problem, certain assumptions will be made and certain factors will be neglected for the sake of this simplicity. It might also be worthwhile to carry out some further empirical studies of the possible existence of different kinds of (stated and unstated) preferences relating to the sex of offspring; of the changes in these preferences with time or with exposure to various experiences (e.g. the experience of having a daughter might affect the parents' preferences); of the relationships that might be observed between the initial preferences of (married) couples, the number of children that they have, and the proportion of sons that they have; of the possible effects of these preferences on the parents' decisions (if they make such decisions) as to whether or not to have another child; of the possible effects of other considerations (e.g. various attitudes concerning family size regardless of the sex of the offspring) on the parents' decisions as to whether or not to have another child; of the extent of the use and the effectiveness of various methods available for carrying out these decisions; of the nature of the likelihood of a male birth for particular parents; of the changes in this likelihood with time or with physiological changes in the parents; of the variation in this likelihood in the population.*

THE SEX RATIO

Let p_i denote the probability that a child born to the ith couple, in a population of n couples ($i = 1, 2, ..., n$), will be a boy. Let $q_i = 1 - p_i$. Throughout the major part of the present article we shall assume, for the sake of simplicity, that this probability is a constant for the ith couple, that it does not change with time, and that the sexes of the children born to a particular married couple are statistically independent. These assumptions are identical with those made implicitly by Weiler (1959), with those made implicitly by Edwards (1958) in his derivation and application of the modified binomial distribution and in his presentation of the posterior probability distribution of p_i (except for the fact that Edwards made the additional assumption that the distribution of the p_i in the population of married couples could be described by the β-distribution), and with those made by Robbins (1952) (except for the fact that Robbins made the additional assumption that $p_i = 1/2$ for all $i = 1, 2, ..., n$). We shall also assume, as was done implicitly by Weiler and Robbins, that multiple births and births where the sex of the

* There have been a number of studies dealing with the physiological factors governing the proportions of the sexes, the variation in the sex ratio, etc. References to some of this literature appear in articles by Goodman (1953) and Edwards (1958) and (1959). The interested reader is also referred to Szilard (1960).

child is unknown are sufficiently rare events so that these phenomena can be ignored, for the sake of simplicity, in the mathematical analysis. Finally, we shall assume, as was done implicitly by Weiler, that in the situation where there is no birth control, the expected number, c_i, of children that will be born to the ith couple will be uncorrelated with p_i. Although some of these assumptions may, in fact, not be altogether correct, we shall for the sake of simplicity make them here.

In the present note, it will be convenient to define the sex ratio (at birth) to be the ratio, S, of the expected number of boys born in the population and the expected number of children born in the population. Thus, $S = \sum_{i=1}^{n} (p_i c_i) \bigg/ \sum_{i=1}^{n} c_i$, where c_i is the expected number of children by the ith couple. In the situation where there is no birth control (i.e. where c_i and p_i are uncorrelated), the sex ratio is then equal to $S_0 = \sum_{i=1}^{n} p_i/n$.

EFFECTS OF BIRTH CONTROL

Winston (1932), in discussing the motivation for his own study, states that 'influencing this query are the rather commonly accepted statements that men desire at least one male heir, and also the less often heard statement that women desire a male child'. Weiler (1959) assumes, in the derivation of the results presented in his paper, that a preference for male offspring would lead to the decision of a married couple to continue to bear children until a boy is born and then to use birth control so as to bear no further children. Robbins (1952) also discusses this situation where couples decide to continue to bear children until a boy is born and then to bear no further children. We shall call such couples type I couples. Using methods that are similar to those used by Weiler, it is possible to prove that, in the situation where all couples in the population are of type I, the sex ratio is $S_1 = n \bigg/ \sum_{i=1}^{n} (1/p_i)$, which is always less than or equal to S_0 computed in the situation when birth control is absent. Thus, in the situation where the population consists of type I couples, a preference for male offspring would either *decrease* the sex ratio or it would leave it unchanged.

A possible effect of a preference for male offspring, which is quite different from the one obtained with type I couples, is the following: Parents might decide, if their first child is a boy, that they will continue to bear children (perhaps being encouraged to continue by the birth of a boy as the first child) until a girl is born and then bear no further children; they might decide, if their first child is a girl, that they will continue to bear children until a boy is born (perhaps because of their desire to have at least one male offspring) and then bear no further children (since they might believe that, if they have had one or more girls and only one boy, they will be more likely, or no less likely, to have a girl, rather than a boy, as their next child). Such couples we call type II couples. Using methods similar to those used by Weiler, it is possible to prove that, in the situation where the population consists of type II couples, the sex ratio at birth is *[See page 317 for footnote.]

$$S_2 = \left\{ \sum_{i=1}^{n} (1/q_i) - \sum_{i=1}^{n} p_i \right\} \bigg/ \left\{ \sum_{i=1}^{n} [1/(p_i q_i)] - n \right\} = \sum_{i=1}^{n} (t_i/q_i) \bigg/ \sum_{i=1}^{n} [t_i/(p_i q_i)],$$

where $t_i = p_i^2 + q_i = q_i^2 + p_i$. It can be seen by simple numerical examples that the relation between S_2 and S_0 will depend on the particular distribution of the p's in the population. In some cases S_2 will be larger than S_0 (so that a preference for males would increase the sex ratio), and in other cases S_2 will be less than or equal to S_0.

Still another possible effect of a preference for male offspring might be that parents might decide, if their first child is a boy, that they will continue to bear children until a girl is born and then bear no further children; and, if their first child is a girl, that they will bear no further children (since they might believe that, if they have had one girl and no boys, they will be more likely to have a girl, rather than a boy, as their next child, or they might simply feel discouraged to continue by the birth of a girl as the first child). Such couples we call type III couples. It is possible to prove that, in the situation where the population consists of type III couples, the sex ratio is

$$S_3 = 1 - \left[n \Big/ \sum_{i=1}^{n} (1/q_i) \right],$$

where S_3 is always more than or equal to S_0. Thus, in this situation, a preference for male offspring either increases the sex ratio or leaves it unchanged.

These three types of couples described here represent, of course, oversimplification of reality. Weiler (1959) had concerned himself with type I only. It may, however, be the case that a preference for male offspring might lead some couples to become type II or type III, rather than type I. It would also be possible to describe still different types of couples whose decision patterns are affected by a preference for male offspring in ways other than those mentioned here; but it will not be necessary to go into these details in the present note. (The reader will note that couples who become type I as a result of the preference for boys might have tended to become type III if there had been a comparable preference for girls, since type III couples decide to continue to bear children until a girl is born and then bear no further children.)

If the ith couple in the population is of type I, then the expected number of children born to it will be $1 + (q_i/p_i) = 1/p_i$. Thus, if p_i is relatively small, the expected number of children will be large. From this we see that type I couples who are less likely to bear boys than are other type I couples will have a larger expected number of children. This observation helps to explain why, for type I couples, the sex ratio can decrease (since in this case the couples who are less likely to bear boys will have a larger expected number of children and will thus be more heavily weighted in the computation of the sex ratio than are the other couples).

If the ith couple in the population is of type II, then the expected number of children born to it will be $t_i/(p_i q_i) = [1/(p_i q_i)] - 1$. Thus, if p_i is 1/2, the expected number of children born to the ith couple will be a minimum, while if p_i is either more than 1/2 or less than 1/2 the expected number of children born to the ith couple will be larger. From this we see that type II couples who have an equal chance of bearing a boy or a girl will have a smaller expected number of children than will other type II couples. This observation helps to explain why, for type II couples, the sex ratio can either increase, decrease, or remain unaffected, depending on the distribution of the p's in the population (since in this case the couples who are less likely to bear boys and the couples who are more likely to bear boys are more heavily weighted in the computation of the sex ratio than are the couples who have an equal chance of bearing a boy or a girl).

If the ith couple in the population is of type III, then the expected number of children born to it, will be $(p_i/q_i) + 1 = 1/q_i$. Thus, if q_i is relatively small, the expected number of children will be large. From this we see that type III couples who are more likely to bear boys than are other type III couples will have a larger expected number of children. This observation helps to explain why, for type III couples, the sex ratio can increase (since in this case the couples who are more likely to bear boys are more heavily weighted in the computation of the sex ratio than are the other type III couples).

The sex ratio for the ith couple (i.e. the ratio of the expected number of boys born to the ith couple and the expected number of children born to the ith couple) is simply p_i, regardless of whether this couple is of types I, II, or III. Thus, we see that the sex ratio for the ith couple does not depend on the particular type of couple it is; it does, of course, depend on the value of p_i. We observed earlier in this paper that the reason why the (general) sex ratio (for the population) did depend on the particular types of couples present in the population was that the computation of the sex ratio weighted more heavily those couples who had a larger expected number of children and that the relationship between the expected number of children and p_i was different for the three different types of couples described here.

The preceding discussion leads us to suggest that some further empirical study of the relationship between observed size of family and the observed sex ratio of the children born to the family, analysed for different types of couples, might be of real interest.

The formulas discussed in this present note for the (general) sex ratios, S_0, S_1, S_2, S_3, can be summarized as follows. We have that

$$S_0 = E(p),$$
$$S_1 = 1/E(1/p),$$
$$S_2 = \{E(1/q) - E(p)\}/\{E[1/(pq)] - 1\}$$

and
$$S_3 = 1 - [1/E(1/q)],$$

where
$$\sum_{i=1}^{n} p_i/n = E(p), \quad \sum_{i=1}^{n} (1/p_i)/n = E(1/p),$$

$$\sum_{i=1}^{n} [1/(p_i q_i)]/n = E[1/(pq)] \quad \text{and} \quad \sum_{i=1}^{n} (1/q_i)/n = E(1/q).$$

These formulas can be modified in a straightforward fashion to deal with populations that include all three types of couples (and other types as well) in certain specified proportions; but we shall not go into these details in this note.

In the special situation where all p_i are equal (i.e. where the likelihood of a male birth is the same for each of the couples in the population considered), then $S_0 = S_1 = S_2 = S_3 = p$, where $p = p_i$ for $i = 1, 2, ..., n$. Thus, in this special situation, we observe that the sex ratio does not depend on the particular types of couples present in the population and that this (general) sex ratio is unaffected by birth control.

The special situation where all p_i equal $1/2$ (i.e. where the likelihood of a male birth is $1/2$ for each of the couples in the population considered) has been studied by Robbins (1952). He has shown that, if it is assumed that the expected family size is finite and that $p_i = 1/2$ for $i = 1, 2, ..., n$, then an observed preponderance of male offspring in a given population cannot be explained by the fact that male offspring may be regarded as more desirable. This conclusion is in agreement with the result presented in the preceding paragraph for the situation where $p_i = p$ for $i = 1, 2, ..., n$. While the result presented in the preceding paragraph is somewhat more general in a certain sense (since it was not necessary to assume there that $p = 1/2$), Robbins's conclusion is, in a different sense, more general (since his results were derived using a more general definition of the various 'types of couples', which would include the three types explicitly defined and studied in the present article). It is possible to generalize Robbins's conclusion, by applying the same method that is presented in his article or by applying some results on cumulative sums (see, for example, Johnson (1959)), in order to show that, if it is assumed that the expected family size is finite and that $p_i = p$ for $i = 1, 2, ..., n$, then an observed preponderance of male offspring in a given population cannot be explained by the desirability of male offspring; which is again in agreement with the result presented in the preceding paragraph for the situation where $p_i = p$ $(i = 1, 2, ..., n)$.

As we have seen earlier in the present article, it may be possible to explain an observed preponderance of male offspring in a given population by the desirability of male offspring, if it is not assumed that all p_i are equal (i.e. if it is not assumed that the likelihood of a male birth is the same for each couple in the population). In addition, if p_i is not a constant for the ith couple (e.g. if p_i is a function of the age of the mother, the age of the father, the number of preceding births, etc.), as has been suggested in some of the published literature (see, for example, some of the articles referred to by Goodman (1953) and Lancaster (1950)), then it may also be possible to explain an observed preponderance of male offspring by the desirability of male offspring even in the special case where the p_i are the same for each couple in the population (i.e. even where the probability $p_i(t)$, written as a function of all relevant variables, t, such as age of mother, age of father, etc., is identical for all i, so that $p_i(t) = p(t)$ for all $i = 1, 2, ..., n$). Further empirical studies are needed in order to explore the various possible considerations arising from the present discussion.

In conclusion, we take note of the fact that Slater (1944), Winston (1932), and Weiler (1959) have commented also upon the sex ratio for the last-born child in (completed) families; we add the following brief comment with regard to this sex ratio. Defining this as the expected proportion of the families in the population that have a son as the last-born child, it is possible to prove that, for a population consisting of type I couples, this sex ratio is one; for a population consisting of type II couples, this ratio is $\sum_{i=1}^{n} q_i/n = E(q)$; and for a population consisting of type III couples, this ratio is zero.

SUMMARY

The discussion presented here is intended to clarify some of the problems arising in an analysis of the possible effects of birth control on the human sex ratio. Formulas are presented indicating some of the ways in which the sex ratio can be modified as a result of the use of birth-control methods. These formulas lead to different conclusions from those presented in the earlier literature on this subject. Further empirical research, along lines suggested by the considerations arising from the present discussion, is needed. The overall effect of birth control on the sex ratio will depend upon, among other things, the particular kinds of preferences for male offspring that influence the married couples in the population, the particular kinds of preferences for female offspring that influence the married couples in the population, the particular ways in which these preferences affect the parents' decisions as to whether or not to have another child (if they make such decisions), the relation between the parents' decisions and their probability, p_i, of bearing a boy, the effectiveness with which these decisions are carried out, the relation between family size and p_i, the distribution of the p_i in the population, and the nature of the p_i as a function of all relevant variables.

REFERENCES

EDWARDS, A. W. F. (1958). An analysis of Geissler's data on the human sex ratio. *Ann. Hum. Genet., Lond.,* **23**, 6.

EDWARDS, A. W. F. (1959). Some comments on Schützenberger's analysis of data on the human sex ratio. *Ann. Hum. Genet., Lond.,* **24**, 233.

GINI, C. (1951). Combinations and sequences of sexes in human families and mammal litters. *Acta genet.* **2**, 220.

GOODMAN, L. A. (1953). Population growth of the sexes. *Biometrics,* **9**, 212.

JOHNSON, N. L. (1959). A proof of Wald's theorem on cumulative sums. *Ann. Math. Statist.* **30**, 1245.

LANCASTER, H. O. (1950). The sex ratio in sibships, with special reference to Geissler's data. *Ann. Eugen., Lond.,* **15**, 153.

PIERRE SIMON, MARQUIS DE LAPLACE (1819). *A Philosophical Essay on Probabilities.* Translation by Truscott, F. W. and Emory, F. L. (1902) of the Sixth French Edition. London: Chapman and Hall, Ltd.

ROBBINS, H. (1952). A note on gambling systems and birth statistics. *Amer. Math. Mon.* **59**, 685.

SLATER, E. (1944). A demographic study of a psychopathic population. *Ann. Eugen., Lond.,* **12**, 121.

SZILARD, L. (1960). Dependence of the sex ratio at birth on the age of the father. *Nature, Lond.,* **186**, 649

WEILER, H. (1959). Sex-ratio and birth control. *Amer. J. Sociology,* **65**, 298.

WINSTON, S. (1932). Birth control and the sex-ratio at birth. *Amer. J. Sociology,* **38**, 225.

*To derive this expression, the expected number of children, c, given p, must be calculated. Here

$$c = 2(pq + qp) + 3(p^2q + q^2p) + \ldots + (j+1)(p^jq + q^jp) + \ldots$$

$$c = q \sum_{1}^{\infty} (j+1)p^j + p \sum_{1}^{\infty} (j+1)q^j = q/(1-p)^2 - q + p/(1-q)^2 - p$$

$$c = 1/q + 1/p - 1 = 1/pq - 1.$$

Substituting this value for c_i in the general equation for S, the desired result is obtained.

[EDITORS' NOTE: In a later paper ("Some Possible Effects of Birth Control on the Incidence of Disorders and on the Influence of Birth Order," *Annals of Human Genetics,* 1963, pp. 41–52), Goodman continues study begun in the above paper. There he considers whether the relative incidence of some disorder would be affected if parents were to stop having children after the birth of one with the disorder; and whether such decisions would lead to an apparent relation between incidence of the disorder and birth order.

He finds that the decision to stop having children would tend to reduce the relative incidence of the disorder, under the assumptions that each birth is an independent event, with constant probability of the disorder appearing (for any particular parents), and that the disorder is not correlated with family size in the absence of birth control. A correlation between birth order and incidence of the disorder will also occur, under these conditions, but the relation may appear to be positive or negative, depending on how the comparison between "normals" and "disordereds" is made.]

Probability Models for Mobility

Isadore Blumen, Marvin Kogan, and **Philip J. McCarthy**   *Cornell University*

[EDITORS' NOTE: The data studied by the authors were drawn from the continuous work sample of the Bureau of Old Age and Survivor Insurance, and consisted of the employment records of 16,391 individuals for twelve consecutive quarters (1947–49). The workers were distinguished by sex and age; three age groups were sampled: 20–24, 40–44, and 60–64. The industries were coded into ten categories, with an eleventh category for the unemployed and those in jobs not covered by insurance. The data thus locate each worker in the sample in exactly one of these eleven categories at every quarter, and it is this pattern of mobility that was studied. In the early chapters of their monograph the authors examine a simple Markov chain as a model for this mobility.

Consider the *transition matrix* P_{12}, whose (i,j) entry is the probability that a worker in industry i at time 1 will be in industry j at time 2. If it is assumed that this matrix is the same for any two consecutive quarters — that is, $P_{n,n+1} = P_{12} = P$ — and that the potential mobility of a worker depends only on the industry he is in at a particular time, then P is the transition matrix of a Markov chain.*

Evaluation of the fit of a Markov chain to observed data is usually based on two implications of the model.† First, the transition matrices $P_{n,n+1}$ can be examined to see whether it is reasonable to assume that they are all sample estimates of the same matrix, P. If this is accepted, then higher-order transitions can be examined, according to the following argument. Let $P^{(n)}$ be the matrix of nth-order transition probabilities: that is, the probabilities of moving from one state to another in exactly n steps are the entries of this matrix. The Markov chain model implies that $P^{(n)} = P^n$, the nth power of P, for every n. The fit of the model to the data can be tested by comparing the observed nth order matrix, $P^{(n)}$, with P^n.

For these data the authors found that $P^{(n)}$ differed from P^n by a sizable amount when $n = 8$. In particular, the entries along the diagonal of $P^{(8)}$ were larger than the corresponding entries of P^8, showing that the simple model

---

*For an elementary introduction to Markov chains, see Kemeny, Snell, Mirkil, and Thompson, *Finite Mathematical Structures* (Englewood Cliffs, N.J.: Prentice-Hall, 1959), Chap. 6.

†See T. W. Anderson and L. A. Goodman, "Statistical Inference About Markov Chains," *Annals of Mathematical Statistics,* 1957, pp. 89–110.

underpredicted the number of workers who were in their original industry after eight quarters. Because of this and other information about how the data deviated from the simple model, the authors constructed the more complicated "Stayer-Mover" model described below.]

1. General Approach

As an approximation to some of the more complex models that might be considered, we will divide the workers into two groups, the "Stayers" and the "Movers." The Stayers are workers who in some sense or other have become attached to an industry, who move out infrequently for such reasons as illness or layoff, and who have a high probability of returning to the industry if they do move out. The Movers, on the other hand, are assumed to be workers who have developed relatively little "attachment" to an industry, and whose interindustry movement does follow a simple Markov process. The Movers may or may not stay in the same industry between two consecutive quarters, but their behavior is described by the probabilities of an appropriate one-quarter transition matrix.

In practice, it is quite clear that there will be some form of interchange between these two types of workers (Movers may develop into Stayers, and vice versa), or that there may be varying degrees of "Staying" and "Moving." However, for the sake of simplicity, we shall assume here that workers remain in one or the other of the two groups throughout the period under study. Finally, we shall make one further simplifying requirement, namely, that Stayers remain in an industry code group with probability one. This assumption is perhaps not overly restrictive, since the data indicate that a consistently small fraction of such workers would move between two consecutive quarters, and that a high fraction of them would return to the same industry within a very short period of time if they did move.

Probability models can be set up without these restrictions, as will be shown later, but for purposes of exposition and for checks against observation, it is desirable to keep the model as simple as possible.

2. Formal Description of the Modified Process

Proceeding along the lines described in the preceding section, we assume that the workers employed in a code group in a particular quarter may be separated into two groups, the Stayers and the Movers. To keep the notation and illustrative material manageable, let us treat a simple situation in which there are two industries, 1 and 2, and a classification U for workers "not in covered employment." Under these circumstances the division into Stayers and Movers is given by three numbers s_1, s_2, and s_U, each lying between zero and one inclusive. The number s_1 is to be interpreted as the fraction of workers in industry 1 in a designated quarter who are Stayers, while s_2 and s_U are the fractions for the other two groups. The complementary fractions, $(1 - s_1)$, $(1 - s_2)$, and $(1 - s_U)$, are, of course, the fractions of Movers in these three industry groups in the same quarter. It is again convenient to use matrix notation for these quantities, and this is:

$$S = \begin{Vmatrix} s_1 & 0 & 0 \\ 0 & s_2 & 0 \\ 0 & 0 & s_U \end{Vmatrix}$$

and*

$$(I - S) = \begin{Vmatrix} 1 & 0 & 0 \\ 0 & 1 & 0 \\ 0 & 0 & 1 \end{Vmatrix} - \begin{Vmatrix} s_1 & 0 & 0 \\ 0 & s_2 & 0 \\ 0 & 0 & s_U \end{Vmatrix}$$

$$= \begin{Vmatrix} (1 - s_1) & 0 & 0 \\ 0 & (1 - s_2) & 0 \\ 0 & 0 & (1 - s_U) \end{Vmatrix}$$

Finally, we must give the one-quarter transition matrix which describes the manner in which the Movers behave. This is

$$M = \begin{Vmatrix} m_{11} & m_{12} & m_{1U} \\ m_{21} & m_{22} & m_{2U} \\ m_{U1} & m_{U2} & m_{UU} \end{Vmatrix}$$

where the letter M has been used to emphasize that this matrix refers *only* to Movers.

By using the foregoing quantities and assumptions, we can now describe the movement of all workers among industry code groups. For example, suppose we compare the industry location in the first of two consecutive quarters with that in the second of the pair. The probability that a worker starts in 1 and ends up in 1 is equal to

$$(s_1)1 + (1 - s_1)m_{11}.$$

That is, it is the probability that he is a Stayer, and therefore remains with probability one, plus the probability that he is a Mover and still remains in 1. Similarly, the probability that a worker starts in 1 and ends up in 2 is

$$(s_1)0 + (1 - s_1)m_{12}.$$

---

*The matrix I is referred to as the identity matrix. Also, two or more matrices are added or subtracted by adding or subtracting the corresponding elements.

Similar arguments for the other possibilities give the one-quarter transition matrix for *all* workers (Movers and Stayers combined) as

$$P = \left\| \begin{array}{ccc} s_1 + (1-s_1)m_{11} & (1-s_1)m_{12} & (1-s_1)m_{1U} \\ (1-s_2)m_{21} & s_2 + (1-s_2)m_{22} & (1-s_2)m_{2U} \\ (1-s_U)m_{U1} & (1-s_U)m_{U2} & s_U + (1-s_U)m_{UU} \end{array} \right\|$$

which can be written in matrix notation as

$$P = S + (I-S)M.$$

Having obtained this one-quarter transition matrix, we next consider the transition matrix for two quarters of second order. This matrix will be designated as $P^{(2)}$, where the superscript is placed in parentheses to emphasize that this matrix cannot be obtained by multiplying P by itself. Let us focus our attention on several terms in $P^{(2)}$ and the general rule of formation will then be clear. For example, the probability that a worker starts in 1 and ends up in 1 two quarters later can be easily obtained if we consider the following table, which illustrates the possible paths:

	Industry in First Quarter	Industry in Second Quarter	Industry in Third Quarter	Probability of Path
Stayers	1	1	1	1
	1	1	1	$m_{11}m_{11}$
Movers	1	2	1	$m_{12}m_{21}$
	1	U	1	$m_{1U}m_{U1}$

Thus, we see that Stayers starting in 1 remain in 1 and that Movers starting in 1 may end up in 1 either by remaining there or by moving out and back in again. Finally, these results can be put together to obtain the required probability, as

$$s_1 + (1-s_1)(m_{11}m_{11} + m_{12}m_{21} + m_{1U}m_{U1})$$
$$= s_1 + (1-s_1)m_{11}^{(2)},$$

where $m_{11}^{(2)}$ is the probability that a Mover starting in 1 ends up in 1 two quarters later.

Arguments similar to the above can be made for the other possibilities, and we obtain

$$P^{(2)} = \left\| \begin{array}{ccc} s_1 + (1-s_1)m_{11}^{(2)} & (1-s_1)m_{12}^{(2)} & (1-s_1)m_{1U}^{(2)} \\ (1-s_2)m_{21}^{(2)} & s_2 + (1-s_2)m_{22}^{(2)} & (1-s_2)m_{2U}^{(2)} \\ (1-s_U)m_{U1}^{(2)} & (1-s_U)m_{U2}^{(2)} & s_U + (1-s_U)m_{U}^{(2)}{}_U \end{array} \right\|$$

Finally, we note that the m_{ij}'s and $m_{ij}^{(2)}$'s do describe a simple probability process, and thus obtain

$$P^{(2)} = S + (I-S)M^2,$$

where M^2 is actually computed by multiplying M by itself. This process can be extended indefinitely and $P^{(n)}$, the transition matrix for *all* workers for two quarters of nth order, is equal to

$$P^{(n)} = S + (I-S)M^n.$$

As a simple illustration of the foregoing, let us define S and M as follows:

$$S = \begin{Vmatrix} .40 & 0 & 0 \\ 0 & .50 & 0 \\ 0 & 0 & .30 \end{Vmatrix}$$

$$(I-S) = \begin{Vmatrix} .60 & 0 & 0 \\ 0 & .50 & 0 \\ 0 & 0 & .70 \end{Vmatrix}$$

$$M = \begin{Vmatrix} .90 & .05 & .05 \\ .10 & .80 & .10 \\ .20 & .20 & .60 \end{Vmatrix}$$

Some values of $P^{(n)}$ are

$$P = \begin{Vmatrix} .40 + (.60)\,(.90) & (.60)\,(.05) & (.60)\,(.05) \\ (.50)\,(.10) & .50 + (.50)\,(.80) & (.50)\,(.10) \\ (.70)\,(.20) & (.70)\,(.20) & .30 + (.70)\,(.60) \end{Vmatrix}$$

$$= \begin{Vmatrix} .940 & .030 & .030 \\ .050 & .900 & .050 \\ .149 & .140 & .720 \end{Vmatrix}$$

$$P^{(4)} = \begin{Vmatrix} .40 + (.60)\,(.73) & (.60)\,(.16) & (.60)\,(.11) \\ (.50)\,(.33) & .50 + (.50)\,(.50) & (.50)\,(.17) \\ (.70)\,(.44) & (.70)\,(.34) & .30 + (.70)\,(.22) \end{Vmatrix}$$

$$= \begin{Vmatrix} .838 & .096 & .066 \\ .165 & .750 & .085 \\ .308 & .238 & .454 \end{Vmatrix}$$

$$P^{(32)} = \begin{Vmatrix} .40 + (.60)\,(.57) & (.60)\,(.29) & (.60)\,(.14) \\ (.50)\,(.57) & .50 + (.50)\,(.29) & (.50)\,(.14) \\ (.70)\,(.57) & (.70)\,(.29) & .30 + (.70)\,(.14) \end{Vmatrix}$$

$$= \begin{Vmatrix} .742 & .174 & .084 \\ .285 & .645 & .070 \\ .399 & .203 & .398 \end{Vmatrix}$$

It should be recognized that the matrix $P^{(32)}$ approximates the limiting or stable form of the process that is being discussed. That is, the Movers are following a simple Markov process described by the one-quarter transition matrix M and as a consequence $m_{ij}^{(n)}$, the probability that a Mover located in industry i in the first quarter is in industry j n quarters later, approaches a limit m_j as n becomes large. The limit of M, to within the accuracy of our computations, has been reached by the time 32 quarters have elapsed and is equal to

$$\operatorname*{Lim}_{n \to \infty} M^n = \begin{Vmatrix} .57 & .29 & .14 \\ .57 & .29 & .14 \\ .57 & .29 & .14 \end{Vmatrix}$$

Therefore we have

$$\operatorname*{Lim}_{n \to \infty} P^{(n)} = S + (I - S) \operatorname*{Lim}_{n \to \infty} M^n$$

$$= \begin{Vmatrix} .40 & 0 & 0 \\ 0 & .50 & 0 \\ 0 & 0 & .30 \end{Vmatrix} + \begin{Vmatrix} .60 & 0 & 0 \\ 0 & .50 & 0 \\ 0 & 0 & .70 \end{Vmatrix} \cdot \begin{Vmatrix} .57 & .29 & .14 \\ .57 & .29 & .14 \\ .57 & .29 & .14 \end{Vmatrix}$$

$$= \begin{Vmatrix} .742 & .174 & .084 \\ .285 & .645 & .070 \\ .399 & .203 & .398 \end{Vmatrix}$$

This limiting matrix for *all* workers does not have equal rows, as is the situation for the simple Markov process. That is, the probability that a worker starting in a particular industry code group ends up in a specified code group a large number of quarters in the future now *depends* upon the code group in which he started. This is, of course, a natural consequence of introducing Stayers into the model. It becomes necessary, therefore, to discuss the actual distribution of workers among code groups. This is done in the remainder of this section, but may be omitted on first reading if desired, since it is not essential to the main theme of our treatment.

In addition to examining the movement pattern which this type of process produces, we will also want to discuss the absolute fraction of workers in each of the code groups for any given quarter. For example, let us assume that in Q(1) a fraction $g_1^{(1)}$ of all workers are in code group 1, a fraction $g_2^{(1)}$ are in code group 2, and a fraction $g_U^{(1)}$ are in code group U. Since each worker is in one or the other of these three groups, we have

$$g_1^{(1)} + g_2^{(1)} + g_U^{(1)} = 1.$$

Now, we ask, what is the distribution of workers among the three groups in Q(2)? The argument can be given for $g_1^{(2)}$ — the fraction of workers in code group 1 in Q(2) — and the results will then be clear for the other two desired values, $g_2^{(2)}$ and $g_U^{(2)}$. First of all, a fraction, s_1, of the workers in code group 1 are Stayers. In absolute terms, these constitute a fraction $s_1 g_1^{(1)}$ of all workers. Second, among the Movers in code group 1, a fraction m_{11} will remain, and in absolute terms these constitute a fraction $(1-s_1)g_1^{(1)}m_{11}$ of all workers. Finally, Movers who start in 2 or U may move into 1. Thus, we have

$$g_1^{(2)} = s_1 g_1^{(1)} + (1-s_1)g_1^{(1)}m_{11} + (1-s_2)g_2^{(1)}m_{21} + (1-s_U)g_U^{(1)}m_{U1}.$$

Similar expressions hold for $g_2^{(2)}$ and $g_U^{(2)}$.

This procedure can be extended indefinitely, and we find that $g_1^{(n+1)}$, the absolute fraction of all workers in code group 1 in the $(n+1)$st quarter (after n possibilities for change) is equal to

$$g_1^{(n+1)} = s_1 g_1^{(1)} + (1-s_1)g_1^{(1)}m_{11}^{(n)} + (1-s_2)g_2^{(1)}m_{21}^{(n)}$$
$$+ (1-s_U)g_U^{(1)}m_{U1}^{(n)}$$

where the $m_{ij}^{(n)}$ are the appropriate elements in the nth-order transition matrix for Movers. These results can be compactly summarized if we let $g^{(1)}$ be a row vector (a matrix with one row) having components $g_1^{(1)}$, $g_2^{(1)}$, and $g_U^{(1)}$, that is,

$$g^{(1)} = \| \, g_1^{(1)} \qquad g_2^{(1)} \qquad g_U^{(1)} \, \|$$

Similarly

$$g^{(n+1)} = \| \, g_1^{(n+1)} \qquad g_2^{(n+1)} \qquad g_U^{(n+1)} \, \|$$

Therefore

$$g^{(n+1)} = g^{(1)} P^{(n)}$$
$$= g^{(1)} \, S \, + g^{(1)} \, (I-S) M^n$$

As an illustration, let us use the same values for S and M as we did previously and, in addition, let $g_1^{(1)} = .20$, $g_2^{(1)} = .50$, and $g_U^{(1)} = .30$. Then we have

$$
\begin{aligned}
g^{(1)} &= \|\ .200 \qquad .500 \qquad .300\ \| \\
g^{(2)} &= \|\ .255 \qquad .498 \qquad .247\ \| \\
g^{(5)} &= \|\ .342 \qquad .466 \qquad .192\ \| \\
g^{(33)} &= \|\ .410 \qquad .418 \qquad .172\ \|
\end{aligned}
$$

Since $P^{(32)}$ approximates the limiting of the matrix, the vector $g^{(33)}$ is approximately the limiting or stable distribution of *all* workers among the three industry code groups. Although Movers are still behaving according to the matrix M, their moves do not affect this distribution.

As a final point, we note that the fraction of Stayers in any given industry group is a continually changing number until the limiting distribution is reached. Once this limiting distribution is attained, the fraction of Stayers is constant for each industry group. This is illustrated for the present example by the following values:

$$
\begin{aligned}
s_1^{(1)} &= .40 \\
s_1^{(2)} &= .31 \\
s_1^{(5)} &= .23 \\
s_1^{(33)} &= .20
\end{aligned}
$$

$s_1^{(1)}$ is the fraction of Stayers in industry 1 in $Q(1)$, $s_1^{(2)}$ is the fraction in $Q(2)$, and $s_1^{(33)}$ is the fraction of Stayers after the entire process has reached the "steady state." Except when the process is in the steady state, the fractions of Stayers (the elements of the matrix S) depend upon the time when one examines the process, and in the following we shall therefore assume that the process *was* in the steady state. This is not unreasonable when we consider that interindustry movement had been going on for some time before our observation period of 1947–1949.

[EDITORS' NOTE: In the remainder of Chapter VI the authors go on to estimate the parameters of the Stayer-Mover model for their mobility data and compare the long-range predictions of this model with the observed transitions. While the fit of the model to the data was improved over the original Markov chain model, systematic deviations were still found to occur.

In a later paper ("Statistical Methods for the Mover-Stayer Model," *Journal of the American Statistical Association,* 1961, pp. 841–68), Leo A. Goodman has derived improved estimators for the parameters of this model and reexamined the fit of some of the data to the model. Rather than continue with the discussion of estimation and fit, however, we have chosen to include a portion of Chapter VII of the monograph, in which the authors develop some interesting ideas for the generalization of this kind of model.]

3. Further Generalization of the Model

In the preceding examination of industrial mobility we deliberately used simple probability models. This enabled us to see rather easily the directions in which we ought to proceed if more adequate models were to be developed. It also enabled us to emphasize the basic structure of our process and to develop an understanding of the Markov process. This expository advantage was gained at the expense of the greater realism and flexibility that would be inherent in a more general attack on the problem of mobility. However, it does make it possible for us to treat some more general probability models as easy modifications of a Markov process.

In this section we discuss a model which includes the Stayer-Mover model as a special case. Instead of having only two groups, however, we allow for an arbitrary number of groups, in which the amount of movement is allowed to vary from zero, as in the Stayers group, to almost certain movement. The general line of approach is similar to that in the treatment of "proneness" and "experience" in the literature on accidents,* absenteeism,† and illness.** An account of the general theoretical framework for dealing with such problems has been given by Feller.††

3.1 Exposure to a process. In Section 2 we divided our population into two parts, the Stayers and the Movers. In each industry, there was a fraction of workers who were certain to remain in it and a fraction whose pattern of movement from one quarter to the next was determined by a matrix M.

Let us now divide up the quarter into m time intervals. Instead of just two categories, Stayers and Movers, consider the possibility of $m + 1$ categories. One category will include those workers who were Stayers in each interval and, therefore, throughout the quarter. Another category will include those who were Stayers in all but one time interval of this quarter. Another will include those who were Stayers in all but two intervals, and so on.

---

*A. G. Arbous and J. E. Kerrich, "Accident Statistics and the Concept of Accident Proneness," *Biometrics,* 1951, **7**, 340–432.

†A. G. Arbous and H. S. Sichel, "New Techniques for the Analysis of Absenteeism Data," *Biometrika,* 1954, **41**, 77–90.

**Ove Lundberg, *On Random Processes and Their Application to Sickness and Accident Statistics* (Uppsala: Almqvist and Wicksella Boktryckeri-A-B, 1940).

††W. Feller, "On the Theory of Stochastic Processes with Particular Reference to Applications," *Proceedings of Berkeley Symposium on Mathematical Statistics and Probability* (Univ. of California Press, 1949), pp. 403–32.

We will argue that, in the intervals in which they were not Stayers, the movements of these workers are described by the simple Markov process. That is, the group of workers who are Stayers in all but one interval will have their movements determined by the probabilities of a first order matrix M. Those workers with two intervals in which they are not Stayers will have their movements determined by M^2, and so on. (In this chapter the first order matrix M is a Markov matrix for an interval that is less than a quarter.)

To use a convenient term, we will say that those who are not Stayers in x of the m intervals have had x exposures to the Markov process. The one-quarter distribution of these workers will be determined by M^x, where $x = 0, 1, 2, \ldots, m$.

We will let r_0 designate the fraction of Stayers; r_1 the fraction with one exposure; and generally, r_x the fraction with x exposures. These fractions are each less than one and their total will include all our workers—that is, $r_0 + r_1 + r_2 + \ldots + r_m = 1$. From the point of view of constructing a model, these r_x are the probabilities that an individual chosen at random will be exposed to x stages of a Markov process. We take r_x to be the same for all industries. (In Section 2 the fractions of Stayers were different in different industries.)

When we treated the two-group process of the preceding chapter we obtained the probability that an individual in any state was in the same state, or a different one, a quarter later as the sum of the elements of two matrices, appropriately weighted. For the present model, with $m + 1$ categories, we will add $(m + 1)$ matrices. The movement pattern of those who were exposed x times is M^x and this matrix is weighted by r_x, the fraction of the population exposed x times. For the Stayers we write $M^0 = I$ and weight this matrix by r_0, the fraction of the population who are Stayers. Adding these terms* for all x, we find that the one-quarter transition matrix for a situation in which there are m intervals of exposure is

$$P = r_0 I + r_1 M + r_2 M^2 + \ldots + r_m M^m.$$

We illustrate this procedure of "mixing" by a fictitious example. Suppose that in our time interval the movement matrix M is

$$M = \begin{Vmatrix} .70 & .15 & .15 \\ .20 & .60 & .20 \\ .25 & .25 & .50 \end{Vmatrix}$$

---

*The reader is reminded that every element in a matrix is multiplied by a number placed before the matrix and that matrix addition is performed by adding corresponding elements of the matrices.

For M^2 we have*

$$M^2 = \begin{Vmatrix} .56 & .23 & .21 \\ .31 & .44 & .25 \\ .35 & .31 & .34 \end{Vmatrix}$$

and

$$M^3 = \begin{Vmatrix} .49 & .28 & .24 \\ .37 & .37 & .26 \\ .39 & .32 & .28 \end{Vmatrix}$$

In this example we will take $r_0 = .67$, $r_1 = .27$, $r_2 = .05$, and $r_3 = .01$. That is, 67 percent of our group have no exposure to movement, 27 percent have one exposure, and so on. If this is so, the fraction of workers who start in any industry and are in the same industry one quarter later is, to take industry 2 as an example,

$$.67 + (.27)(.60) + (.05)(.44) + (.01)(.37) = .86.$$

The sum is composed of the 67 percent never exposed, the 27 percent exposed once for whom the probability of staying is given by the element in the second row and column of M; the 5 percent who are still in industry 2 with probability given by the second row and column of M^2; and the 1 percent taken from M^3. Thus 67 percent never move, 16 percent are exposed once but remain in industry 2, and 3 percent are exposed at least twice but are in industry 2 at the end of the quarter.

A similar procedure can be followed for all other combinations of industries of origin and destination. It will be equivalent to multiplying each element of the identity matrix by .67, each element of M by .27, each element of M^2 by .05, each element of M^3 by .01, and then obtaining a new matrix by adding the elements in the corresponding positions of these matrices. If we designate the one-quarter transition matrix corresponding to the process described above by P, we have

$$P = .67I + .27M + .05M^2 + .01M^3$$

$$= \begin{Vmatrix} .67 & 0 & 0 \\ 0 & .67 & 0 \\ 0 & 0 & .67 \end{Vmatrix} + \begin{Vmatrix} .19 & .04 & .04 \\ .05 & .16 & .05 \\ .07 & .07 & .13 \end{Vmatrix}$$

---

*All computations were carried to more significant figures than are indicated. Results obtained by using two decimal places will not always agree exactly with figures given here.

$$+ \begin{Vmatrix} .03 & .01 & .01 \\ .02 & .02 & .01 \\ .02 & .02 & .02 \end{Vmatrix} + \begin{Vmatrix} \text{Matrix whose ele-} \\ \text{ments are all less} \\ \text{than } .005 \end{Vmatrix}$$

$$= \begin{Vmatrix} .89 & .05 & .05 \\ .07 & .86 & .07 \\ .09 & .09 & .82 \end{Vmatrix}$$

We now turn our attention to relating the transition matrices that span two or more quarters to the one-quarter transition matrix. That is, we try to connect short-term and long-term movements.

We will write $P^{(2)}$ for the two-quarter matrix. Then, if we subdivide both the first and second of our quarters into m intervals, the matrix will be given by

$$P^{(2)} = r_0^{(2)} I + r_1^{(2)} M^2 + \ldots + r_{2m}^{(2)} M^{2m}.$$

In this equation we introduce the probability $r_0^{(2)}$ for workers who are not exposed to movement in two quarters, $r_1^{(2)}$ for those exposed once to movement and, more generally, $r_x^{(2)}$ for those who are exposed to movement x times in two quarters. For a transition matrix of arbitrary order we will have

$$P^{(n)} = r_0^{(n)} I + r_1^{(n)} M + r_2^{(n)} M^2 + \ldots + r_{nm}^{(m)} M^{nm}.$$

What we have is a process which is determined by two sets of elements. One set consists of the probabilities $r_0^{(n)}$, $r_1^{(n)}$, $r_2^{(n)}$, $\ldots$, $r_{nm}^{(n)}$, which determine the number of exposures to the process, and the other is a matrix M, which determines patterns of movement of those who have been exposed. For the time being, let us assume that the pattern of movements — that is, M — is constant over all the time intervals that we are using to build up our one-quarter transition matrices. If this is so, the relation between P and matrices of higher order, such as $P^{(2)}$, is determined by the relations between the various r's — for example, r_0 and $r_0^{(2)}$, r_1 and $r_1^{(2)}$, r_0 and $r_1^{(2)}$, and so on. Under some circumstances these relations can be obtained from rather straightforward considerations. To show how this can be done, we will simultaneously generalize our process slightly by the use of a "limiting" argument and restrict ourselves somewhat by considering a simplified situation. As the reader would expect, we intend to modify these restrictions considerably in what follows.

Let us, for the moment, consider a group of workers who are relatively homogeneous with respect to exposure to our movement pattern. That is, in any time interval they all have essentially the same chance of exposure to movement. Furthermore, let us suppose that exposure probabilities are constant over our period of observation and that an exposure has no effect on further chances of exposure during this period. Suppose, further, that each quarter is divided up into an arbitrarily large number of time intervals. It then follows from an argument involving differential equations that the probabilities, r_x, are those of a Poisson distribution. That is, if the average number of exposures in any quarter is called a, then $r_x = e^{-a} \dfrac{a^x}{x!}$, where $e = 2.718 \ldots$ is a standard mathematical constant. Hence

$$P = e^{-a} \left(I + aM + \frac{a^2}{2!} M^2 + \ldots \right).$$

This argument can also be used to give us $P^{(2)}$. In this instance the mean number of exposures will be $2a$ and the probability of x exposures in two quarters will be given by the Poisson probability, $r_x{}^{(2)} = e^{-2a} \dfrac{(2a)^x}{x!}$. Thus we have $P^{(2)} = e^{-2a} \left(I + (2a)M + \dfrac{(2a)^2}{2!} M^2 + \ldots \right).$

Now, suppose we multiply P by itself, obtaining P^2. It is not difficult to show that the coefficient of M^x in the resulting series is also $e^{-2a} \dfrac{(2a)^x}{x!}$. That is, if we multiply our one-quarter transition matrix by itself, we should get our second-order transition matrix. (Symbolically, $P^{(2)} = P^2$.) The argument can be extended to higher order matrices and, in general, $P^{(n)} = P^n$.

A numerical example may serve to illustrate the argument of the last paragraph. The r_x we used earlier in this section were the probabilities of a Poisson distribution within which 0.4 is the average number of exposures in one quarter. When we consider a two-quarter period, the average number of exposures becomes 0.8. In this instance the probability of 0 exposures becomes .45, of one exposure .36, of two exposures .14, of three exposures .04, and of four exposures .01. For $P^{(2)}$ we then have

$$P^{(2)} = .45I + .36M + .14M^2 + .04M^3 + .01M^4$$

$$= \begin{Vmatrix} .80 & .10 & .10 \\ .13 & .75 & .12 \\ .16 & .15 & .69 \end{Vmatrix}$$

Straightforward matrix multiplication of

$$P = \begin{Vmatrix} .89 & .05 & .05 \\ .07 & .86 & .07 \\ .09 & .09 & .82 \end{Vmatrix}$$

by itself yields the same result.

The importance of this result is that it tells us that we can ignore the number of movements made by individuals between the points of time at which we take our observations. Hence we have partial justification for the procedure of assigning the workers who had worked in more than one industry in any quarter to a principal industry.

3.2 Proneness to movement. In testing the fit of the simple Markov chain model to the data, we found that multiplication of one-quarter matrices by themselves did not yield higher-order transition matrices that gave an adequate description of our process. In particular, there were considerable discrepancies between the observed and expected principal diagonal elements. We will now modify the approach of the preceding subsection with an eye to improving our model in this respect.

The argument which led us to Poisson probabilities for exposure to the process was based on homogeneity with respect to chance of exposure for all individuals in the process. We now recognize that the population may be composed of many groups, each relatively homogeneous with respect to chance of exposure, but not all groups having the same chance of exposure. The differences may be due to race, personality, unionization, or other factors. These differences imply that each group will have its own average exposure during a quarter. We will write a_k as the average exposure for the kth group.

In any single quarter, of course, not all members of the same group will be exposed the same number of times. In the kth group, the probability of x exposures for an individual chosen from that group is $\dfrac{(a_k)^x}{x!} e^{-a_k}$.

Let q_k be the fraction of the population falling into the kth group. Then the probability that an individual chosen at random will be in the kth group and also be exposed to movement x times is $q_k \dfrac{(a_k)^x}{x!} e^{-a_k}$. Adding these probabilities for all groups, we see that the probability that an individual chosen at random will have x exposures is given by $r_x = \displaystyle\sum_{k=1}^{\infty} q_k \dfrac{(a_k)^x}{x!} e^{-a_k}$. (We have allowed the sum to run over all positive integers to indicate that there may be an arbitrarily large number of groups. We can also introduce the possibility of continuous variation of the a's by letting $dF(a)$ be the fraction of the population with a particular average exposure. In that event,

$$r_x = \int_0^{\infty} \frac{a^x}{x!} e^{-a} \, dF(a).)$$

The expression for P, the one-quarter transition matrix, will have the same general form as in Section 3.1, $P = r_0 I + r_1 M + r_2 M^2 + \ldots$, where we note that the fraction of the population with x exposures, r_x, is given by the equation above. Our problem now is to examine the relation between P and the higher-order transition matrices $P^{(n)}$ and to discuss the limiting distribution. We will treat the limiting distribution first.

If the one-quarter transition matrix for Movers is given by M, and if we assume that the Movers follow a Markov process, then the probability that an individual who is a Mover would be in a particular industry after a sufficiently long time does not depend on his industry of origin. These limiting probabilities can be obtained by multiplying M by itself a sufficiently large number of times, and we use the notation $\underset{n \to \infty}{\text{Lim}} M^n = M^{\text{lim}}$.

Let us now return to our one-quarter transition matrix P, which is the weighted sum of various powers of a matrix M, where M is the matrix that determines the pattern of movement whenever there is exposure to movement. Let us multiply P by itself an arbitrarily large number of times. It can be readily shown that this operation gives us a limiting matrix and that $\underset{a \to \infty}{\text{Lim}} P^n = M^{\text{lim}}$.

We now compare this result with the result of watching the process for a long time — that is, with $\underset{n \to \infty}{\text{Lim}} P^{(n)}$ — and discover that $\underset{n \to \infty}{\text{Lim}} P^{(n)}$ is also equal to M^{lim}. That is, multiplication of the one-quarter transition matrices should give us the same distribution of workers among industries as is actually observed.*

We now turn our attention to the relation between short- and long-term movements, that is, between P and $P^{(n)}$. The interesting fact we now observe is that the introduction of heterogeneity of exposure to movement implies that we cannot obtain higher-order transition matrices by simply multiplying the first-order matrix by itself an appropriate number of times. That is, it is *not* true that $P^{(2)} = P^2$ and, more generally, it is not true that $P^{(n)} = P^n$. Furthermore, if the elements on the main diagonal of the first-order transition are relatively large, we will find this reflected, after a number of periods, by larger diagonals of the observed nth-order matrix than the simple Markov model would lead one to expect.

We can illustrate these remarks by a simple numerical example before discussing their implications in the light of our data. Suppose that we have just two groups of workers of the same size, one with an average exposure in any quarter of 0.1 and another with an average exposure of 0.7. The average exposure in the two groups combined will be the same as that of the workers in the preceding example.

We will then have that $r_0 = (.5)e^{-0.1} + (.5)e^{-0.7}$, $r_1 = (.5)(.1)e^{-0.1} + (.5)(.7)e^{-0.7}$, and so on. Thus, $r_0 = .70$, as compared with .67 in the pure Poisson situation, $r_1 = .22$ as compared with .27, $r_2 = .06$, and $r_3 = .01$. (In view of the small contributions made by r_4 and r_5, it will make numerical work simpler if we ignore r_4 and r_5 and take $r_3 = .02$.)

---

*We assume that there is no group of individuals who are certain to stay, that is, $F(O) = 0$.

Similarly, for probabilities of exposure in two time periods, we have $r_0{}^{(2)} = .5e^{-0.2} + .5e^{-1.4}$, and so on. Thus, $r_0{}^{(2)} = .53$ as compared with .45 in the pure Poisson situation, $r_1{}^{(2)} = .25$ against .36, $r_2{}^{(2)} = .13$, $r_3{}^{(2)} = .06$, $r_4{}^{(2)} = .02$, and $r_5{}^{(2)} = .01$.

The transition matrices P and $P^{(2)}$ now become

$$P = .70I + .22M + .06M^2 + .02M^3$$

and

$$P^{(2)} = .53I + .25M + .13M^2 + .06M^3 + .02M^4 + .01M^5.$$

Using M as previously defined

$$M = \left\|\begin{array}{ccc} .70 & .15 & .15 \\ .20 & .60 & .20 \\ .25 & .25 & .50 \end{array}\right\|$$

we have

$$P = \left\|\begin{array}{ccc} .90 & .05 & .05 \\ .07 & .87 & .06 \\ .08 & .08 & .84 \end{array}\right\|$$

and

$$P^{(2)} = \left\|\begin{array}{ccc} .82 & .09 & .09 \\ .12 & .77 & .11 \\ .14 & .13 & .73 \end{array}\right\|$$

Computing $P^2 = P.P$

$$= \left\|\begin{array}{ccc} .81 & .10 & .09 \\ .13 & .76 & .11 \\ .15 & .14 & .71 \end{array}\right\|$$

we see that discrepancies begin to arise between $P^{(2)}$ and P^2. The discrepancies are relatively small.

If we extend our period of observation, however, and therefore have matrices of a somewhat higher order, the differences become substantial. Thus

$$P^{(8)} = \left\|\begin{array}{ccc} .63 & .21 & .17 \\ .26 & .55 & .19 \\ .28 & .23 & .48 \end{array}\right\|$$

and

$$P^8 = \begin{Vmatrix} .54 & .25 & .21 \\ .33 & .44 & .24 \\ .35 & .30 & .36 \end{Vmatrix}$$

$P^{(8)}$ is the expected eighth-order transition matrix for this *mixture* of Markov processes. P^8 is the expected eighth-order transition matrix if we assume that we have the simple Markov model and, therefore, also for the model of Section 3.1, where all workers have the same chance of exposure. We see that the differences between P^8 and $P^{(8)}$ are of the same sort as those found in our data. That is, the Markov model understates the probabilities on the main diagonal for transitions of high order.

Thus one model that might reasonably be expected to fit the data fairly well could be obtained by arguing that workers, when they move, do so in accordance with the same or similar transition matrices. The essential difference from the simple model is that we will now allow workers to have differing probabilities of exposure to the movement process. That this approach has possibilities is evidenced by the considerable improvement in "fit" of model to data accomplished by the procedure of dividing the population into Stayers and Movers.

How well such a model describes industrial mobility could be determined only by estimating the parameters of our model from actual data and testing observation against hypothesis. Before this could be done, the model would have to be given more explicitly than has been done in this brief discussion. This would not be difficult if one were willing to make reasonable simplifications in the assumptions underlying the model. There might be difficulties, however, in devising procedures for estimation and testing hypotheses and manipulating the data according to these procedures.

A Comparison of Eight Models[1]

Robert R. Bush   *University of Pennsylvania*
Frederick Mosteller   *Harvard University*

Introduction

In the testing of a scientific model or theory, one rarely has a general measure of goodness-of-fit, a universal yardstick by which one accepts or rejects the model. Indeed, science does not and should not work this way; a theory is kept until a better one is found. One way that science does work is by comparing two or more theories to determine their relative merits in handling relevant data. In this paper we present a comparison of eight models for learning by using each to analyze the data from the same experiment.[2]

A primary goal of any learning model is to predict correctly the learning curve—proportions of correct responses versus trials. Almost any sensible model with two or three free parameters, however, can closely fit the curve, and so other criteria must be invoked when one is comparing several models. A criterion that has been used in recent years is the extent to which a model can reproduce the fine-grain structure of the response sequences. Many properties can be and have been invented for this purpose. Fourteen such properties are used in this paper.

A summary index of how well one model fits the fine-grain detail of data compared with another model is the likelihood ratio. There are three objections to this measure, however. First, for many models it is very difficult to compute. Second, its use obscures the particular strengths and weaknesses of a model and so fails to suggest why the model is inadequate. Third, it may be especially sensitive to uninteresting differences between the model and the experiment. Therefore we do not use likelihood ratios in this paper.

A satisfactory prediction of the sequential properties of learning data from a single experiment is by no means a final test of a model. Numerous other criteria—and some more demanding—can be specified. For example, a model with specific numerical parameter values should be invariant to changes in independent variables that explicitly enter in the model. Such requirements we do not investigate in this paper. Our analyses are restricted to the problem

[1] Support for this research was received from the Ford Foundation, the National Science Foundation (grant NSF-G2258), and the Laboratory of Social Relations, Harvard University.

[2] [EDITORS' NOTE: The authors use the same data in testing another model in a later chapter.]

of predicting sequential details. We believe that this is a sensible second step once the learning curve has been handled.

The particular data used for comparing the eight models were obtained by Solomon and Wynne from an experiment on the avoidance training of dogs [8]. On each of 25 trials, a dog could avoid an intense electric shock by jumping over a barrier within ten seconds after the occurrence of a conditioned stimulus. The basic data are sequence of shocks (S) and avoidances (A) for 30 dogs. In an earlier work ([1], chap. 11) we analyzed these data with a two-operator linear model. This is one of the eight models being compared in this paper, and so the results are summarized below.

For most learning models of the type to be discussed, one can derive formulas for the expected values and variances of several sequential statistics. Such formulas are of great value in the application of models to data. It often turns out, however, that for a particular model certain explicit formulas are very difficult if not impossible to obtain. Therefore, for the purpose of this paper, we resort to Monte Carlo computations with each model ([1], p. 129). This allows a direct comparison of the models on each of the fourteen statistics chosen. One exception to this procedure occurs in our treatment of the Markov model. For some properties of some models, we include explicit formulas even though they are not used in the final comparisons.

To standardize notations, we use p_n to represent the probability of avoidance (A) on trial n and $q_n = 1 - p_n$ to denote the probability of shock (S). Trials are numbered $n = 1, 2, \cdots$.

The Two-Operator Linear Model

The model previously applied [1] to the Solomon-Wynne data asserts that

$$q_{n+1} = \begin{cases} \alpha_2 q_n & \text{if } S \text{ occurs on trial } n \\ \alpha_1 q_n & \text{if } A \text{ occurs on trial } n, \end{cases}$$

where $0 \leq \alpha_1, \alpha_2 \leq 1$, and $q_1 = 1.00$. Several procedures for estimating α_1 and α_2 from the data were used, but the final estimates were $\hat{\alpha}_1 = 0.80$ and $\hat{\alpha}_2 = 0.92$. With these parameter values we ran 30 stat-dogs and calculated the values of the fourteen statistics listed in Table 1 (p. 305).

A Hullian Model[3]

Clark Hull does not explicitly consider the problem of avoidance training in his *Principles of Behavior*, but he does give a general theory of acquisition [2]. He asserts that the increment in habit strength occurring on each trial is a constant proportion of the "potential habit strength yet unformed." He further says (in one place at least) that an index of habit strength is "per cent of correct reaction evocation." This suggests that if p_n is the probability

---

[3] To each of the remaining models we attach the name of the man judged by us to be most closely associated with it. This does not imply that any of these men has explicitly proposed a model for the Solomon-Wynne experiment, nor that our interpretations would be acceptable to them. At best we are simplifying if not wrenching their notions, but it may help the reader if we use these names as labels.

of avoidance on trial n, then

$$p_{n+1} = p_n + (1 - \alpha)(1 - p_n) ,$$

where $(1 - \alpha)$ is the constant of proportionality. In terms of q_n, the probability of shock, this transition law is $q_{n+1} = \alpha q_n$. Note that this rule is equivalent to the basic assumption of the two-operator linear model when $\alpha_1 = \alpha_2 = \alpha$.

In this Hullian model, the expectation of T, the total number of shocks in 25 trials, is

$$E(T) = \sum_{n=1}^{25} q_n = \sum_{n=1}^{25} \alpha^{n-1} q_1 = q_1 \frac{1 - \alpha^{25}}{1 - \alpha} .$$

As before, we take $q_1 = 1$. From the data we get the average number of shocks per dog to be $\overline{T} = 7.80$. By equating $\overline{T}$ and $E(T)$, we get $\hat{\alpha} = 0.88$. With this value of α, 30 stat-dogs were run and statistics of the sequences were computed. The results are shown in Table 1.

A Hullian Model with Individual Differences

Inspection of Table 1 shows that the Hullian stat-dogs are less variable than the real dogs and so one might suspect that the Hullian model would apply to individuals, but that different dogs would have different values of the parameter α. To construct a model that allows for such individual differences we need to make some assumptions about the distribution of α, and we need to estimate parameters of this distribution from the data.

Values of α are restricted to the unit interval. A reasonable, convenient, and well-known probability density function on the unit interval is the beta-distribution [5],

$$f(\alpha) = \frac{(r + s + 1)!}{r! \, s!} \alpha^r (1 - \alpha)^s ,$$

where the parameters r and s must both be greater than -1. The mean and variance of this distribution are

$$E(\alpha) = \frac{r + 1}{r + s + 2} , \qquad \text{var}\,(\alpha) = \frac{(r + 1)(s + 1)}{(r + s + 3)(r + s + 2)^2} .$$

We shall assume that the values of α have this distribution and estimate r and s from the Solomon-Wynne data.

In order to estimate r and s, we compute the mean and variance of the total number of shocks in terms of r and s, set these expected values equal to the observed values, and thereby solve for the desired estimates. A particular value of α determines the parameter of a binomial distribution for a single trial, and so we need expectations over these binomials as well as expectations over the assumed beta-distribution. Subscripts b and β will be used on the expectation operator E to indicate whether the binomial or the beta-distribution, respectively, is involved. The total number of shocks received by a dog in an infinite number of trials is represented by a random variable T. We then see that for fixed α,

$$E_b(T) = \sum_{n=1}^{\infty} q_n = \sum_{n=1}^{\infty} \alpha^{n-1} = \frac{1}{1-\alpha},$$

and the variance of T is

$$\text{var}(T) = \sum_{n=1}^{\infty} q_n(1-q_n) = \sum_{n=1}^{\infty} \alpha^{n-1}(1-\alpha^{n-1}) = \frac{1}{1-\alpha} - \frac{1}{1-\alpha^2}.$$

Therefore

$$E_b(T^2) = \frac{1}{1-\alpha} - \frac{1}{1-\alpha^2} + \frac{1}{(1-\alpha)^2}.$$

We now need expectations over the beta-distributions (we assume they exist):

$$\begin{aligned}
E_\beta E_b(T) = E_\beta\left(\frac{1}{1-\alpha}\right) \\
= \int_0^1 \frac{1}{1-\alpha} f(\alpha) d\alpha = \int_0^1 \frac{(r+s+1)!}{r!\, s!} \alpha^r (1-\alpha)^{s-1} d\alpha \\
= \frac{r+s+1}{s} \int_0^1 \frac{(r+s)!}{r!\,(s-1)!} \alpha^r (1-\alpha)^{s-1} d\alpha.
\end{aligned}$$

The last integral is unity because the integrand is a beta density function with parameters r and $s-1$. Thus, dropping the subscripts, we have

$$E(T) = \frac{r+s+1}{s}.$$

By a similar process we can easily show that

$$E_\beta\left(\frac{1}{(1-\alpha)^2}\right) = \frac{(r+s)(r+s+1)}{(s-1)s}.$$

To compute $E_\beta E_b(T^2)$, we need also

$$E_\beta\left(\frac{1}{1-\alpha^2}\right) = \int_0^1 \frac{(r+s+1)!}{r!\, s!} \alpha^r \frac{(1-\alpha)^{s-1}}{1+\alpha} d\alpha.$$

This integral causes some minor difficulty but we can expand $1/(1+\alpha)$ into a series as follows:

$$\begin{aligned}
\frac{1}{1+\alpha} = \frac{1}{2-(1-\alpha)} = \frac{1}{2} \frac{1}{1-(1-\alpha)/2} \\
= \frac{1}{2}\left[1 + \frac{1-\alpha}{2} + \frac{(1-\alpha)^2}{4} + \frac{(1-\alpha)^3}{8} + \cdots \right].
\end{aligned}$$

The integration can be carried out term by term to give

$$E_\beta\left(\frac{1}{1-\alpha^2}\right) = \frac{r+s+1}{2s} + \frac{1}{4} + \frac{s+1}{8(r+s+2)} + \frac{(s+1)(s+2)}{16(r+s+2)(r+s+3)} + \cdots.$$

This result enables us to write

$$E(T^2) = \frac{(r+s)(r+s+1)}{(s-1)s} + \frac{r+1}{2s} + \frac{1}{4} - \delta,$$

where

$$\delta = \frac{s+1}{8(r+s+2)}\left[1 + \frac{s+2}{2(r+s+3)} + \cdots\right].$$

The variance of T is then

$$\mathrm{var}\,(T) = \frac{(r+1)(r+s+1)}{s^2(s-1)} + \frac{r+1}{2s} + \frac{1}{4} - \delta.$$

This equation and our previous expression for $E(T)$ are the desired estimation equations.

To simplify computations, we let

$$\mu = E(T) = \frac{r+s+1}{s}, \qquad \sigma^2 = \mathrm{var}\,(T).$$

We then can solve for s to get

(1)
$$s = \frac{\mu(\mu-1)}{\sigma^2 - \dfrac{1}{2}(\mu-1) - \dfrac{1}{4} + \delta},$$

with

$$\delta = \frac{s+1}{8(s\mu+1)}\left[1 + \frac{s+2}{2(s\mu+2)} + \cdots\right].$$

Having estimated s from Equation 1, we can estimate r from the equation $r = s(\mu-1) - 1$.

The Solomon-Wynne data give $\hat{\mu} = 7.80$, $\hat{\sigma}^2 = 6.58$, which in turn yield the estimates $\hat{s} = 19$, $\hat{r} = 128$. In terms of these values, we get

$$E(\alpha) = 129/149 = 0.866,$$

$$\mathrm{var}\,(\alpha) = \frac{(129)(20)}{(150)(149)^2} = 0.000775,$$

$$\sigma(\alpha) = 0.0278.$$

In order to use available tables, we choose $s = 19$, $r = 130$, which give $E(\alpha) = 0.868$, $\sigma(\alpha) = 0.0275$.

From tables [6], the cumulative of the beta-distribution $F(\alpha)$ with $r = 130$, $s = 19$, and the first differences were determined as shown below.

α	$F(\alpha)$	$\Delta F(\alpha)$	α	$F(\alpha)$	$\Delta F(\alpha)$
.76	.000		.88	.657	.285
.78	.003	.003	.90	.887	.230
.80	.013	.010	.92	.983	.096
.82	.051	.038	.94	.999	.016
.84	.158	.107	.96	1.000	.001
.86	.372	.214			

To approximate this distribution with 30 animals, the following frequency table was constructed.

α	Number	α	Number
.81	1	.89	7
.83	3	.91	3
.85	6	.93	1
.87	9		

The mean is 0.871 and the standard deviation is 0.0271. These values were considered sufficiently close to the desired values of 0.866 and 0.0278.

With the above set of α's, 30 stat-dogs were run and they yielded the statistics given for them in Table 1.

An Early Thurstone Model

In 1917, Thurstone proposed a hyperbolic law of learning [9],

$$y = \frac{a(n + c)}{n + c + b},$$

where y is the number of successes per unit time, n is the number of trials, and a, b, and c are constants. If y is to be the probability of avoidance, which is zero when $n = 1$ and approaches unity as $n \rightarrow \infty$, Thurstone's equation becomes

$$p_n = \frac{n - 1}{n - 1 + b},$$

and the probability of shock is

$$q_n = \frac{b}{n - 1 + b}.$$

The expected number of shocks during the first N trials is

$$E(T) = \sum_{n=1}^{N} q_n = \sum_{n=1}^{N} \frac{b}{n - 1 + b}.$$

The sum can be approximated by the integral

$$\int_{1/2}^{N + (1/2)} \frac{b\,dn}{n - 1 + b} = b \log \frac{b + N - (1/2)}{b - (1/2)}.$$

For $N = 25$ and $\overline{T} = 7.80$, we get $\hat{b} = 3.5$. Furthermore, a direct evaluation of the sum with $b = 3.5$ gives the correct value of 7.80. With this value of b, the values of q_n were computed and 30 stat-dogs run. The results are given in Table 1.

A Late Thurstone Model

One of the first stochastic learning models with differential effects for success and failure was Thurstone's urn scheme [10]. His idea was that an urn containing black and white balls represented the probability of the responses in a two-choice situation. Thus if a randomly drawn ball is white, response 1 occurs; if black, response 2 occurs. The contents of the urn can be altered by the effects of events. For example, if event i occurred, a_i white and b_i

black balls could be added to the urn. While the a's and b's can take negative values, some arrangement must be made to assure that the number of balls of any color is never negative, and that the urn always has at least one ball in it. In the model that follows, we shall add only white balls.[4]

Suppose that immediately preceding some trial n, the contents of the urn are (a_n, b_n) in white and black balls. Then the probability of shock on trial n is

$$q_n = \frac{b_n}{a_n + b_n}.$$

If a white ball is drawn, an avoidance occurs. The white ball is replaced and c_1 whites added to the urn. If a black ball occurs, then shock occurs, and the black ball and c_2 whites are added to the urn. Thus both shock and avoidance improve the probability of an avoidance if we assume the c's are positive.

In the dog data, the initial probability of an avoidance has been taken to be zero. Thus initially we can take $q_1 = 1$, i.e., $b_1 = 1$, $a_1 = 0$. We shall not actually work with the concept of balls but with continuous parameters. This does no violence to Thurstone's original idea. He obviously used the balls for intuitive appeal. Then in general on trial n, the probability of shock is

$$(2) \qquad q_{ij} = \frac{1}{1 + ic_2 + jc_1} \qquad (i + j = n - 1),$$

where i is the number of previous shocks and j is the number of previous avoidances.

Several estimation procedures have been considered for obtaining values of c_1 and c_2. Some of these are rather tedious. We settled upon a rather inexpensive method.

We note first that $\hat{q}_{ij} = x_{ij}/n_{ij}$, where n_{ij} is the number of dogs with i previous shocks and j previous avoidances, and where x_{ij} is the number of those dogs shocked on trial $n = i + j + 1$. Then we could rewrite by analogy with Equation 2

$$x_{ij}(1 + ic_2 + jc_1) \triangleq n_{ij},$$

where $\triangleq$ means "estimates" or "is estimated by."

There are two parameters to estimate, c_1 and c_2, and so we wish to obtain a pair of simultaneous equations. These can be obtained by summing over two different sets of i, j pairs. Suppose these sets are called A and B; then we get the equations

$$c_2 \sum_A ix_{ij} + c_1 \sum_A jx_{ij} = \sum_A (n_{ij} - x_{ij}),$$

$$c_2 \sum_B ix_{ij} + c_1 \sum_B jx_{ij} = \sum_B (n_{ij} - x_{ij}).$$

[4][EDITORS' NOTE: The authors point out that if the number of white balls added were proportional to the number already in the urn, Thurstone's model would be essentially equivalent to the beta model discussed by them in a later chapter.]

The coefficients of the c's suggest how we might pick the sets A and B. Generally speaking, in one of the equations we wish the coefficient of c_1 to be large and that of c_2 to be small, and in the other equation we want this relation reversed. We might therefore pick for our set A those i, j pairs such that $i > j$, for B those i, j pairs for which $j \geq i$. While we are not thereby guaranteed that the result is satisfactory, because the x_{ij} have their contribution to make, we can hope that the general effect is about right. The values we got from such an approach gave us a preliminary estimate. (We actually used $i > j + 1$ for A, and $i \leq j + 1$ for B.)

It seemed wise to try to improve this estimate by forming weights for the various cells. We decided to weight the equations of the form

$$x_{ij}(1 + ic_2 + jc_1) = n_{ij}$$

reciprocally by their variances. The variance of the left side is

$$(1 + ic_2 + jc_1)^2 n_{ij} \left(\frac{1}{1 + ic_2 + jc_1} \right) \left(\frac{ic_2 + jc_1}{1 + ic_2 + jc_1} \right) = n_{ij}(ic_2 + jc_1) .$$

Dividing both sides by this result and then multiplying through by n_{ij} again gives

$$x_{ij} \left(\frac{1 + ic_2 + jc_1}{ic_2 + jc_1} \right) \triangleq \frac{n_{ij}}{ic_2 + jc_1} .$$

The initial estimates of c_1 and c_2 gave c_1 as about three times c_2, so the weights finally used were $1/(i + 3j)$. The same summations were performed, and estimates $\hat{c}_1 = 0.446$, $\hat{c}_2 = 0.111$ were obtained. Using these values for the c's, we then ran 30 stat-dogs and computed the several statistics.

A Markov Model

A simple model for a learning situation is a two-state Markov chain. Such models were discussed by G. A. Miller [4]. Recall that S stands for shock and A for avoidance. The two conditional probabilities, $\Pr\{S|S\}$ and $\Pr\{A|A\}$, are assumed constant. $\Pr\{X|X\}$ means the probability of X occurring on a trial given that X occurred on the previous trial. We need the initial probability of shock $q_1(S)$, but from the data we see that the appropriate value is 1.00. Furthermore, Solomon and Wynne report that for many trials beyond the 25th, no dogs were shocked. Thus we take $\Pr\{A|A\} = 1.00$. This leaves us with one parameter, $a = \Pr\{S|S\}$, to be estimated from the data. It is easily shown that the expected total number of shocks is

$$E(T) = \frac{1}{1 - a} .$$

Using $\overline{T} = 7.8$, we get $\hat{a} = 0.872$. Further, it can be shown that

$$\text{var}(T) = \frac{a}{(1 - a)^2} .$$

For $a = 0.872$, we have $\text{var}(T) = 53.1$, $\sigma(T) = 7.30$.

Because $\Pr\{A \mid A\} = 1$, as soon as an avoidance occurs, the model predicts that the dogs will continue avoiding forever. Thus, all of the statistics listed in Table 1 can be computed from theory without running stat-dogs. These theoretical results are shown in Table 1.

A Restle Model

F. Restle has described a model for discrimination experiments [7], and a modification of his model might be appropriate for avoidance training. Assume with Restle that the stimulus situation contains r relevant cues and i irrelevant cues. A relevant cue may or may not be conditioned to a response (avoiding shock, in our problem) on trial n; the probability that any single relevant cue is conditioned on trial n, according to Restle, is $c_n = 1 - (1 - \theta)^{n-1}$. Irrelevant cues become "adapted," i.e., cease to exist for the subject. The probability that on trial n any irrelevant cue is adapted is $a_n = 1 - (1 - \theta)^{n-1}$. Another of Restle's main assumptions is that $\theta = r/(r + 1)$.

In writing down an expression for the response probability on trial n, we depart from Restle's model. We assume that only conditioned cues contribute toward avoidance. Thus, we take

$$p_n = \frac{rc_n}{r + i(1 - a_n)} .$$

From the previous equations, one gets

$$p_n = 1 - \frac{(1 - \theta)^{n-1}}{\theta + (1 - \theta)^n} .$$

The probability of shock is

$$q_n = \frac{(1 - \theta)^{n-1}}{\theta + (1 - \theta)^n} .$$

The expected total number of shocks is

$$E(T) = \sum_{n=1}^{\infty} q_n = \sum_{n=1}^{\infty} \frac{(1 - \theta)^{n-1}}{\theta + (1 - \theta)^n} .$$

By replacing the sum with an integral from 1/2 to ∞, we get the approximation

$$E(T) = \frac{\log \theta - \log (\theta + \sqrt{1 - \theta})}{(1 - \theta) \log (1 - \theta)} .$$

The right-hand side of this equation is 7.82 when $\theta = 0.23$. The sum is 7.78 when $\theta = 0.23$. Thus, we take $\hat{\theta} = 0.23$. With this value of θ, the values of q_n were computed and 30 stat-dogs run. The results are shown in Table 1.

A Krechevsky Model

For ten years or more, beginning about 1930, there was a controversy between the "continuity" and "noncontinuity" theorists [3]. The latter school (Lashley, Krechevsky) argued that an initial presolution period was followed by sudden learning; the continuity theorists (Hull, Spence) contended that learning occurred from the beginning.

One possible formalization of the noncontinuity position is described in this section.

Define a random variable

$$x_{in} = \begin{cases} 1 \text{ if } A \text{ on trial } n \text{ by } i\text{th animal} \\ 0 \text{ if } S \text{ on trial } n \text{ by } i\text{th animal.} \end{cases}$$

Then $p_{in} = \Pr\{x_{in} = 1\}$, and $q_{in} = \Pr\{x_{in} = 0\}$. Assume that the ith animal is in some "state" S_0 at the start of the experiment and at the start of some trial N_i changes to another state S_1 and then remains in S_1 for the remainder of the experiment. We shall speak of the change of state on trial N_i as the occurrence of an event E.

We then postulate that the probability of avoidance obeys the following law:

$$p_{in} = \begin{cases} p \text{ if } i\text{th animal is in state } S_0 \text{ on trial } n \\ 1 \text{ if } i\text{th animal is in state } S_1 \text{ on trial } n. \end{cases}$$

It is next assumed that event E (change from S_0 to S_1) occurs with some fixed probability on every trial that the animal is in state S_0:

$$\Pr\{S_1 \text{ on } n \mid S_0 \text{ on } n - 1\} = \beta \ .$$

It then follows that the random variable N_i (the trial number of insight or complete learning) has a negative binomial distribution given by

$$\Pr\{N_i = j\} = \beta(1 - \beta)^{j-1} \qquad (j = 1, 2, \cdots) \ .$$

These axioms specify a stochastic process which has some simple properties.

A group learning curve is obtained by plotting the proportion of animals that have a success on trial n versus n. The ordinate is

$$\bar{x}_n = \frac{1}{I} \sum_{i=1}^{I} x_{in} \ ,$$

where I is the number of animals in the group. The theoretical curve is obtained from the expected value of x_{in} which we now compute.

From the axioms of the model

$$\Pr\{x_{in} = 1 \mid n < N_i\} = p \ , \qquad \Pr\{x_{in} = 1 \mid n \geq N_i\} = 1 \ ,$$

and

$$\Pr\{N_i \leq n\} = \sum_{j=1}^{n} \beta(1 - \beta)^{j-1} = 1 - (1 - \beta)^n \ ,$$

$$\Pr\{N_1 > n\} = (1 - \beta)^n \ .$$

It then follows that

$$E(x_{in}) = 1 - (1 - p)(1 - \beta)^n \ .$$

Thus, a theoretical group learning curve can be computed in terms of the two model parameters, p and β. It is interesting to note that the learning function just derived can also be obtained from a "Hullian-type" model. Of course, this model makes very different predictions about other aspects of the data.

Denote the total number of shocks made by the ith animal by T_i. On trials before event E occurs, T_i has a binomial distribution

$$\Pr\{T_i = k \mid N_i = j + 1\} = \binom{j}{k} q^k p^{j-k} \qquad (k \leq j).$$

We have already seen that

$$\Pr\{N_i = j + 1\} = \beta(1 - \beta)^j.$$

and so

$$\Pr\{T_i = k\} = \sum_{j=k}^{\infty} \binom{j}{k} q^k p^{j-k} \beta(1 - \beta)^j.$$

The summation can be carried out to yield

$$\Pr\{T_i = k\} = \gamma(1 - \gamma)^k \qquad (k = 0, 1, \cdots),$$

where

$$\gamma = \frac{\beta}{1 - p(1 - \beta)},$$

Thus T_i has a negative binomial distribution with parameter γ.

It is well known that the expected value and variance of T_i are

$$E(T_i) = \frac{1 - \gamma}{\gamma} = q\frac{1 - \beta}{\beta},$$

(3)

$$\mathrm{var}(T_i) = \frac{1 - \gamma}{\gamma^2} = q\frac{1 - \beta}{\beta^2}[1 - (1 - q)(1 - \beta)].$$

Denote by L_i the trial number of the last shock by the ith animal. We must have $L_i < N_i$ and so we can define a new random variable, $Y_i = N_i - L_i - 1$, which corresponds to the number of trials after trial L_i and before trial N_i. If one thinks of the trials occurring in reverse order, it is readily seen that Y_i has a negative binomial distribution

$$\Pr\{Y_i = h\} = qp^h \qquad (h = 0, 1, 2, \cdots).$$

We already know that

$$\Pr\{N_i = j + 1 + h\} = \beta(1 - \beta)^{j+h},$$

and so the joint distribution of Y_i and N_i is

$$\Pr\{N_i = j + 1 + h, Y_i = h\} = \beta(1 - \beta)^{j+h} qp^h.$$

From this we can get the distribution of L_i because

$$\Pr\{L_i = j\} = \sum_{h=0}^{\infty} \Pr\{N_i = j + 1 + h, Y_i = h\}$$

$$= \sum_{h=0}^{\infty} \beta(1 - \beta)^{j+h} qp^h.$$

Performing the summation gives

$$\Pr\{L_i = j\} = \frac{q\beta(1 - \beta)^j}{1 - p(1 - \beta)}.$$

This function is not a normalized density function; in fact

$$\sum_{j=1}^{\infty} \Pr\{L_i = j\} = 1 - \frac{\beta}{1 - p(1 - \beta)}.$$

This is so because L_i may not have a value—it may happen that no shocks occur. We already know that

$$\Pr\{T_i = 0\} = \gamma = \frac{\beta}{1 - p(1 - \beta)}.$$

Therefore, it is more convenient to deal with the conditional probabilities

$$\Pr\{L_i = j \mid T_i \neq 0\} = \frac{\Pr\{L_i = j\}}{\Pr\{T_i \neq 0\}}.$$

We obtain

$$\Pr\{L_i = j \mid T_i \neq 0\} = \beta(1 - \beta)^{j-1},$$

which is precisely the distribution of N_i.

The mean and variance are

$$(4) \qquad E(L_i \mid T_i \neq 0) = \frac{1 - \beta}{\beta}, \qquad \mathrm{var}\,(L_i \mid T_i \neq 0) = \frac{1 - \beta}{\beta^2}.$$

These theoretical values can be compared with empirical values obtained from the values of L_i for animals that obtain at least one shock.

Equations 3 and 4 were used to estimate the two parameters, p and β. Equating expectations and observed means for the Solomon-Wynne data, we have $q(1 - \beta)/\beta \cong 7.80$, $(1 - \beta)/\beta \cong 11.33$. Solving for the estimates, we have $\hat{\beta} = 0.081$, $\hat{p} = 0.312$. These values were used in 30 Monte Carlo computations and the obtained values of the fourteen statistics are given in Table 1.

The process defined by the model is binomial on trials before event E occurs. Thus the distribution of alternations is essentially that for a binomial. In j binomial trials with probabilities p and q of success and failure, respectively, the expected number of runs is well known to be

$$2(j - 1)pq + 1 \qquad (j = 1, 2, \cdots).$$

The number of alternations is one less than the number of runs. Avoidance necessarily occurs on trial N_i, and if trial $N_i - 1$ is a shock trial, one more alternation occurs. Thus, if A_i is the number of alternations by the ith animal,

$$E(A_i \mid N_i = j \neq 1) = 2(j - 2)pq + q.$$

We know that $E(N_i \mid N_i \neq 1) = (1/\beta) + 1$. Thus

$$E(A_i) = 2\frac{1 - \beta}{\beta}pq + q.$$

Discussion

A study of Table 1 reveals a great deal about the relative weaknesses of the eight models. It appears that the Markov model is the least satisfactory; the first and second avoidances occur too late, the last shock occurs too soon, and there are far too few alternations. This is no surprise in view of the design of the model—all learning occurs on a single random trial. For a similar reason, the Krechevsky model is quite unsatisfactory. With this model, the first and second avoidances occur too soon, the last shock occurs too soon, and there are too few alternations. Therefore, we can conclude that neither of these "discontinuity" models is adequate.

TABLE 1

Comparisons of the Eight Models with the Dog Data

Statistic		Dog data	Two-operator linear	Hullian	Hullian with individual differences	Early Thurstone	Late Thurstone	Markov	Restle	Krechevsky
Trials before first avoidance	Mn	4.50	4.13	3.17	3.57	3.13	4.10	7.80	4.40	1.77
	SD	2.25	2.08	1.79	1.81	1.17	2.91	7.30	1.73	2.11
Trials before second avoidance	Mn	6.47	6.20	5.03	5.33	4.87	6.53	8.80	6.37	4.03
	SD	2.62	2.06	1.82	1.71	1.28	2.74	7.30	1.83	2.52
Total number of shocks	Mn	7.80	7.60	7.57	7.50	8.50	8.67	7.80	7.73	6.07
	SD	2.52	2.27	1.73	1.62	2.23	2.80	7.30	1.76	5.37
Trials before last shock	Mn	11.33	12.53	17.57	15.80	19.97	18.97	6.80	12.97	7.73
	SD	4.36	4.78	4.09	5.36	4.70	5.11	7.30	4.60	7.46
Number of alternations	Mn	5.47	5.87	7.40	7.10	9.17	7.37	1.00	5.87	3.87
	SD	2.72	2.11	2.04	2.94	3.28	2.62	0.00	2.56	3.34
Length of longest run of shocks	Mn	4.73	4.33	3.53	3.70	3.40	4.44	7.80	4.47	3.43
	SD	2.03	1.89	1.57	1.69	1.04	2.73	7.30	1.59	2.45
Trials before first run of 4 avoidances	Mn	9.70	9.47	7.83	10.03	10.13	9.57	7.80	10.03	7.50
	SD	4.14	3.48	3.00	4.20	5.78	3.59	7.30	3.34	6.96

The Hullian model has several weaknesses: the first and second avoidances occur too soon, the last shock occurs too late, and there are too many alternations. All of the SD's are too small. Similar weaknesses are found in the Hullian model with individual differences, although it is a decided improvement over the simpler Hullian model.

Like the Hullian models, the early Thurstone model predicts that avoidances occur too soon, that the last shock occurs too late, and that there are too many alternations. It is evident that a satisfactory model must have some mechanism for delaying the early avoidances and at the same time speeding up the occurrence of the last shock. The late Thurstone model accomplishes the former but fails at the latter; in this model learning does not occur rapidly enough near the end.

The two models that seem most satisfactory are the two-operator linear model and the Restle model. Both models predict about the correct means on all seven properties. However, both predict SD's that are somewhat small on all properties except the number of trials before the last shock. The two-operator model and the Restle model are both sufficiently close that the data of Table 1 do not allow one to choose between them. Thus, we ask if there exists a statistic which is more sensitive to the differences between those models. One major difference between them is that the Restle model assumes that all organisms have a single value of q_n on trial n, whereas the two-operator model generates a distribution of q_n for $n > 1$. We now investigate one consequence of this difference.

The estimates of α_1 and α_2 in the two-operator model show that shock has a smaller effect than avoidance. Thus, those dogs that receive five shocks on the first five trials, for example, have a higher probability of shock on the sixth trial than any dog that receives fewer than five shocks on the first five trials. Therefore, the total number of shocks received after the fifth trial should be greater for those dogs that are shocked on each of the first five trials. The Solomon-Wynne data show that 13 dogs obtained shock on all of the first five trials and that these dogs obtained a mean of 4.77 shocks thereafter; the other 17 dogs obtained a mean of 2.70 shocks on trials beyond the fifth. This difference is significant, as a Mann-Whitney test shows ($P < .01$). The Restle model, like all models that have a single q_n for all organisms on trial n, predicts that no such difference will occur.

Conclusion

From the discussion in the previous section it is clear that among the models presented the two-operator model described the data best. A critic might point out that the game played in this paper is easily rigged by the authors to favor their own model. Though one reply to such a critic would be that the authors have not suppressed any models, that reply would be entirely out of the spirit of this paper. We freely admit that several of the models can be considerably improved, though at some expense in mathematical and statistical research. (Parameter estimation is the main difficulty.) What we are trying to do here is to present a sequence of models each of which has some relation to past psychological thinking about learning, and to discover just where our versions of these models are weak in describing one experiment.

A person with a special bent toward one of the psychological theories represented here can take our formulation as a first approximation and see wherein it was weak. Such a step may suggest to him directions in which the model needs improvement and may indicate those aspects of the more general psychological theory that have been especially neglected in our formulation.

The work in this paper might be regarded as mathematical experimentation, as distinguished from laboratory experimentation. The former is needed to get some feeling for the variety of models there can be, and to prevent premature acceptance of any one model just because it has been worked on and others have not.

The authors feel that in the past too little attention has been given to the ability of various models to reproduce the fine structure of a set of data, and they present this paper as an illustration of one kind of study that is needed.

REFERENCES

1. Bush, R. R., and Mosteller, F. *Stochastic models for learning.* New York: Wiley, 1955.
2. Hull, C. L. *Principles of behavior.* New York: Appleton-Century-Crofts, 1943. Chap. 8.
3. Krechevsky, I. A study of the continuity of the problem-solving process. *Psychol. Rev.*, 1938, **45**, 107-33.
4. Miller, G. A. Finite Markov processes in psychology. *Psychometrika*, 1952, **17**, 149-67.
5. Mood, A. M. *Introduction to the theory of statistics.* New York: McGraw-Hill, 1950. P. 115.
6. Pearson, K. *Tables of the incomplete beta function.* London: Cambridge University Press, 1932.
7. Restle, F. A theory of discrimination learning. *Psychol. Rev.*, 1955, **62**, 11-19.
8. Solomon, R. L., and Wynne, L. C. Traumatic avoidance learning: acquisition in normal dogs. *Psychol. Monogr.*, 1953, **67**, No. 4 (whole No. 354).
9. Thurstone, L. L. The learning curve equation. *Psychol. Monogr.*, 1919, **26**, No. 3 (whole No. 114).
10. Thurstone, L. L. The learning function. *J. gen. Psychol.*, 1930, **3**, 469-91.

Information Theory and Psycholinguistics:
A Theory of Word Frequencies

Benoit Mandelbrot   *International Business Machines Corporation*

This paper describes the brief encounter between two important streams of thought, information theory and psycholinguistics, and presents the theory of word frequencies born of their interaction. By now the two protagonists have gone their own separate ways, but their offspring remains. One could even describe it with hardly any reference to its parents, but this would be unfair. It would also be pointless, since the main purpose of this paper is to illustrate one form of the interplay between the new forms of mathematical thinking and certain problems that constituted the mainstream of traditional sciences. Broad logical relations will be given primacy over manipulations by postponing the latter to appendixes.*

The stage having been set, let us introduce the actors.

The great distinction of information theory, born fully armed in 1948 from two celebrated papers by Claude Shannon, was the novel manner in which it recombined two of the oldest and most fundamental ideas of formalized science: the concept of algorithm and the concept of chance. These two ideas have, of course, never been far from each other, starting with games of pure chance in the seventeenth and eighteenth centuries and continuing through statistical mechanics around 1900 and quantum theory around 1925. Therefore Shannon's theory was in no way the beginning of something entirely new, and now—as time goes by—it begins to fit very well within probability theory as another interesting chapter. Before 1948, however, there were only a few scattered attempts to formalize the fact that human discourse is both highly structured and highly unpredictable. Shannon's work stressed the possibility of describing its structure by the algorithms of coding and of describing its unpredictability by a systematic exploitation of Markov's pure chance model (1913) of Pushkin's novel *Eugene Onegin*. By reinterpreting the physical concept of entropy as a measure of "quantity of information," Shannon also showed a way of

---

*These appendixes have been added for the purposes of the present revised reprint. For more detailed and more general derivations, and for answers to a number of comments, the reader is referred to Mandelbrot (1961) and also to Mandelbrot (1954). A less complete account, but perhaps a better-written one, is given in Miller and Chomsky (1963). For further developments addressed to the philosopher of science, see Mandelbrot (1957).

describing the degree of structure of a system by its degree of disorder, itself measured by a function of the probabilities of various events (Appendix A). This "quantity of information" was, of course, never claimed to exhaust the loose verbal idea of "information," and many experts soon found that the best way of presenting Shannon's theory was to follow its author in *not* giving the top billing to the "quantity of information." It is also true that "information theory" was meant to be applicable not only to human discourse, but to every type of message; but the actual techniques of the theory have turned out to be most inconvenient except for messages similar to discourse.

The importance of Shannon's contribution has always been obvious. Fifteen years later, however, it is difficult and somewhat puzzling to think of one's reactions, and of those of one's peers, when the original papers appeared, a part of the backlog of novelties accumulated during the war and readied for publication during the three years from 1945 to 1948. The supply and the demand for the new things being then at their highest, the ink was not yet dry when enthusiasts started going around promising prompt rewards from the application of information theory to any problem one could think of. Conservatives balked, some saying that it would be too easy to be true, and others adding that one should really not expect so much from a mathematical panacea of which professional mathematicians were taking such an indifferent view. These quarrels have now died, since – as is often the case – most predictions were rather poor. Indeed, application of information theory turned out not to be easy, and it did not solve everything; but the honest toil which it generated has – in my opinion – served as a most effective wedge through which mathematics was helped to conquer new fields of application. As to professional mathematicians, they sought to compensate by great activity for their lateness in getting involved in these problems. To sum up, information theory has indeed become a quite well-established chapter of the calculus of probability. In the meantime the limitations of its practical usefulness in its field of origin have also become fairly clear (see Mandelbrot, 1965).

Let us now turn to the second actor of our story. The term *psycholinguistics* fits him, and I also think that there is no problem in extending the shorter term *linguistics* to cover the features of human discourse with which we shall deal, and in particular to cover the astonishing statistical law, the discovery of which is associated with the names of Jean Baptiste Estoup and of George Kingsley Zipf, and the story of which will be our primary concern for the remainder of the present paper.

Let us again begin with a few words of history. Among the technological problems concerning natural discourse, the most ancient are without question those of cryptography and of stenography or telegraphy. All these problems have now become parts of information theory, and I wish to show that they ought also to be considered part of linguistics. Let us recall the purposes that the cryptographer and the stenographer set for their special transformations of the usual phonic and graphic signs—which are of course quite "arbitrary," in Saussure's sense. The cryptographer wishes to achieve a code as devoid as possible of any kind of structure that can be used by his adversary to break the secrecy of his message. As to the stenographer and the telegraphist, their common aim is to achieve a code which the hand or a machine handling Morse can note in as short a time as possible. We must investigate these two kinds of code somewhat more closely.

First of all, we shall neglect the technological constraints that are obviously present in both cases. For that, let us grant for a while that the encoding and decoding machines may be as complicated as the designer may wish, and that the memory of the human links—in the common sense of the word *memory*—is unbounded. Under those ideal circumstances it is obvious that any improvement of our understanding of the structure of language and of discourse will bring a possibility of improvement of the performance of the cryptographer or the stenographer. For example, a knowledge of the rules of grammar will show that such and such a phrase will never be encountered in grammatically correct discourse; thus, if his employer were to speak only grammatical English, a stenographer would not need any special set of signs to designate the incorrect sentences. Similarly, a knowledge of the statistics of discourse will suggest that clichés be represented by special short signs; in this way the stenogram will be shortened and—since deciphering is very much helped by clichés—the cryptogram will be made more robust. That is, the ideal cryptographer and stenographer should make the utmost use of any available linguistic information. Conversely, the empirical findings of language engineers should widen our knowledge of language and discourse.*

Let me indulge at this stage in a brief epistemological aside, pointing out that one could hardly have expected the empirical facts most important to language engineers to be the kind that interests the traditional linguists most. As a matter of fact, the following is likely to happen and has indeed been observed: using the margin of error allowed by empirical observation, grammarians and language engineers may very well envision their common object of study in such divergent ways that their final theories are, strictly speaking, logically incompatible. The discovery of such occurrences has had a rather traumatic effect on some linguists, whose previous experience did not include sufficiently long logical deductions to ever lead to logical contradiction. Practitioners of supposedly "hard" fields, such as physics, are on the contrary very familiar with the fact that a total description of a given reality may require the use of several logically incompatible theories.

---

*A similar interplay between theory and practice is encountered by another group of language engineers: those concerned with translation from one language to another with the help of automatic dictionary look-up. However, the scope of the present work excludes this question and any other topic of the field of mechanical translation.

There is also good reason for the psychologist to envy the physicist's luck in his attempts to explain complicated facts on the basis of very simple assumptions: after all, practitioners of the "hard science" of physics have succeeded —for centuries—in being excused for using arguments about the imaginary realm of atoms; nobody could go and check the properties assumed for these entities, so that the philosopher's strictures against such "nonoperational" procedures were paid little heed to. (This is a good example of what the physicist Eugene P. Wigner refers to as "the unreasonable effectiveness of mathematics in the natural sciences.") How embarrassing, by contrast, is the situation encountered in the social sciences: any set of assumptions— however fruitful, reasonable, and useful it may be—is susceptible of some kind of experimental verification which, however rough it may be, is very likely to show the inapplicability of these assumptions.

Feeling sure that nobody will take quite seriously the above aside, let me resume our examination of the cryptographer and the stenographer. It is clear that they work under such obvious practical constraints that they could hardly take advantage of the possibilities of making use of linguistics. Conversely, the professional literature of those fields is hardly known to outsiders; from the viewpoint of information theory, the most important exceptions are the frequency properties relative either to "average samples of discourse," to mixtures of various sources, or to samples from particular authors. The striking fact here is the difference in simplicity between the two most commonly studied "articulations"—that of the letter or phoneme and that of the word. The frequencies of single letters and of "n-grams" made up of successive letters have been taken into account by cryptographers and telegraphers since the earliest times. Decades before the justification provided by information theory, Samuel Morse knew that he should use the shortest combinations of dots and dashes to designate the most frequent letters, and cryptographers dealt with letter frequencies centuries before information theory. Moreover, recurrent attempts have been made to relate the frequency of a phoneme to some measure of its articulatory "difficulty." But all this has not gone very far. Indeed, it seems that, from the viewpoint of statistical modelmaking, isolated letters are too small to be intrinsic units: little is implied about longer bits of discourse by knowing the frequencies of the contributing letters. As to n-grams, they are more useful, but linguistically very artificial.

Words are better bets for the theoretician: although their exact linguistic standing is not free of problems, there is no question that perception of discourse is based upon units whose length approximates that of a word, and there are good practical reasons for beginning the study of those units by examining words, defined as the sequences of letters between two successive space symbols.

Such a study was indeed performed quite early, and, according to my sources, the first worker in this area was a stenographer of the French parliament, Jean Baptiste Estoup. His work seemed to be motivated by a politicotechnical dispute concerning the respective advantages of several systems of French stenography, and—very commendably—he sought scientific fact to support the design that he favored. Similar investigations were repeated, this time for the sake of healthy intellectual curiosity, by many other investigators. But theirs were isolated and brief efforts in comparison with the lifetime of toil devoted to the question of word frequencies by George Kingsley Zipf, the author of several books that combine fact and folly in an unusually intimate fashion. To describe the findings of these various authors we need the following definitions.

Take a long sample of discourse from a given individual and rank all the words that occur in this sample in the order of decreasing frequencies. The word given rank one is the most frequently observed sequence of letters contained between two successive space signs; in English it is usually *the,* but for some subjects it is *I.* The word given rank two is that which becomes the most frequent when the word of rank one has been put aside. The word of rank three is the most frequent when one excepts those of ranks one and two, and so on. Let us designate by the symbol $W(r)$ the word that occupies the rank r in this special ordering. We should note that there are many rare words that occur once or twice in the given sample. Their order is indeterminate, but also indifferent; that is, they can be ranked arbitrarily.

With use of these definitions, the empirical findings can be expressed as follows:

In the first approximation, the ratio $i(r, k)/k$, which is the relative number of repetitions of the word $W(r)$ in the sample of length k, is inversely proportional to ten times r:

$$i(r,k)/k = 1/(10r) = (1/10)(1/r).$$

The numerical factor $1/10$ was obtained empirically. It should also be stressed that the definition of rank only implies that r and $i(r,k)$ vary in *inverse directions*; the fact that $i(r,k)$ is *inversely proportional* to r is therefore not obvious and must be established empirically. The usual method of checking relationships of this form is to use doubly logarithmic paper, in which the abscissa is the logarithm of r and the ordinate is the logarithm of $i(r,k)$. The first approximation law of word frequencies is then expressed by stating that the graph of $\log[i(r,k)]$ as a function of $\log r$ is a straight line of slope minus one, or—in other terms—that it is parallel to the second bissectrix of the coordinate axes, as shown by the bold line of Fig. 1.

The second approximation. According to certain authors, the law $i(r,k) = k(1/10)(1/r)$ would hold for every writer, irrespective of the language that he happened to use. One finds in fact that most empirical graphs differ markedly

from a straight line of slope minus one. *To begin with*: The few most frequent words seem not to follow the law at all. As a matter of fact, in a language such as French, the definition of "word" is unclear in the case of
abbreviated forms such as *l'* which are among the most frequent ones, so
that "the" distribution of the most frequent words is actually undetermined. *Second remark*: One finds that the bulk of the graphs of log $i(r,k)$
are not parallel to the second bissectrix, and that the law of word frequencies
depends upon what is often loosely referred to as the "wealth of vocabulary"
of the subject; such a dependence is hardly unexpected. To sum up, data
can be analytically represented by the following formula, which corresponds
to curves similar to the dashed line of Fig. 1.

$$i(r,k) = Pk(r + V)^{-B}$$

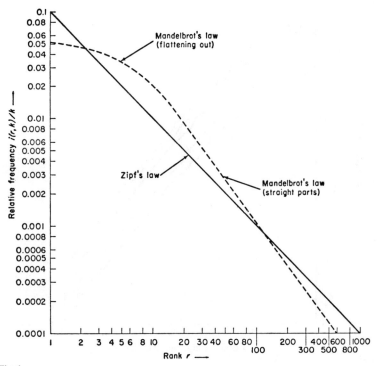

Fig. 1.

The rank r has been defined. As to P, V, and B, they are parameters — that
is, they are fixed for a given subject but are different for different subjects;

they do not characterize a language, although it may well be that different languages "favor" different ranges of values for the parameters. The easiest to measure is the parameter B, which is the absolute value of the slope of the doubly logarithmic graph of log $[i(r,k)]$ as a function of log r (excluding the most frequent words). The first-approximation law is a particular case of the second approximation: by writing it as $i(r,k) = (1/10)kr^{-1}$, one sees that it corresponds to the following values of the parameters: $B = 1$, $V = 0$, and $P = 1/10$. As to the general law $i(r,k) = Pk(r + V)^{-B}$, it seems worth pointing out that it has *not* been obtained by "mere curve fitting": in attempting to explain the first approximation law, $i(r,k) = (1/10)kr^{-1}$, I invariably obtained the more general second approximation, and only later did I realize that this more general formula was necessary and basically sufficient to fit the empirical data.* Examples are presented in Fig. 2.

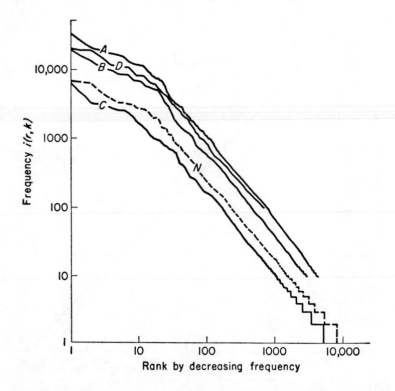

*It is worth pointing out here that the evidence of doubly logarithmic graphs is *very reliable* when their slope B is in the vicinity of 1 (see Mandelbrot, 1963). We need not be concerned here with the well-documented fact that doubly logarithmic graphs are very unreliable when their slope B is large (for example, when it exceeds 4).

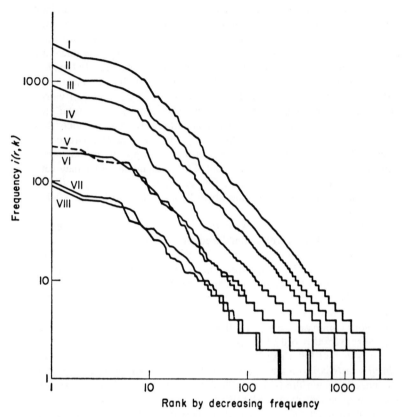

Fig. 2. Some examples of plots of the frequency of a word (vertically in the logarithmic scale) versus its rank (horizontally in the logarithmic scale). *First:* A, B, C, and D are samples from German writers, N, from a Norwegian writer; *second:* samples of increasing length from the writings of the same English-speaking individual, who happened to be a schizophrenic.

Social science statistics being what it is, the law $i(r,k) = Pk(r+V)^{-B}$ is among the best-established results in that field, and in fact is one of the very few laws that are constantly reconfirmed by all the new evidence that keeps accumulating. Since such a law is in fact observed, there could be nothing absurd in imagining that some general law is applicable to word frequencies. To show that there is indeed no conflict between the facts and most people's "intuition" of the properties of discourse, let us consider the word *coffee*. There is no question that it is usually observed when the subject wishes to express some idea, without reference to any desire to attribute a given frequency to the sequence of letters *c-o-f-f-e-e*. But, first of all, the probabilistic conception of the structure of discourse determines the relative frequency of a word only on the average. This is very similar to well-known facts concerning the tossing of coins or dice: if the ace appears exactly once in a long succession of plays, one can be sure that the game is unfair. In the ideal model of random tosses, the observed frequencies of the ace must vary around the ideal value (1/6). Similarly, the observed frequencies of words should be expected to fluctuate. Naturally, as seen by the emitter, the fluctuations of word frequencies are not generated by "pure chance" but rather are associated with what he "has to say"; but, as seen by the receiver, the occurrences of the words are (hopefully) at least partly unpredictable, and "pure chance" is nothing but a model of unpredictability. One may very well find that this model is inadequate for certain refined purposes, but one certainly cannot say that it is a priori absurdly in conflict with some kind of intuition.

Let us proceed. The law $i(r,k) = Pk(r+V)^{-B}$ does not limit itself to say that every word has a well-defined frequency; it also proposes a relation between the frequencies of different words. This is not absurd either. First of all, the law says nothing of the frequencies of *coffee, tea,* or *chocolate* as such; its prediction is rather the following: Paul tells me that he has established that *coffee* has the rank 177 in his vocabulary, while Peter found that it has rank 315 in his. In the first approximation this suggests to me that Paul uses the word *coffee* once every 1770th word on the average, and that Peter uses it every 3150th word. That is, the law of word frequencies relates to the entire system of Peter's or Paul's words, taken as one whole. Moreover, *system of words* is in no way synonymous with *system of ideas*. The correspondence between the two is sufficiently arbitrary to allow one system of words to represent many systems of ideas, and conversely.

Having convinced (hopefully) milder skeptics of the reasonableness of the existence of a law of word frequencies, it remains to "explain" why this law takes the form described above. It happens that this expression is formally one of the simplest encountered by statisticians; but most professionals neglected it until now, so that almost all the explanations (beginning with Zipf's "least effort" arguments) used very primitive tools or handled mathematics incorrectly. Hence — so far as I know — the only acceptable models are the numerous variants of an idea that I suggested in 1951 and that was developed in various directions by several writers. These variants are fully equivalent mathematically, but they appeal to such different intuitions that the strongest critics of one may be the strongest partisans of another; certain variants were in fact rediscovered by constructive critics! But their author has long since given up trying to determine which is best. It is useful to note here that a problem of prediction is called "well posed" in physics if slight changes in initial conditions do not change the result more than slightly. Similarly, my "explanatory" setup can be called well posed, since changes in assumptions do not lead to disproportionate changes in the results; if, however, the assumptions are modified drastically enough, quite different results will be obtained.

The two basic variants of my model of word frequencies are readily interpreted in terms of the problems of cryptography and telegraphy that were mentioned earlier. One can prove this: Suppose that the cryptographer or the telegrapher were forced to use a given coding alphabet, and that he were required to encode word by word, the code of each word being followed by a special symbol that plays the same role as the "space" of ordinary spelling. Then, information theory shows that the same rule of coding is best for both secrecy and economy; this is so because any symbol that could be spared for purposes of economy in transmission might also provide a clue for deciphering. However, the coding procedures thus suggested by the theory will in general have to cut across words and to use longer units. Thus the constraint imposed by the use of word-by-word coding may a priori be expected to lead to decreased economy in transmission and to decreased "robustness" against attempts to decipher. It happens, however, that in the case of actually observed word statistics, and in this case alone, no loss whatsoever is entailed by the need to use word delimitations and to follow the words by space symbols. In other terms, one may say that, so far as the use of a space is intrinsic to the concept of a word, the only case where the word is a natural segment of discourse is when its statistics follow the law which they happen precisely to follow (Appendix B).

The form of these criteria is very familiar in physics, which is inclined to characterize the observed facts with the help of such statements as "the principle of least action," "the principle of largest entropy," "the principle of smallest entropy production." The initial idea of those principles was borrowed from introspective criteria of optimal human behavior, and, after a long detour through physics, they returned to social science under the guise of such things as Zipf's "principle of least effort." As a matter of fact, it was the title of Zipf's book that triggered my derivation of the law of word frequencies, in which "telegraphic optimality" was characterized by maximizing Shannon's quantity of information under certain constraints. It seems, unfortunately, that many readers were greatly confused by the inevitable association of such a model with Zipf's peculiar idea of a perfect world and by the inevitable association of Shannon's quantity of information with the many aspects of the word *information* that Shannon never remotely claimed to cover. It turned out therefore to be more politic to stress the optimality of observed word statistics with respect to cryptography, an activity less readily associated with the idea that the works of man are perfect.

Besides the approaches based upon problems of telegraphy and secrecy, a third variant of my basic model also deserves brief mention. It is clear indeed that as time goes by the structure of the system of word frequencies slowly changes, both for individuals and for the averages relative to groups. Concerning the nature of this change, I made certain hypotheses that are simple and would have seemed reasonable in the framework of the "unreasonable effectiveness of mathematics in natural science," to which I referred. Since the model thus obtained is only a reinterpretation of the two criteria of optimality, it leads again to the empirically observed law. Again, there is little chance that a universe generated by haphazard diachronic chance can be considered "perfect" in any real way.

I suddenly realize that I have not done justice to psychology as such. Let me therefore end up by commenting upon a curious aspect of some of my models. Independently of the specific variant that one may prefer, they all ultimately rest upon the decomposition of words into more elementary units. For example, in the last analysis cryptographic or telegraphic optimality implies the representation of words with the help of special signs such as Morse dots and dashes. As a matter of fact, this decomposition is the key to the success of our models, since, using appropriate new forms of the "law of large numbers," we could show that the same law of word frequencies should correspond to a wide range of microscopic structures; this is an application to linguistics of a method of "macromodel" making in the absence of "microdata," which is one of the most powerful tools of the physicist (a different tool bearing the same name is greatly used in economics). This being granted, and even though word frequencies are surely independent of the technical details of Samuel Morse's contraption, one could have expected them to be linked to phoneme frequencies, and—in the first approximation—to letter frequencies. For example, the more general forms of the models sketched in Appendix B require a concept of "the cost" of a word; it would be tempting indeed to identify the cost of a word with the number of letters it contains, as is implied through most of Appendix B. This is unfortunately impossible, and the best that one can do is to look for the cost within the recoding of discourse by the higher nervous system of the receiver of the message and, perhaps, even that of its emitter.

Even though hardly anything is known about these stages, it is likely that this recoding uses certain units shorter than the phrase or the idea and longer than the phoneme or the letter. It is natural to try to see whether these units are the words; if so, our models would refer to the mutual adaptation between the codes of those words and their frequencies. Unfortunately, the only simple tests of this hypothesis are the tachitoscopic measurements of the time for recognition of words. These tests are favorable to my hypothesis, but the recourse to higher brain functions may still seem to be a dodge. Let us hope, however, that the situation is not worse than that of statistical physics in the heyday of the energetists: those who dared brave the philosophers of science freely spoke of the effects of the shape of the unobservable atoms; the more cautious scholars preferred to work with the so-called phenomenological method, for which theories that predict well the results of possible experiments need not be explained any further. As it happens, I am personally rather in favor of phenomenology these days, so that we shall not continue this tale any further.

Appendix A. The Quantity of Information

To make this paper more self-contained, it is good to define Shannon's quantity of information and to comment upon its motivation.

A discrete probability distribution is a set of positive numbers p_n adding to 1. Shannon's information of such a distribution is defined as being equal to

$$H = -\Sigma\, p_n \log_2 p_n,$$

where the sum Σ is carried over all values of n, from $n = 1$ to $n = N$ (N may be infinite).

I shall now list three broad justifications of this definition. To state them unambiguously, it will be useful to establish a distinction between two common uses of the term "word." On the one hand, one says that "the dictionary is a list of words"; such elements of a dictionary will be called *word-types*. On the other hand, one says that "discourse is a sequence of words"; such elements of discourse will be called *word-tokens*. One can speak of the "probability of a word-type," but not of the "probability of a word-token"; therefore, to avoid pedantry, we shall often speak of the "probability of a word." By order of increasing content and increasing vulnerability, the three motivations of the definition of H are as follows:

1. There is a theorem due to Shannon, that H is the lower limit to the number of binary digits necessary — on the average — to transmit a message, when its successive tokens are independent, and its types W_n have the probabilities p_n (a binary digit is a symbol that can take only two values, say -1 and $+1$). When any expression plays a role of such importance, it is naturally useful to give it a name, even if it was originally introduced purely as a mathematical device without intuitive basis, as is the case in certain of the proofs of Shannon's theorem.

    If one adopts this hard-boiled approach, one will consider that the choice of the term *quantity of information* to designate H is purely a matter of convention.

2. Other proofs of Shannon's theorem introduce H in a more intuitive way: In a random sequence of k tokens, let k_n be the number of repetitions of W_n. By elementary combinatorial considerations, one finds that the number of different messages, each characterized by the same set of values of the k_n, is equal to

$$Q = \frac{k!}{\Pi k_n!},$$

where Π designates a product carried over n ranging from 1 to N. Suppose now that k is very large and that Stirling's formula can be applied to each of the factorials $k_n!$. In a long message, k_n/k tends towards p_n, and the combinatorial expression Q is approximately

$$2^{-k\Sigma p_n \log_2 p_n} = 2^{kH}.$$

kH is thus interpreted as the binary logarithm of the number Q of messages of k words characterized by the mean word frequencies $k_n = kp_n$. This number Q turns out to summarize all that one may wish to know about messages of k words — at least for purposes of communication. It is, however, better to deal with $\log_2 Q$ instead of Q, because $\log_2 Q$ increases less precipitously with k, and because it can be apportioned equally among the k word-tokens contained in our message: $\log_2 Q/k$ being equal to H, one can say that every word-token carries an amount H of the "stuff" that messages carry, and this "stuff" is then designated as "information."

3. Many authors have taken the term *information* much more seriously than is suggested above (under either 1 or 2). They argue that H *must* be called information because the loose intuitive idea of "information" can be reexpressed with the help of certain axioms that H happens to satisfy. If those axioms are chosen in a certain seemingly necessary fashion, one can even show that H is the only possible function of the p_n that can legitimately be called information.

I believe that this axiomatic approach has been more often harmful than useful. Its main drawback is that it has been found necessary to use other concepts of information in other contexts — for example, R. A. Fisher's concept, relative to parameter estimation. In each case, it has also been found possible to extract a set of axioms. Their necessity is therefore illusory or at least questionable, and axiomatics turns out to be a most slippery approach that ought to be avoided.

Appendix B. Derivations of the Law of Word Frequencies

Consider a long random sequence of k word-tokens. The word-type $W(r)$ of rank r has the relative frequency $i(r,k)/k$, which can be closely approximated by a probability $p(r)$. The present appendix presents several derivations of the relationship linking p and r.

B1. Word frequencies when discourse is a random sequence of independent symbols: the letters and the space that marks the boundaries between words

In a first stage, we shall assume the following: (a) the probability of occurrence of the space is p_o; (b) there are $M > 1$ letter types, each of which has the same probability $(1 - p_o)/M$; (c) discourse is generated by monkeys handling typewriters and is a random sequence of independent successive letters and spaces. Then, if a word contains m letters, its probability will be equal to the product of the probabilities of the component letters and space; that is, it will equal

$$p_o \left[\frac{1 - p_o}{M}\right]^m = p_o \exp \{-m \log [M/(1 - p_o)]\}.$$

This can be written as $p_o \exp \{-\beta m\}$, where $\beta = \log [M/(1 - p_o)]$ is a positive quantity that depends upon M and p_o.

It is now necessary to establish a relation between the number of letters m and the rank that a word of m letters occupies in the ordering of all words by decreasing frequencies. For that, one must note that two spaces can follow each other in an independent sequence of letters and spaces; there is therefore a "word" that is made of zero letters; there are moreover M words of 1 letter, M^2 words of 2 letters, etc., M^m words of m letters. By the very definition of rank, the most frequent word has rank 1, the next most frequent has rank 2, etc.; if, however, two words have the same probability or frequency, they can be ranked arbitrarily. If, therefore, a word has m letters, its rank r is contained between the following bounds:

r is larger than the total number of different words that contain $m - 1$ letters or less; that is,

$$r > 1 + M + M^2 + \ldots M^{m-1} = (M^m - 1)/(M - 1),$$

or, alternatively,

$$m < \frac{\log [(M - 1) \, r + 1]}{\log M}.$$

r is also at most as large as the total number of different words that contain m letters or less; that is,

$$r \leqslant 1 + M + M^2 + \ldots M^m = (M^{m+1} - 1)/(M - 1),$$

or, alternatively,

$$m \geqslant -1 + \frac{\log [(M - 1) \, r + 1]}{\log M}.$$

It follows that the relation between rank and probability is given by a step function that remains constant when r varies between two expressions of the form $(M^m - 1)/(M - 1)$, corresponding to any successive values of m. Such a relation cannot be represented by any simple analytic expression; if, however, m is very large, the above two bounds on r differ little in relative value, and one can write approximately

$$m \sim \frac{\log\left[(M - 1)r\right]}{\log M}.$$

Under these conditions, the probability $p_o \exp\{-\beta m\}$ of a word of m letters can be restated in the following forms (in which B is defined as $B = \beta/\log M$ and P as $P = p_o (M - 1)^{-B}$):

$$p(r) = p_o \exp\left\{-\frac{\beta}{\log M} \log\left[(M - 1)r\right]\right\} = p_o(M - 1)^{-B} r^{-B} = Pr^{-B}.$$

This relation between probability and rank is almost identical to the "second approximation" mentioned in the text.

Thus, *speaking in somewhat broad terms,* the once-amazing law of word frequencies can be considered the consequence of a set of almost ridiculously simple assumptions. *From a more exacting viewpoint,* four principal features of the above result are worthy of further discussion. *First,* the number of different word-types is necessarily infinite. *Second,* the parameter B being equal to $1 - \log(1 - p_o)/\log M$, it is necessarily greater than 1. *Third,* the relation between p and r is a step-function. *Fourth,* there is no trace as yet of the parameter V mentioned in the text. In certain bodies of data, all these features are acceptable; in other cases, however, one or more of these features is contrary to experience. Something must therefore be done about them, and they will be tackled in turn, in Appendices B2 and B3, after the following *Discussion.*

Discussion. The above model makes very little difference between the proper letters and the space. As a result, if this model could be taken entirely seriously, a distribution of the form $p(r) = Pr^{-B}$ would hold for "pseudowords," defined by successive recurrences of some proper letter. G. A. Miller and E. Newman have checked this prediction for the pseudowords of natural language defined by the letter e; they find that pseudowords do not follow our $p(r)$ law with $B > 1$, as they should if the model of random generation were entirely true; they seem rather close to our $p(r)$ law with $B < 1$. In other terms, the properties of the recurrence of space seem more intrinsic in some ways than those of the recurrence of any proper letter. This also seems supported by even the crudest psychological experiments, which suggest that the reading of written discourse (or the perception of speech signals) is not performed letter by letter and is closer to being performed word by word. If so, it would be more natural to consider that randomness applies to the sequence of some more abstract cerebral coding elements, rather than to letters. The only element common to all coding systems would be the space, so that our $p(r)$ relation for the ordinary words would provide the only conceivable check of the randomness of the higher coding elements. However, more evidence concerning e-words is needed to elaborate this conjecture.

Let us now return to the four difficulties that were mentioned just before the preceding *Discussion*. The third and fourth of those problems can be settled by replacing the model of Appendix B1 by a model to be discussed in the following Appendix B2.

B2. Informationally optimal systems of word frequencies, that is, word frequencies for which discourse requires the smallest possible mean number of letters for a given Shannon's information, or carries the largest amount of Shannon's information given the mean value of the number of letters

Suppose now that the number of different words, R, has an arbitrary value that may be finite or infinite. Thus, among word types defined as sequences of letters followed by space, only R have a nonvanishing probability. The minimization of the mean number of letters is then performed in two steps. In order to simplify the notation, $\Sigma_{r=1}^{R}$ will be shortened to Σ.

First Step: It is clear that, given any prescribed set of word probabilities, the average number of letters per word is minimized if the list of words, ranked by decreasing probability, coincides with the list of the R shortest letter sequences, ranked by increasing number of letters. Let $m(r)$ be the number of letters per word, a function that has been derived in Appendix B1.

Second Step: By definition of probability, the set of quantities $p(r)$ must satisfy the relation

$$\Sigma\, p(r) = 1.$$

Moreover, our informationally optimal system of probabilities $p(r)$ is constrained to carry a given amount H of Shannon's information, so that the set of $p(r)$ must also satisfy the relation

$$-\Sigma\, p(r)\, \log_2 p(r) = H.$$

This quantity H may take any value between 0 and $\log_2 R$.

Under these two constraints on the numbers $p(r)$, we wish to minimize the mean number of letters per word-token, namely,

$$\Sigma\, p(r)\ m(r).$$

Such a problem of minimization under constraints is classically solved by the method of "Lagrange multipliers," which involves two steps:

1. One picks quite arbitrarily two numbers α and β, and one chooses the various $p(r)$ so as to minimize the linearly weighted expression

$$-\Sigma\, p(r)\ \log p(r) - \beta\, \Sigma\, p(r)\ m(r) + \alpha\, \Sigma\, p(r).$$

It is therefore required that the derivative of this form with respect to every one of the $p(r)$ be identically zero; this yields the R relations

$$-1 - \log p(r) - \beta\, m(r) + \alpha = 0.$$

This can be rewritten

$$p(r) = \exp\,(\alpha - 1)\ \exp\,[-\beta\, m(r)].$$

2. In the second step of Lagrange's method, one picks α and β so as to satisfy the two original requirements: The parameter α is eliminated through $\Sigma\, p(r) = 1$, which yields $\exp\,(1-\alpha) = \Sigma_{s=1}^{R} \exp\,[-\beta\, m(s)]$ and hence

$$p(r) = \frac{\exp\,[-\beta\, m(r)]}{\Sigma_{s=1}^{R} \exp\,[-\beta\, m(s)]}.$$

As to the parameter β, it is determined by the requirement that

$$-\Sigma p(r)\ \log_2 p(r)$$

be equal to the given H. The range of possible values of β depends upon the total number R of word-types. If R is finite, the values of β are unrestricted; if R is infinite, on the contrary, β turns out to be necessarily greater than log M.

The result thus obtained by Lagrange's method has an alternative and most interesting interpretation: the same manipulations would indeed be encountered if one wished to *maximize information given the mean number of letters*, rather than the contrary. The only difference would be in the very last step, where β would naturally be determined through the mean number of letters rather than through its information.

For $r \leqslant R$, the formal dependence of $p(r)$ upon m is precisely the same as in the case of the law $p_o \exp\,(-\beta m)$ obtained in Appendix B1 (using a very different-sounding basis). Therefore, by inserting the relation between r and m, one finds again, for large r, the relation

$$p(r) \sim Pr^{-B}.$$

We have thus obtained an alternative derivation of the law of word frequencies, in which the total number of words may be finite and the slope B may be less than unity; Note that the parameter P now depends upon R and does not have the same value as in the model of Appendix B1.

Having indicated how one can settle two of the four difficulties mentioned before the *Discussion* of Appendix B1, we shall now say a few words about methods of settling the other two difficulties.

B3. The concept of the cost of a letter-type and Markovian models of discourse

Let us now assume that each letter can be characterized by a positive quantity, to be called its cost, which is such that the cost of a word is the sum of the costs of the component letters. The basic criterion of communication optimality can then be reexpressed by requiring that the mean cost per word be as small as is compatible with a prescribed value of the quantity of information. Let us then designate by $C(r)$ the cost of the rth word in the ranking of all words by increasing cost; it is easy to see that the method of Lagrange multipliers yields

$$p(r) = P \exp\left[-\beta\, C(r)\right].$$

It is moreover possible to show that, for large values of r, one still has an exponential relation between C and r, of the form

$$C(r) \sim (1/\beta')\, \log r,$$

where β' is some positive number that depends upon the set of letter costs and may be either smaller or larger than β, because the quantities β and β' are determined by entirely independent mechanisms. After this relation between C and r is replaced within the relation between p and C, we again obtain the asymptotic law $p(r)$ of appendix B2. The domain of validity of that law therefore extends to the case of unequally costly letters.

But the use of the latter also yields a way of getting rid of the difficulties number three and four, listed before the *Discussion* of Appendix B1. We must necessarily be brief. *First,* it is inevitable that steps exist in the theoretical law $p(r)$, but the amplitude of these steps decreases with the value of the greatest common divisor of the letter costs. As a result, it is thinkable that a smoothly varying function $p(r)$ should represent the law of word frequencies for values of r too small to belong to the asymptotic range. The *second* "bonus" of the use of unequally costly letters is that one can choose for $p(r)$ the function $P(r+V)^{-B}$, where V may range widely according to the distribution of letter costs. This is how the parameter V is introduced, solving the fourth difficulty listed in Appendix B1.

A final remark: If there is no harm in the restrictions that $B > 1$ and $R = \infty$, the results obtained with unequally costly letters may be rederived along the lines of Appendix B1. It suffices to assume that the successive letter tokens are not independent but rather generated by a Markov chain (see Mandelbrot, 1954).

References

ESTOUP, JEAN BAPTISTE. *Les Gammes Sténographiques*, Paris: privately printed for the Institut Sténographique, 1916.

MANDELBROT, BENOIT. "Adaptation d'un message à la ligne de transmission," *Comptes Rendus des Séances Hebdomadaires de l'Académie des Sciences de Paris*, **232**, 1951, 1638–40.

———. "On Recurrent Noise Limiting Coding," in *Information Networks, the Brooklyn Polytechnic Institute Symposium*, 1954, 205–21.

———. "Linguistique statistique macroscopique," in L. Apostel, B. Mandelbrot, and A. Morf, *Logique, Langage et Théorie de l'Information*. Paris: Presses Universitaires de France, 1957.

———. "On the Theory of Word Frequencies and on Related Markovian Models of Discourse," in Vol. XII, *Structure of Language and Its Mathematical Aspects, Proceedings of Symposia on Applied Mathematics*, ed. ROMAN JAKOBSON. Providence, R.I.: American Mathematical Society, 1961.

———. "New Methods in Statistical Economics," *Journal of Political Economy*, **71**, 1963, 421–40, or *Bulletin of the International Statistical Institute*.

———. "La théorie de l'information est-elle *encore* utile?" in *Le Concept d'Information dans la Science Contemporaine, Cahier de Royaumont*. Paris: Gauthier-Villars & Les Editions de Minuit, 1965, 78–98.

MARKOV, A. "Essai d'une recherche statistique sur le texte du roman *Eugène Onéguine*," *Bulletin de l'Académie Impériale des Sciences de Saint-Pétersbourg*, VII, 1913.

MILLER, GEORGE A., and CHOMSKY, A. NOAM. "Finitary Models of Language Users," in Vol. II, *Handbook of Mathematical Psychology*, eds. R. R. BUSH, E. GALANTER, and R. D. LUCE. New York: Wiley, 1963.

SHANNON, CLAUDE A. "Mathematical Theory of Communication," *Bell System Technical Journal*, **28**, 1948, 379–423, 623–56.

ZIPF, GEORGE KINGSLEY. *Human Behavior and the Principle of Least Effort*. Reading, Mass.: Addison-Wesley, 1949.

Suggestions for Further Reading (Section Five)

ANDERSON, T. W. "Probability Models for Analyzing Time Changes in Attitudes," in *Mathematical Thinking in the Social Sciences,* ed. PAUL F. LAZARSFELD. Chicago: Free Press, 1954. Anderson presents the basic ideas of finite Markov chains and uses the model to study the patterns of changing vote intentions preceding the 1940 presidential election. Problems of estimation and of testing hypotheses about the process are emphasized, and the generalization of the model to take into account more than the previous interview is discussed.

ESTES, WILLIAM K. "Individual Behavior in Uncertain Situations: An Interpretation in Terms of Statistical Association Theory," in *Decision Processes,* eds. ROBERT M. THRALL and others. New York: Wiley, 1954. Estes considers two problems of decision making in an experimental situation: (1) predicting an uncertain event and (2) attempting to control an uncertain event. In both cases he reports results of experiments where the subject, at each trial, must choose one of two possible alternatives. He presents the mathematical models for each case and shows that they are consistent with the data, especially in terms of the *asymptotic behavior* predicted by the models. In Case 1 the model predicts that the proportion of times the subject chooses alternative j approaches the proportion with which that alternative j is actually appearing. Estes' earlier paper "Towards a Statistical Theory of Learning" (*Psychological Review,* 1950, **57,** 94–107) derived the equations of his model from assumptions about the nature of learning.

FELLER, WILLIAM. "On the Theory of Stochastic Processes, with Particular Reference to Applications," in *Berkeley Symposium on Mathematical Statistics and Probability,* ed. JERZY NEYMAN. Berkeley: Univ. of California Press, 1949. This paper remains the best short introduction to stochastic processes of the continuous-time, discrete-state Markov type. These include the widely applicable Poisson process, more general birth-and-death processes, and the Polya process that is the model for many theories of contagious events, such as epidemics. Of particular value to social scientists is Feller's discussion of the "nature of contagion," in which he shows how the Polya distribution can arise when a mixture of Poisson processes is at work as well as when a truly "contagious" process is operating. These results are especially pertinent to the study of accidents, where the existence of accident-prone individuals has often been debated, with statistical "evidence" cited on both sides of the argument.

GOODMAN, LEO A. "Mathematical Methods for the Study of Systems of Groups," *American Journal of Sociology,* 1964, **70,** 170–92. The models discussed here describe the changes in the sizes of groups that belong to some system. The fundamental assumption is that a group will attract new members at a rate directly proportional to its size, whereas there is a constant rate of departure from a group. This basic scheme is examined under different conditions, as when there is an infinite pool of potential members and when there is a fixed, finite population. Also, the number of groups may be a fixed number or a random variable. The latter case would arise in considering "freely forming" groups, which have little or no formal structure. A general "emigration-immigration" model is also analyzed, wherein the arrival and departure rates may vary from one group to another. Equilibrium distributions and estimators for the parameters are derived, as well as tests of goodness-of-fit.

MCPHEE, WILLIAM N. "Survival Theory in Culture," in his *Formal Theories of Mass Behavior.* New York: Free Press, 1962. McPhee proposes a theory to account for the rates of survival of cultural items such as plays, musical works, TV shows, and popular music. He proposes what is essentially a latent-structure model in discrete time and applies it to data on the mortality of TV shows from 1950 to 1960. McPhee assumes that three grades of material are offered each year, in differing quantities and having different probabilities of survival. He develops procedures for estimating these parameters and makes the distinction between "single-screening" cultures (such as popular music), which is either hit or miss, and

370

"repetitive-screening" cultures (such as TV shows), which are constantly subject to reexamination as long as they endure. The implications of the model for these two types of culture are discussed in some detail.

MILLER, G. A., and CHOMSKY, A. N. "Finitary Models of Language Users," in *Handbook of Mathematical Psychology,* eds. R. DUNCAN LUCE, ROBERT BUSH, and EUGENE GALANTER. Vol. II. New York: Wiley, 1963. The authors discuss a number of models of the sources, channels, and receivers of language, including the Markov models for generating word sequences and the construction of efficient codes for transmission of messages. They consider, in addition to probability models, algebraic models for language interpreters: axioms describing the operation of a device for comprehending a string of symbols when the rules of the grammar are known.

Major Reference Books in Mathematical Social Science

(in order of publication)

LAZARSFELD, PAUL F. (ed.). *Mathematical Thinking in the Social Sciences*. Chicago: Free Press, 1954.

THRALL, R. M.; COOMBS, C. H.; and DAVIS, R. L. (eds.). *Decision Processes*. New York: Wiley, 1954.

BUSH, R. R., and MOSTELLER, C. F. *Stochastic Models for Learning*. New York: Wiley, 1955.

LUCE, R. DUNCAN, and RAIFFA, HOWARD. *Games and Decisions*. New York: Wiley, 1957.

TORGERSON, WARREN S. *Theory and Methods of Scaling*. New York: Wiley, 1958.

BUSH, ROBERT R., and ESTES, WILLIAM K. (eds.). *Studies in Mathematical Learning Theory*. Stanford, Calif.: Stanford Univ. Press, 1959.

CHURCHMAN, C. WEST, and RATOOSH, PHILBURN (eds.). *Measurement: Definitions and Theories*. New York: Wiley, 1959.

GULLIKSEN, HAROLD, and MESSICK, SAMUEL (eds.). *Psychological Scaling*. New York: Wiley, 1960.

ARROW, K. J.; KARLIN, S.; and SUPPES, P. (eds.). *Mathematical Methods in the Social Sciences*. (Proceedings of the Stanford Symposium on Mathematical Methods in the Social Sciences.) Stanford, Calif.: Stanford Univ. Press, 1960.

SUPPES, PATRICK, and ATKINSON, RICHARD C. *Markov Learning Models for Multiperson Interactions*. Stanford, Calif.: Stanford Univ. Press, 1960.

LUCE, R. DUNCAN (ed.). *Developments in Mathematical Psychology*. Chicago: Free Press, 1961.

SOLOMON, HERBERT (ed.). *Studies in Item Analysis and Prediction*. Stanford, Calif.: Stanford Univ. Press, 1961.

CRISWELL, JOAN; SOLOMON, HERBERT; and SUPPES, PATRICK (eds.). *Mathematical Methods in Small Group Processes*. Stanford, Calif.: Stanford Univ. Press, 1962.

LUCE, R. DUNCAN; BUSH, ROBERT R.; and GALANTER, EUGENE (eds.). *Handbook of Mathematical Psychology*. New York: Wiley, 1963. Vols. I and II.

————.*Readings in Mathematical Psychology*. New York: Wiley, 1963. Vol. I.

FLAMENT, CLAUDE. *Applications of Graph Theory to Group Structure*. Englewood Cliffs, N. J.: Prentice-Hall, 1963.

COLEMAN, JAMES S. *Introduction to Mathematical Sociology*. New York: Free Press, 1964.

COOMBS, CLYDE. *A Theory of Data*. New York: Wiley, 1964.

LUCE, R. DUNCAN; BUSH, ROBERT R.; and GALANTER, EUGENE (eds.). *Handbook of Mathematical Psychology*. New York: Wiley, 1965. Vol. III.

MASSARIK, FRED, and RATOOSH, PHILBURN (eds.). *Mathematical Explorations in Behavioral Science*. Homewood, Ill.: Richard D. Irwin, 1965.

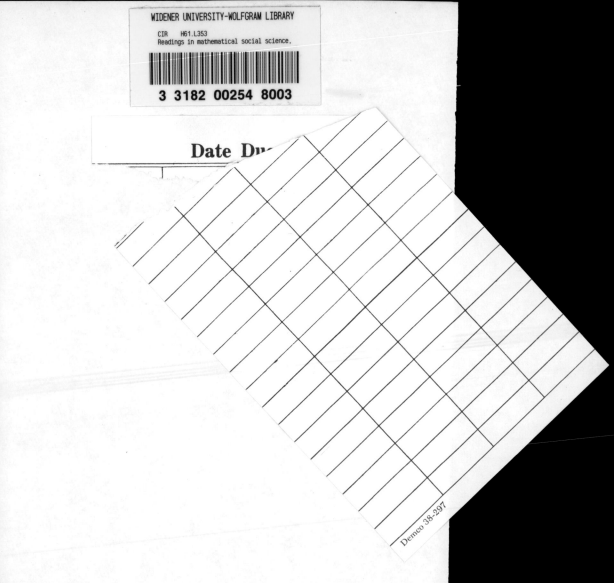

Date Due

Demco 38-297